"Some people would say the universe is pretty much the same everywhere, and we live on an ordinary chunk of rock circling an ordinary star located well out from the center in a galaxy that is nothing special. In *Designed to the Core* astronomer Hugh Ross provides a thoroughly documented discussion of evidence for an enormous amount of fine-tuning for where our galaxy lies, what kind of galaxy we live in, and where we are in the galaxy. He also explains the fine-tuned details of the formation of the solar system, and the internal as well as external properties of the Sun and Earth. The evidence points to everything having been made appropriate for humans to exist right here, right now. Readers are encouraged to examine this evidence that the God revealed in the Bible has also revealed himself through this fine-tuning."

—Kyle M. Cudworth
Professor Emeritus, Department of Astronomy and Astrophysics
University of Chicago
Director of Yerkes Observatory

"I have read books and articles that describe the rare Earth hypothesis; that is, that our planet enjoys a remarkable place in the solar system and that our solar system resides in an optimal place in the Milky Way. *Designed to the Core* is the first book I've ever read that explains how the Milky Way Galaxy itself is special and unique—the 'rare galaxy hypothesis!' Hugh Ross has a remarkable ability to gather and synthesize enormous amounts of technical data and then present it in a way that a scientific layperson (like me) can understand. Very well done."

—Ken Keathley
Director of the L. Russ Bush Center for Faith and Culture
Southeastern Baptist Theological Seminary

"Reading a Hugh Ross book is like drinking from a fire hydrant, and *Designed to the Core* is no exception. Breathtaking! Encyclopedic! Detailed! Clear! Conclusive! Psalm 8 says, 'When I consider your heavens, the work of your fingers, the moon and the stars, which you have set in place . . . Lord, our Lord, how majestic is your name in all the earth!' I will never read that Psalm the same way again. Read this book and sing the Hallelujah chorus with gusto!"

—Steve Brown
Author, seminary professor, broadcaster,
host of the syndicated talk show *Steve Brown, Etc.*

"Dr. Ross is uniquely qualified among scientists to give a comprehensive overview of up-to-date evidence for design. In *Designed to the Core*, Dr. Ross explains 'evidence for the exquisite fine-tuning observed at all astronomical levels, from the farthest reaches of the cosmos to the ground beneath our feet.' As with all his books, Dr. Ross brilliantly synthesizes research from hundreds of peer-reviewed research publications to bring to light the layers of fine-tuning within our universe that makes human life possible and highlights our significance."

—Eric R. Hedin
Professor, Department of Chemistry, Physics, and Engineering,
Biola University

"The anthropic principle (the observation that the universe appears highly fine-tuned for our existence) is now widely acknowledged. However, much of the discussion of this remarkable fact focuses on the largest scales in time and space. In *Designed to the Core*, Hugh Ross surveys a vast range of scales, from the grand cosmic to our planetary, to show this fine-tuning appears at every level. Concise, yet well-documented, this book is a compelling invitation to wonder at the care our Creator has for us, and the transcendent intricacy of his design for our universe. For the scholar and apologist, this work also serves as an excellent launch point into any number of research areas pointing to evidence for design in the cosmos."

—Bijan Nemati
Principal Research Scientist,
University of Alabama in Huntsville

"In *Designed to the Core*, Dr. Hugh Ross takes us on an unprecedented journey to explore the necessary requirements for a planet to support complex life. His truly comprehensive approach to the subject examines every aspect of Earth's life-friendly environment, from the cosmic supercluster that we inhabit to our location in the Milky Way to our unusual solar system and even deep inside Earth's core. The sheer number and scope of the needed parameters is mind-boggling and unambiguously answers the question of whether Earth is unique in its capability of supporting complex life. The only question left for the reader to ponder is how such a fortunate planet could have come into existence at all. Many of us who have pondered that question will agree with Dr. Ross, that such exquisite design requires an intelligent and powerful Designer."

—Michael G. Strauss
David Ross Boyd Professor of Physics
University of Oklahoma

HUGH ROSS

DESIGNED
TO THE CORE

Covina, CA

Cover design: 789, Inc.
Interior layout: Christine Talley
Figure design: Heather Lanz

Names: Ross, Hugh (Hugh Norman), 1945-, author.
Title: Designed to the core / by Hugh Ross.
Description: First edition. | Includes bibliographical references and index. | Covina, CA: RTB Press, 2022.
Identifiers: ISBN: 978-1-956112-01-6
Subjects: LCSH Religion and science. | Creation. | Astronomy--Religious aspects--Christianity. | God--Proof, Cosmological. | God--Proof, Teleological. | Anthropic principle. | BISAC RELIGION / Religion & Science | SCIENCE / Physics / Astrophysics | SCIENCE / Physics / Geophysics | SCIENCE / Space Science / Astronomy | SCIENCE / Space Science / Stellar & Solar
Classification: LCC BT102 .R667 2022 | DDC 231.7/65--dc23

Printed in the United States of America

First edition

2 3 4 5 6 7 8 9 10 11 / 27 26 25 24 23

For more information about Reasons to Believe, contact (855) REASONS / (855) 732-7667 or visit reasons.org.

Contents

List of Figures and Tables

Figures

Tables

Acknowledgments

This book culminates a multiyear project that included combing the scientific literature, preparing short articles on what the latest data reveal, developing short presentations plus lengthier talks, and responding to feedback. My livestreamed Paradoxes class, which engages a variety of scientists, engineers, students, and lay people, served as my primary sounding board. Class participants' questions, challenges, critiques, and suggestions helped shape the content, specifically the crafting of multiple explanations and descriptions. These individuals strongly encouraged me to include plentiful photos, figures, and diagrams, and, as you can see, I accepted their advice.

My partner in life and ministry, Kathy, took on a host of practical responsibilities to protect my research and writing time, as well as protect me from COVID-19. As usual, she also took the lead in editing the manuscript, which the pandemic made more efficient by confining us to our shared office space at home. Kathy did her utmost to achieve the nearly impossible goal of a balance between the scientists' demand for accuracy and thoroughness and the lay readers' need for understandability. If any opaqueness remains, that's on me.

My colleagues here at Reasons to Believe (RTB) and several of our Scholar Community members deserve thanks for taking the time to discuss with me the insights and integration I sought to develop and for offering helpful recommendations. I'm especially thankful to astrophysicists John Zuhone and Kyle Cudworth and theologian Ken Keathley, who reviewed the final manuscript. Their suggested revisions and additional citations strengthened the book's argument.

Six more members of RTB's editorial team stepped up to assist: Linda Hucks, Joe Aguirre, Sandra Dimas, Brett Tarbell, Helena Heredia, and Ruth

Alvarado. Together they improved the book's readability, checked citations and quotations, performed detailed copyediting, prepared the index, and helped keep this book on schedule. RTB's graphic designer, Heather Lanz, transformed my figures and diagrams into print-ready format, and Christine Talley designed the book's interior. I owe a big thanks to each of them and also to Charley Bell, Richard Silva, Crystal Casunuran, and Kimberly Skorheim of 789, Inc., whose creative skills are colorfully displayed on the book's cover.

Others who deserve special mention include members of RTB's ministry care, advancement, and marketing teams, and none more than Diana Carrée, my executive assistant, whose diligent efforts provided Kathy and me with such essentials as food and toilet paper at moments of critical shortage during the early days of the COVID-19 pandemic. Your support, extra effort, and gatekeeping allowed us to focus intensely for many months on writing and editing. Finally, I am truly blessed by all the love and encouragement I receive from my family, friends, teammates, and countless others who take the time and care to stay in touch.

Lastly, to our ever-faithful Reasons to Believe donors: Dan and Katy Atwood, Ron and Bett Behrens, Ken and Tracy Camacho, Jamie and Maria Campbell, Mark and Valerie Durham, Rodney and Pam Emery, Otis Graf, Kirby and Karen Hansen, Mike and Marj Harman, Roger and Stefanie Joe, Mathew John, Matt and Janet Jones, Hal and Edie Kirman, Steve and Liz Klein, Francisco and Martha Larzabal, David La Pointe, Perry Lanaro, George and Valerie Leiva, Martin and Cynthia Levine, Steve and Kara Loupe, Moriah Martinez, Helen Masuda, Clark and Alice McKinley, Gary Parks, Steve and Eileen Rogstad, David Singh, Brant and Laura Ullman, Harold and Beverly Van Vuren, Darren and Jennifer Williams, John and Shera Williamson, Colleen Wingenbach, Josh and Kerri Wolcott, and John Yue. We owe the completion of this book to your dedicated partnership and believe God will use your generosity to impact more lives for his kingdom.

Chapter 1

The Anthropic Principle

In a now famous outtake, astrophysicist Neil deGrasse Tyson declared, "The universe is a deadly place. At every opportunity it's trying to kill us."[1] When astronomers look out to the universe, some are struck by all the dangers it poses to life, especially to human life.[2] In every region of the cosmos beyond Earth, they see gravitational disturbances, supernovae, gamma-ray bursts, ultraviolet and x-ray sources, black holes, asteroids, comets, and solar and stellar flares that can easily destroy us.

From a strictly astronomical perspective on time, doomsday for humanity and all life appears to be just around the corner. Long before cosmic expansion brings about the heat death of the universe,[3] the approaching collision of our galaxy with the Large Magellanic Cloud and the Andromeda Galaxy will inevitably do us in. These collisions will collapse our galaxy's spiral structure and greatly augment the mass of its central black hole (see chapters 6 and 7). At any time, the much smaller collision between Earth and an asteroid roughly twice the diameter of the one that struck northwestern Greenland 12,800 years ago would prove fatal.[4]

By the time the universe has aged by only another quarter of a percent, the Sun will be too bright for humanity's survival. In fact, a solar superflare will most likely occur before the universe is another 0.003% older,[5] and it, too, will bring an end to the human species. The instability that characterized the Sun's early luminosity and flaring activity will return as it moves closer to the end of its nuclear-burning cycle.

This dark, doomsday perspective makes sense for astronomers and others who've embraced the beliefs expressed by their predecessor Carl Sagan. His message—that the universe is all there is or was or ever will be—shapes their perspective. One person sees a razor-sharp blade as a deadly weapon, the other as a life-saving scalpel. The motive of the one who wields that blade makes all the difference.

What if all that appears so deadly and dangerous is actually what makes life, especially human life and its flourishing, possible? What if the cosmos is *not* all there is or was or ever will be? Such a perspective would alter the significance of everything about it and within it. Such a perspective would begin to make sense of an observation called "the anthropic principle."

Anthropic Principle Redefined

In its original form, the anthropic principle states that humanity's existence places severe constraints on the physical constants and structure and history of the cosmos as a whole, as well as those of the Milky Way Galaxy, the solar system, Earth, and early life on Earth.[6] Basic astronomy textbooks define the anthropic principle in this way: the presence of intelligent observers (beings capable of measuring astronomical bodies and phenomena) requires that multiple characteristics of the universe and the laws of physics fit within certain narrowly limited ranges. This fine-tuning suggests an external designer. This inference raises some doubt about the Sagan doctrine, causing some researchers to pull back from the implications of their findings.

As Brazilian astrophysicist Marcelo Gleiser[7] points out, what researchers today refer to as the "anthropic" principle amounts to nothing more than the "preconditions for primitive life."[8] These conditions include only the minimum physical and chemical requirements for the feasibility of prebiotic chemistry. Gleiser proposes that "what is currently called the 'anthropic principle' should instead be named the 'prebiotic principle.'"[9]

In his paper, Gleiser demonstrates that the universe's ability to sustain living things through a transition from one stage to another is far from trivial. For the universe to transition from its capacity to sustain prebiotic chemistry to its capacity for single-celled life-forms is no trivial matter. Transitioning to its capacity for sustaining complex, multicellular organisms replete with appendages and internal organs seems even more complex. A still more dramatic step in fine-tuning would be necessary for the universe to provide for the support of any species equivalent to the human race.

I must add that an exponentially greater degree of fine-tuning is needed to allow humans (or their equivalents) the time and resources for development of a global, high-population, highly technological civilization.

Anthropic Principle Debates

Fine-tuning, of course, requires a shaping source. The greater the degree of fine-tuning, and the more pervasive the fine-tuning, the more capable the fine tuner required. The pursuit of fine-tuning evidence, therefore, holds profound personal significance.

If the observed design proves inconsequential, or only vaguely purposeful, one could argue that no intentionality is necessary. Perhaps the apparent design feature is merely a probable outcome of the operation of mysteriously self-existent natural processes. On the other hand, if the observed fine-tuning is multifaceted and every facet crucial to the outcome, then the fine-tuning source must be more than a mindless, impersonal force or process. The more numerous, specific, and purposeful the necessary fine-tuned requirements, the more these required features reveal about the characteristics and identity of the fine tuner.

Not everyone agrees, however, that cosmic fine-tuning is real. Many allege that the design is mere anthropomorphism. They contend that the observed cosmic fine-tuning is akin to a puddle, noting that the hole in which the puddle finds itself is perfectly fit for it. So, the puddle concludes that someone must have manufactured the hole specifically for it.

Astronomers Geraint Lewis and Luke Barnes explain why cosmic fine-tuning is *not* anthropomorphism.[10] The puddle does not realize that given the fluidity of water, the solidity of the hole, and the downward force of gravity, it will *always* take the precise shape of its hole. However, not every conceivable universe will suit physical life. Physical life is not a fluid. It will not and cannot adjust to any old universe. The fine-tuning that astronomers observe indicates that even very slight alterations to the universe's characteristics would rule out the possible existence of physical life.

Some argue that the observational evidence for fine-tuning is merely coincidental. They assert that we humans would not be here to report on the so-called fine-tuned features of the universe unless by pure chance these highly unlikely, intricately intertwined properties converged—and we emerged.

Philosophers Richard Swinburne and William Lane Craig have exposed the fallacious nature of this appeal to chance. As they point out, it ignores the level of specific intentionality implied by the degree and extent of the cosmic fine-tuning.[11] A scientific rebuttal to this pure-chance appeal would be to demonstrate that the anthropic principle wields both explanatory and predictive power, pointing researchers toward productive avenues of inquiry and discovery.

In a previous book, *The Creator and the Cosmos*, 4th edition, I responded to some more obscure attempts to avoid the conclusion that cosmic fine-tuning implies a cosmic fine tuner.[12]

Let's consider the outcome of all this fine-tuning observed to date: scientists know of one planet capable of supporting the existence of a large population of humans, more or less civilized and technologically capable. If a purposeful Tuner exists, it makes sense that the deeper our search into the features of the cosmos, the more evidence of fine-tuning this search will reveal. If no purposeful Tuner exists, then a deeper search will reveal less and less specificity and intentionality. A fine tuner's attributes and purposes will become either increasingly clear or increasingly vague.

I invite readers to join me in a deeper exploration, probing from the exterior layers into the interior features of the cosmos at every scale, from its large-scale structure to our supergalaxy cluster, galaxy cluster, galaxy group, local galactic neighborhood, star, planetary system, moon, and home base, planet Earth. I invite readers to boldly go where they have not gone before to explore strange new realms. I invite readers to ponder what their discoveries mean for humanity and for themselves personally.

Chapter 2

Exterior Design Features

Chapter summary: *The entire physical universe is humanity's "house." It must be precisely as massive, spatially extensive, and old as it is to allow for our existence. All the home's exterior features require precise construction for physical life to be possible anywhere within it. Unless the exterior features are designed just as they are, the cosmic interior features required for complex, enduring, and advanced physical life can neither be established nor maintained.*

On a few occasions, I've had the opportunity to visit grand mansions. I've also visited a mud home in Africa, designed and constructed by a couple who did postgraduate studies, as I did, at the University of Toronto. Given the choice (and I realize *choice* is not always a given), people choose housing that not only keeps them safe, but also allows them whatever comforts they would define, based on their background and preferences, as "home."

The external structure represents the starting place. Its features hold importance primarily in providing the framework, establishing the boundary conditions, and determining what features will be possible inside. At the same time, whatever features are needed and wanted inside have bearing on the scale and design and construction of the floor plan, the walls, doors, windows, access to utilities, and roofing. Although these characteristics do not make a house a home, they hold enormous significance.

Such is the case with our universe. As an astronomer, I see it as the most exquisite mansion for the needs and purposes of a thriving human existence, for a prescribed time. The Laniakea Supercluster, the Milky Way Galaxy, the solar system, and Earth—our house's external features—accommodate the life it holds and sustains. However, the interiors of these external features appear even more exquisite.

To observe and appreciate their exterior qualities requires some visual or exploratory aids. Yet, to explore their interior features requires highly sophisticated instruments. Perhaps because interiors are less easily accessible for observation and investigation, their features have received scant attention in books and articles about our fine-tuned habitat.

No one can take an elevator down to Earth's core. Nor can one personally visit the Sun's nuclear furnace. The Milky Way Galaxy's core is far beyond the reach of any human spacecraft. However, today we possess instruments that permit us to probe the conditions of the deep interior parts of the Moon, Earth, Sun, Milky Way Galaxy, Virgo Cluster, and Laniakea Supercluster.

These instruments are revealing the interiors of heavenly bodies in unprecedented detail. Over the past three decades, many books have been written about the fine-tuned exteriors of the cosmos that make human existence and development of a global, high-technology civilization possible.[1] Throughout these same decades, and for centuries prior, researchers dreamed of probing cosmic interiors to discover what they might reveal about the great mysteries of life. Now that dream is beginning to become a reality.

I wrote this book to showcase the astounding realities discovered to date and, ultimately, to probe the meaning of what can be seen and measured. But, before launching into that exploration and its findings, it may be helpful to review the exterior of our house, the exterior structure that frames the range of the possible components within it. For the sake of context, this chapter provides a brief overview of the universe's exterior features, referred to in the scientific literature as "designs," identifying at least a few of the many that prove essential for the development of a home in which physical life and human beings, in particular, can possibly reside and thrive.

Cosmic Beginning

Within a cosmos once considered boundless, anything seemed possible by pure chance—perhaps even a countless number of planets similar to Earth and lifeforms similar to humans, with a range of remarkable capacities. However, with discovery of the cosmic beginning, including a beginning of the space-time dimensions[2] that define the boundaries of the universe, the view of our "house" came into sharper focus.

Ongoing research has revealed one after another of the universe's external characteristics that must be fine-tuned to allow for the possibility of life's existence at *any locale* and at *any time* within it. An abundance of evidence now indicates that if the cosmic mass, size, age, inflation, elements, and ratio of elemental abundances weren't structured exactly as they are, no one would be here to learn of them or to ponder how they came to be.

Cosmic Mass

The universe is mind-bogglingly massive. The number of stars in the theoretically observable universe (the universe accessible to the largest conceivable telescopes) adds up to about 10^{23} (a hundred billion trillion). The average mass of a star equals 8×10^{29} kilograms (2×10^{30} pounds). Given that stars make up only 0.85% of the total mass of the universe,[3] we can calculate that the total mass of the observable universe equals roughly 10^{55} kilograms (2×10^{55} pounds).

Astronomers who study the geometry of the universe would describe it as spatially flat. In other words, on the largest size scales, it is neither positively nor negatively curved to any significant degree. In the case of a *perfectly* flat universe, the cosmic spatial curvature parameter, Ω_k, would equal exactly zero. The average of the four best cosmic geometry measurements to date looks like this: $\Omega_k = -0.0002 \pm 0.0017$.[4] This geometry measure of Ω_k no greater than 0.0032 allows us to calculate that the actual universe, including that which we cannot observe, must be at least 15 million times more massive than the observable universe.

The universe is a four-dimensional space-time system. The surface of the universe is three-dimensional, not two-dimensional. Astronomers measure the three-dimensional surface of the universe as being very close to a flat shape.

It goes without saying that the massiveness of the cosmos nearly exceeds our capacity to comprehend, and this enormity understandably gives rise to skepticism. Why would such massiveness be essential for our existence? Even without knowing for certain the total mass of the universe, astronomers can determine the significance of its observable mass for the possibility of physical life. All they require is a measure of the cosmic mass density—its mass per unit volume at different epochs in the history of its expansion.

As explained in some detail in my previous books,[5] if the universe were ever so slightly less massive (thus, with an ever-so-slightly lesser cosmic mass density), the periodic table of elements would forever look like figure 2.1. In such a universe, chemistry courses would seem easy to pass, but physical life of any conceivable kind would be impossible. On the other hand, if the universe were ever so slightly more massive (thus, with an ever-so-slightly greater cosmic mass density), then the periodic table would resemble figure 2.2 (soon

1 H

Table of Elements

2 He

Figure 2.1: Periodic Table of Elements for a Slightly Less Massive Universe

Table of Elements

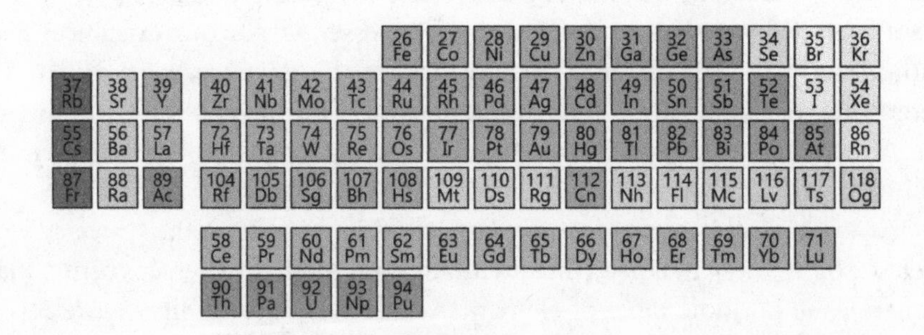

Figure 2.2: Periodic Table of Elements for a Slightly More Massive Universe

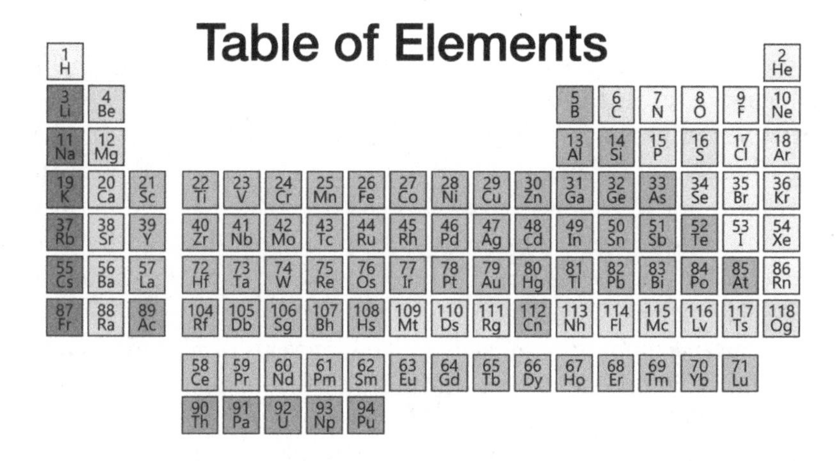

Figure 2.3: Periodic Table of Elements as It Currently Stands

after formation of the first stars). In this periodic table, only iron and heavier elements would exist. In either case, the life-essential elements seen in figure 2.3—carbon, nitrogen, oxygen, sodium, magnesium, phosphorous, sulfur, chlorine, potassium, and calcium—would be missing. No planet like Earth and no physical life would be possible if the universe were not precisely as massive as it is.

The mass of the universe also plays a role in determining whether stars and planets can form because it determines how effectively gravity can slow down the cosmic expansion. In a less massive universe, the universe would expand more rapidly, and gravity would be insufficient to compress the expanding primordial cosmic gas into stars and planets. Such a universe would remain dispersed gas. In a more massive universe, the universe would expand more slowly, and gravity would compress all the primordial cosmic gas into neutron stars and black holes. In such a universe, atoms and molecules would not exist.

As it turns out, the universe must possess its precise mass / mass density for any planet and any physical life to possibly exist.

Cosmic Size

Stars are big. The smallest known nuclear-burning star, EBLM J0555-57Ab, measures 118,000 kilometers (73,000 miles) in diameter, equivalent to Saturn and significantly larger than Earth's 7,915 miles.[6] The largest known nuclear-burning star, NML Cygni, measures 2,280,000,000 kilometers (1,426,000,000 miles) in diameter, or 1,640 times bigger than the Sun.[7]

Stars not only are large, but they also reside far apart from one another. On average throughout the observable universe, stars are separated by about 400 light-years. If one were to take an average-sized star such as the Sun (diameter of 1,391,400 kilometers or 864,576 miles) and scale it down to the size of a large cherry, it would be separated from other cherry-sized stars by an average of 21,000 kilometers (13,000 miles).

The universe took approximately 13.8 billion years to expand to such a size from its initial infinitesimal volume. And only at this precise moment, with stars about 400 light-years apart, could advanced life enter. With stars in the universe jammed more tightly together, planets orbiting the stars would suffer gravitational disturbances and exposure to stellar radiation that would threaten advanced life. On the other hand, with stars dispersed more widely via a more rapid ongoing cosmic expansion, planets would be insufficiently enriched with the heavy elements advanced life requires. (These heavy elements come solely from the ejected debris of massive stars.)

Here, again, the universe must be just as dispersed as it is to provide a home for a diversity of physical life, especially for complex human life.

Cosmic Age

Even the age of the universe plays a role in whether it can provide a suitable habitat for life. The current best measurements tell us the universe is 13.791 ± 0.021 billion years old.[8] Of course, as the universe has aged, it has changed in significant ways. For one, the characteristics of stars have changed and, thus, the relative abundance of elements has changed.

At its origin, the universe possessed just one element: hydrogen. Within the first few minutes after the big bang event, nuclear fusion occurred on a cosmic scale, transforming some of the hydrogen into heavier elements. At this point, 4 minutes after the cosmic creation event, the composition of ordinary matter was 76% hydrogen, 24% helium, and a trace amount of lithium.

About 200 million years later, the first stars formed. Initially, these stars were composed of just hydrogen, helium, and lithium. Then nuclear furnaces inside these stars began to fuse some of the primordial hydrogen, helium, and lithium into elements heavier than lithium. With each successive generation of star formation, the abundance of elements heavier than lithium increased.

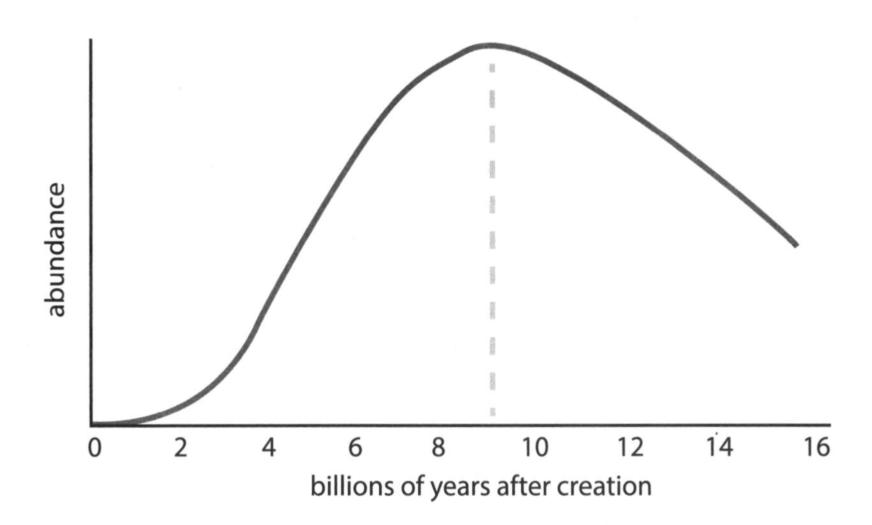

Figure 2.4: Abundance of Thorium and Uranium throughout Cosmic History
Diagram credit: Hugh Ross

This aging process determines whether planets can form and what characteristics those planets will possess. A certain minimum abundance of elements heavier than lithium is required for planets to form at all. The first stars lacked this minimum abundance, and the second generation barely reached it. However, as the universe grew older and older, planets orbiting newly formed stars contained greater and greater concentrations of elements heavier than lithium.

The later a star forms, the higher its ratio of heavy elements to light elements. Any kind of life, and especially advanced life, requires a highly specified abundance of each of the elements in the periodic table.[9] For example, advanced life requires a planet with an enormous abundance of thorium and uranium.

Thorium and uranium arise from only two sources: supernova eruptions and neutron star mergers. The rate at which each of these types of events occur throughout cosmic history has changed with time. As the cosmos expands and bodies disperse, these events become less and less frequent. Given that thorium-232 and uranium-235 and uranium-238 are radioactive isotopes subject to decay with half-lives of 14.05, 0.704, and 4.468 billion years, respectively, they became progressively less abundant after their formation peaked. Their buildup from frequent supernova eruptions and neutron star mergers and subsequent shrinking abundance, due to radioactive decay, is portrayed in figure 2.4.

Figure 2.4 shows that the abundance of uranium and thorium in the universe attained a peak when the universe was slightly more than nine billion years old. The fact that our solar system formed when the universe was slightly more than nine billion years old suggests one of the reasons for Earth's rich abundance of thorium and uranium.

The data displayed in figure 2.4 shows just one of many reasons the universe must be no younger or older than it is to serve as a house for advanced physical life.[10]

Cosmic Inflation

Along with a just-right mass, size, and age, the universe manifests two other characteristics essential for our existence: universal thermal connectedness and a virtually flat geometry. A phenomenon called "inflation" bears significance for understanding how these features came about and how they impact the possibility of life in the cosmos.

Despite vast stretches of space separating the universe's stars and galaxies, every region of the universe manifests the same overall temperature. Without this temperature similarity and temperature smoothness, the universe would be clumpier than it is. In a clumpier universe, the kind of galaxy cluster, galaxy, star, and planetary system physical life requires could never exist. The existing clumps would emit extremely intense and deadly radiation, and strong gravitational tugs-of-war would be common. The vast stretches of space that currently exist between stars and galaxies allow for the possibility that, somewhere in the universe, deadly radiation and gravitational disturbances from nearby stars and galaxies pose no constant threat to advanced life.

Further, if the universe were spherical rather than flat, without a cosmological constant (see figure 2.5), the universe would have expanded from the cosmic origin event, stopped expanding, and then collapsed back on itself before any galaxy, star, and planetary system could form. On the other hand, if the universe were hyperbolic in shape, it would have expanded so quickly from the moment of its origin that the galaxies, stars, and planets advanced life requires would never have been able to form.

To explain how these features—the thermal connectedness across the vast expanse of the universe and the flatness of its geometry—could have come

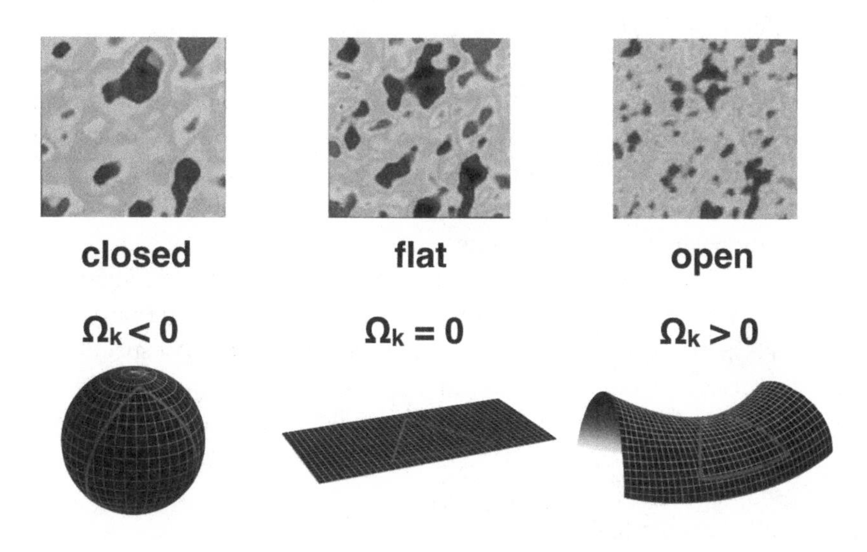

Figure 2.5: Possible Cosmic Geometries
Only one of these geometric options appears suitable for the possibility of advanced life. Closed = spherical. Open = hyperbolic. *Credit: NASA*

about, researchers proposed that a particular event occurred during the first split second after the beginning of the universe. They posited that during a sliver of time, starting no earlier than 10^{-36} seconds after the moment of cosmic origin and ending no later than 10^{-32} seconds, a maximum time duration briefer than a ten millionth of a trillionth of a trillionth of a blink of the eye, the universe expanded from smaller than a proton to about the size of a grapefruit, a factor of 10^{26} times! This rapid inflation episode, exceeding the velocity of light by roughly a trillion trillion times, would perfectly account for the existence of each of these essential features.

The brief and hyperaccelerated expansion of space would have stretched out any initial variations in matter density or temperature to such an extent that the universe became virtually homogeneous and uniform on the largest size scales. On these size scales, nonuniformities and nonhomogeneities would prove no larger than about 1 part in 100,000. Likewise, temperature differences among regions in the universe would never exceed about 1 part in 100,000. The curvature of space would have unfurled so completely as to yield nearly perfect flatness, consistent with actual best cosmic geometry measurements.[11]

These outcomes, all necessary to make life in the universe possible, have been repeatedly affirmed by astronomers' measurements, to date. The ongoing Sloan Digital Sky Survey of galaxies and galaxy clusters,[12] as well as the Planck,[13] WMAP,[14] and Atacama Cosmology Telescope[15] surveys of the cosmic microwave background radiation (CMBR), have all yielded potent affirmations.

Additional confirmation comes from measurements of a characteristic called "the scalar spectral index." The scalar spectral index describes how cosmic density fluctuations vary with size scale. A value for the scalar spectral index, n_s, can be derived based on accurate measurements of a specific feature, the E-polarization mode, that appears in several recent maps of the CMBR. Any universe where n_s does not exactly equal 1.0 must have experienced an inflation event. For a universe with a nearly flat (spatial) geometry that manifests a *simple* inflation event, n_s would equal exactly 0.95. For a universe close to spatially flat that has experienced a *complex* inflation event, n_s would equal 0.96–0.97.

An analysis of the three best CMBR maps currently available, along with the best map to date of a feature called the baryon acoustic oscillations, indicates that $n_s = 0.9676 \pm 0.0038$.[16] This error bar (0.9638–0.9714) implies a less than 1-in-10 quintillion (10,000,000,000,000,000,000) chance that the universe did *not* experience an inflation event very early in its history.[17]

A simple cosmic inflation event, as opposed to a complex inflation event, is ruled out at a confidence level of greater than 99.999%.[18] Thus, there remains a very tiny possibility that the universe experienced a simple versus a complex inflation event. Ongoing observations will soon provide a definitive answer. Whatever kind of inflation occurred, the event must have been exquisitely fine-tuned to allow for the possibility of physical life.[19]

Elemental Abundance Ratios

As mentioned, the universe began with only one element—the lightest element, hydrogen—and the value of the cosmic mass density determined how much of this primordial hydrogen became fused into helium during the first few minutes of the universe's existence. That amount equals 24%, by mass.

The ratio of hydrogen to helium arising in the first few minutes of cosmic history determines which heavier elements, how many of each, and when each will be manufactured in the nuclear furnaces of future stars. Advanced life—whether "as we know it" or "as physics and chemistry allow"—requires highly specified ratios of the abundances of the 94 elements in the familiar periodic table. For advanced life to be possible in the universe at any time, not only must the ratio of hydrogen to helium in the universe's first few minutes be fine-tuned, but so must the number and kinds of stars that form during each epoch throughout the ensuing years. (For a thorough explanation and description, see *Improbable Planet.*[20])

The six cosmic features addressed briefly in this chapter, from mass to size to age to inflation to elements, represent only a modest sampling of the known macro features of the universe that must be designed for physical life to become a reality. More than 140 different "exterior" features of the universe, including the values of the constants that govern the laws of physics, must fit within narrowly specified ranges.[21] This reality reasonably points to a Source with the capacity for intentionality, for deliberate, purposeful design and implementation—in other words, a Creator who transcends the well-crafted cosmos.

Our Itinerary

The following chapters move from this macro, exterior observation toward closer and closer inspection of the interior features of the cosmos. After all, the interior of the universe, along with the characteristics of the various bodies that comprise the whole, are what make this vast house our home. Our journey now takes us, chapter by chapter, from the outermost rooms to the innermost, from our super-supercluster of galaxies to Earth's dazzling interior.

As this adventure takes us inward, the indicators of design become progressively more numerous, more detailed, more beautiful, and more amazing. This progression reflects our observational capabilities. The more distant the objects astronomers observe, the less detail can be observed; the less distant, the more detailed. Only within the last year or two have astronomers seen sufficient detail in the farthest regions of the universe to identify specific design features there. So, some patience will be required as we start with a look at the largest structures of the universe. The interior design features will become dramatically more detailed and astounding in succeeding chapters.

Chapter 3

Large-Scale Cosmic Structures

Chapter summary: *The largest structures in the universe are super-superclusters of galaxies. These super-superclusters would pose a significant threat to life without our particular supercluster, the Laniakea (Hawaiian for "immense heaven"), positioned precisely where it is. The possibility for life also requires that superclusters of galaxies and the galaxy clusters within them be organized as exquisitely fine-tuned cosmic webs. The Laniakea Supercluster not only resides in an area of the cosmos least densely populated by galaxy superclusters but also manifests a structure unlike that of any other known supercluster, realities crucial for advanced life. What's more, the great gravitational attractors in the Laniakea Supercluster's neighborhood are optimally situated and oriented for life in the Milky Way Galaxy.*

On the largest of all size scales, the observable universe could be described as homogeneous and uniform. As noted in the previous chapter, cosmic "smoothness" varies by no more than about 1 part in 100,000.[1] This measure of cosmic homogeneity and uniformity must be precisely as it is for the universe to yield the kinds of galaxies, stars, and planets at the appropriate times in cosmic history for physical life to become possible anywhere within it. However, the small departures from homogeneity and uniformity, aka "clumps," as well as their timing and location, must also be meticulously fine-tuned.

Largest-Scale Structure of the Universe

For more than a decade, astronomers have focused their efforts, as well as some of their most advanced telescopes and imaging instruments, on the goal of producing a detailed map of the structure of the universe at the greatest distance

Observable vs. Current Universe

Astronomers define the observable universe as the full extent of the universe that can conceivably be observed (via light or other radiation) from instruments on Earth. The age of the universe and the speed of light thus impose a constraint on how much of the actual universe astronomers can observe. Because light emitted from distant galaxies must travel through intergalactic space to reach Earth-bound telescopes, that light reveals a picture of the past. The more distant a galaxy, the farther back in time we are seeing it. This lookback time, which is equivalent to the age of the universe, measures 13.791 ± 0.021 billion years. In other words, astronomers are limited to seeing astronomical objects and radiation as far away as 13.79 billion light-years.

The ongoing expansion of the universe means that astronomers see the universe of the past. Based on the known cosmic expansion rate, astronomers can calculate how large the universe they see through their telescopes has become in the present. According to this calculation, the radius of the observable universe at its present moment now extends to 46.5 billion light-years.

If the geometry of the universe is hyperbolic, flat, or slightly positive in curvature, then the size of the entire universe is much larger than the observable universe. Nevertheless, we can be confident that the homogeneity and uniformity in the largest regions of the entire universe do not differ significantly from the homogeneity and uniformity observed in the largest regions of the universe we can see. We know this from the realization that a universe with greater homogeneity and uniformity would contain too few heavy elements for observers to exist, and a less homogeneous and uniform universe would contain too many.

possible. For galaxies and galaxy clusters, that distance is about 13.4 billion light-years away. For hot spots in the cosmic microwave background radiation (CMBR), the spots from which galaxies and galaxy clusters emerge, that distance is about 13.8 billion light-years away. (As the sidebar explains, these distances are light-travel distances, not present-day distances.)

Figure 3.1: Map of the Universe's Largest-Scale Structure
This map shows the positions of superclusters of galaxies and super-superclusters of galaxies out to the full extent of the observable universe (out to 13.5 billion light-years away). The dot in the middle, indicated by an arrow, shows the position of the local superclusters. One of those superclusters is the Laniakea Supercluster, the supercluster in which our Milky Way Galaxy resides. *Credit: Andrew Z. Colvin, Creative Commons Attribution*

The distance limit on our ability to observe and measure is not just a practical limit imposed by existing telescope size and technology. This limit is theoretical, as well as practical (see sidebar, "Observable vs. Current Universe").

Figure 3.1 shows the level of detailed mapping of the observable universe astronomers have been able to achieve to date. In this figure, each dot of light indicates the location and size of a supercluster or super-supercluster of galaxies. A supercluster of galaxies is a cluster of galaxy clusters, and, as the name suggests, a super-supercluster is a cluster of superclusters of galaxies. Each galaxy cluster contains several hundred to several thousand medium-sized, large, and giant galaxies and a hundred to a thousand times that number of small and dwarf galaxies. What's called a galaxy group contains, on average, about fifty medium-sized, large, and giant galaxies and a hundred times that many small and dwarf galaxies.

The largest dots of light in figure 3.1 indicate the locations of super-superclusters of galaxies. One small dot (marked with an arrow) shows the location of our nearest galaxy superclusters. Among them is the Laniakea Supercluster, in which our Virgo Cluster of galaxies, our Local Group of galaxies, and our Milky Way Galaxy (MWG) reside. Among the other members of its super-supercluster, the Laniakea ranks as one of the smallest, least dense, and least globular. Chapter 4 will cover how the Laniakea Supercluster radically differs in shape and structure from other known galaxy superclusters and what these differences imply for physical life's existence.

This same image also reveals the existence of several dozen especially large super-superclusters of galaxies in the observable universe. These super-superclusters contain the most massive galaxies in the universe, and these extremely massive galaxies are typically packed tightly together. For multiple reasons, including deadly radiation and strong gravitational disturbances, such super-superclusters are inhospitable to physical life, both inside and outside their boundaries.

The most energetic (thus, deadliest) radiation in the universe comes from the regions just beyond the event horizons of gigantic supermassive black holes that form in the nuclei of supermassive galaxies (see chapter 5). Tight clusters of supermassive galaxies also exert powerful gravitational attractions that can disturb the long-term stability of galaxy clusters and galaxies even a considerable distance beyond the boundaries of the super-superclusters of galaxies in which they reside.

As figure 3.1 shows, no super-superclusters of galaxies are located near enough to our nearby superclusters, including the Laniakea Supercluster, to pose a threat to life or its possible existence therein. The figure also shows that the Laniakea Supercluster resides in a region of the observable universe characterized by a uniquely low density of superclusters of galaxies.

If the entirety of the observable universe were as devoid of galaxy super-superclusters and superclusters as the region in the immediate vicinity of the Laniakea Supercluster, the universe would not be conducive to life. As noted in the previous chapter, the universe as a whole must manifest a certain level of departure from uniformity and homogeneity for physical life to be at all possible anywhere or anytime in the universe. Figure 3.1 shows that the universe's largest-scale structure is neither too uniform nor too nonuniform, neither too homogeneous nor too inhomogeneous.

The outer parts of figure 3.1 may seem to show a lower density of galaxy superclusters, but this appearance is only a matter of observational limitations.

Astronomers currently lack the telescope power to detect distant superclusters of galaxies as clearly as they do those nearer by, in the vicinity of the Laniakea Supercluster. This limitation will be overcome soon after the James Webb Space Telescope is launched and becomes operational near the end of 2022.

At such enormous observing distances, astronomers are seeing galaxies, galaxy clusters, and galaxy superclusters far back in time, before they were fully formed. As the universe gets older and older, the superclusters of galaxies get progressively larger and brighter because of ongoing merger events and star formation.

Cosmic Web Designs

While the universe on its largest size scales appears to be a relatively homogeneous distribution of randomly located superclusters of galaxies, the appearance of homogeneity and uniformity certainly disappears when astronomers observe the structure of the universe on smaller size scales.

Astronomers who shift their gaze in the opposite direction (from close-up and on relatively small size scales out to extreme distances and extremely large size scales) have described the appearance of cosmic homogeneity and uniformity as the "End of Greatness."[2] The implication is that on smaller scales, evidence of exquisite design, or "greatness," is abundantly clear.[3]

By looking at segments (or volumes) of cosmic space smaller than 840 million light-years in diameter, the seemingly random, homogeneous, uniform jumble of galaxy superclusters gives way to the appearance of ordered structures. This ordered arrangement of gas, galaxies, galaxy clusters, and galaxy superclusters is called the cosmic "web."

Many astronomers have commented that the cosmic web looks like soap foam, with filaments and sheets of gas, galaxy clusters, and galaxy superclusters distributed on bubble surfaces (see figure 3.2). Nearly all the universe's ordinary matter (matter comprised of protons, neutrons, and electrons, which strongly interact with light) and much of the dark matter (matter comprised of particles that do not, or very weakly, interact with light) is distributed along the bubbles' surfaces. The bubbles' interiors are largely void of matter. Animated fly-throughs of cosmic webs can be experienced via three YouTube videos.[4]

Baryon Acoustic Oscillations

After years of intensive research, astronomers now have a plausible explanation as to why, on size scales smaller than 840 million light-years, the cosmos is structured in this weblike, or soap bubbles, way.

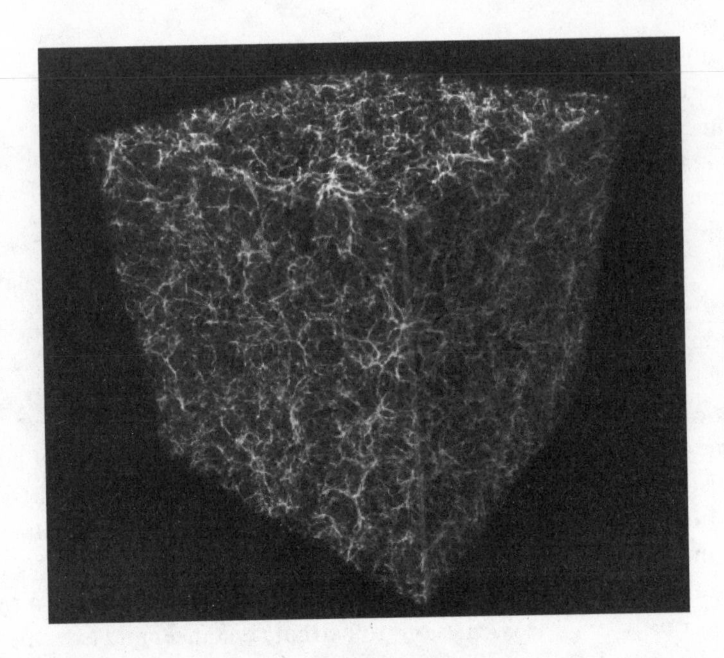

Figure 3.2: 3-D Graphic Portrayal of Cosmic Webs
Membranes comprised of ordinary matter in the form of galaxy clusters, galaxies, dust, and gas encapsulate voids of ordinary matter. *Credit: NASA/ESA/E. Hallman (University of Colorado, Boulder)*

The voids formed from baryon acoustic oscillations arising from the cosmic origin event, the big bang. Baryon acoustic oscillations are fluctuations in the density of baryons (protons and neutrons) caused by acoustic density waves in the plasma (ionized baryonic matter) of the very early universe.

Tiny anisotropies (irregularities) in the quantum fluctuations of the universe when it was much less than a trillionth of a second old amplified as the universe expanded. During this cosmic expansion, high-mass density regions collapsed under the influence of gravity more rapidly than low-mass density regions.

As baryonic matter clumped together, it generated pressure. This pressure came from the photons (radiation) with which baryonic matter strongly interacts. The greater the number of photons and the more energetic the photons, the greater the radiation pressure. This pressure counteracted gravity, creating

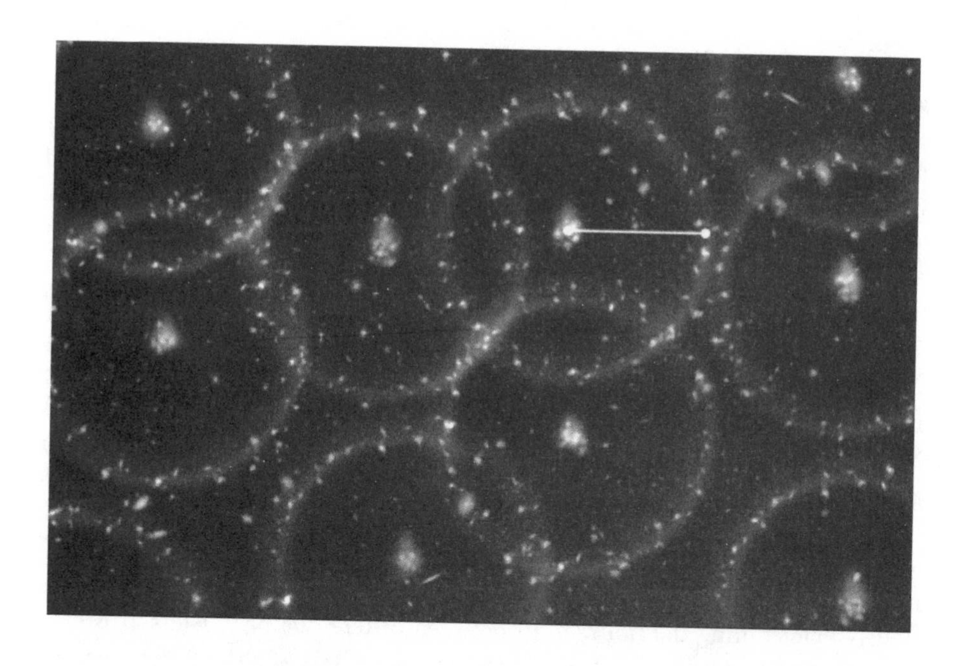

Figure 3.3: Artist's Depiction of the Bubbles of Ordinary Matter Formed by Baryon Acoustic Oscillations *Credit: Zosia Rostomian, Lawrence Berkeley National Laboratory*

ripples that radiated throughout the universe's space-time surface. These ripples are the baryon acoustic oscillations. The Sun provides a helpful analogy: the Sun's mass works to collapse it while its radiation works to expand it.

Since dark matter interacts either very weakly or not at all with photons, the photon pressure that gave rise to the ripples (baryon acoustic oscillations) did not affect dark matter. Thus, most of the universe's dark matter remained at the centers (or cores) of the ripples. Meanwhile, the baryonic matter got pushed outward to form bubbles around the cores or centers of the ripples (see figure 3.3).

A small amount of baryonic matter did fall into the center of each bubble due to the gravitational tug of the dark matter there. However, most of the baryonic matter remained on the surface of the bubbles and only a small amount in the center. The baryonic matter was dispersed along the bubble surfaces as sheets of huge, closely packed aggregates of galaxy clusters and gas, with filaments of galaxy clusters and gas emanating outward from the sheets.

The total quantity of matter, the ratio of baryonic matter to dark matter, the cosmic expansion rate, and, to a much lesser degree, the strength of intergalactic magnetic fields determined the sizes of the cosmic web bubbles. The bubble sizes allow galaxy clusters and the galaxies on them to move apart from each other by the just-right distances at the just-right times (see chapters 4–6) in the history of the universe to allow for the possible future existence of advanced physical life.

Dynamical Definition of a Supercluster

Until recently, astronomers lacked a consistent definition for a supercluster of galaxies. Neither did they know whether the galaxy clusters and galaxy groups within a supercluster were gravitationally bound to one another.

What astronomers did know: galaxy clusters tend to group together to make superclusters of galaxies. Yet astronomers needed a means for unambiguously determining the boundaries between different superclusters. A breakthrough supplied it in 2013 and 2016 with the analysis of a three-dimensional map showing the positions and velocities of 100,000 nearby galaxies.[5]

Astronomer Brent Tully and his team used "the recession velocity measurements" of galaxies in the Cosmicflows-2 galaxy catalog. These measurements indicate the specific velocities by which various galaxies are moving away from our own. The Cosmicflows-2 galaxy catalog provides accurate distances and "peculiar velocities" for 8,188 galaxies, predominantly within 250 million light-years of Earth.[6] (A galaxy's peculiar velocity is its velocity relative to Earth with the contribution from the expansion of the universe subtracted out.) Peculiar velocities reveal the gravitational interactions that galaxies and galaxy clusters exert upon one another.

Tully's team has since released the Cosmicflows-3 galaxy catalog.[7] This newer catalog contains accurate distances and peculiar motions for 17,669 galaxies. The team noted that large-scale maps of thousands of galaxy peculiar motions exposed "basins of attraction."

In a basin of attraction, the peculiar velocity flow fields of huge assemblages of galaxies all flow toward one region. Therefore, the boundaries of a supercluster are defined by the places at which the peculiar velocity flow fields divide, where the flow fields on one side point in opposite directions from the flow fields on the other side (see figure 3.4).[8] This observation yields the first specific definition of a supercluster of galaxies.

Figure 3.4: Peculiar Velocity Map of the Laniakea Supercluster of Galaxies
Every tiny dot in this image is a galaxy. The lines are filaments of galaxies akin to beads on a necklace. The interior lines show peculiar velocity motions of galaxies toward the local part of the Great Attractor, the confluence point slightly above and left of center. The outer edge lines to the extreme left and right show peculiar velocity motions of galaxies away from the Great Attractor. The boundaries between the interior and outer lines delineate the extent of the Laniakea Supercluster. The dot shows the location of the Local Group, the grouping of galaxies that contains our Milky Way Galaxy. Note that the orientation of figure 3.4 is different from that of figures 3.7, 3.8, 3.9, and 4.2. Rather than the Shapley Supercluster being to the upper right of the Laniakea Supercluster, in figure 3.4 it is seen to the upper left. Rather than the Perseus-Pisces Supercluster being to the lower left, in figure 3.4 it is to the right and slightly below. *Credit: Nature/Institut de Recherche sun les Lois Fondamentales de l'Univers*

Figure 3.4 shows how the peculiar velocities (not all of them as accurate as those in the Cosmicflows-3 galaxy catalog) of the nearest 100,000 galaxies define the extent of the local supercluster that is home to the Local Group of galaxies and our Milky Way Galaxy (MWG). Tully and his colleagues named this supercluster Laniakea—a combination of two Hawaiian words, *lani* and *akea*, which mean "heaven" and "immeasurably spacious, broad, and wide," respectively.

Tully's team found not just one basin of attraction in the local universe, but several. Using the same technique, they were also able to define the boundaries of the Shapley, Perseus-Pisces, and Coma superclusters.

While the boundaries of a basin of attraction do define the extent of a supercluster of galaxies, a basin of attraction does not imply that a supercluster will continue to be gravitationally bound. While the Shapley Supercluster is so massive and so dense that it will resist being dispersed by the ongoing accelerating expansion of the universe for at least several tens of billions of years, such is not the case for the Laniakea Supercluster.[9]

The Laniakea Supercluster contains about 100,000 galaxies in 300–500 galaxy clusters and galaxy groups. It stretches out over 250 million light-years of space. It has a total mass about 100,000 times greater than the total mass of the MWG.

Unique Features of the Laniakea Location

Our solar system's address in the universe, if written in a format comparable to that of a typical home or business address, would look like this:

Local Bubble
halfway between the Perseus and Sagittarius spiral arms
Milky Way Galaxy
Local Group
Virgo Cluster
Laniakea Supercluster
Inner neighborhood of galaxy superclusters
Outer neighborhood of galaxy superclusters
Local region of the observable universe

Ongoing research over the years of probing our universe with increasingly advanced technological tools reveals that our address plays a significant role in our existence. Not just any address within the vast cosmos would be suitable, for reasons that become clearer each step of the way, from the cosmic regional scale down to a specific place within the MWG.

Local Region of the Observable Universe

Figure 3.5 takes us from a view of the full extent of the observable universe (figure 3.1) to a slightly closer look at the region where our outer neighborhood and inner neighborhood of galaxy superclusters reside. In this image, even the tiniest white dot is a supercluster of galaxies larger than our own Laniakea Supercluster. Again, as with figure 3.1, because of limitations on

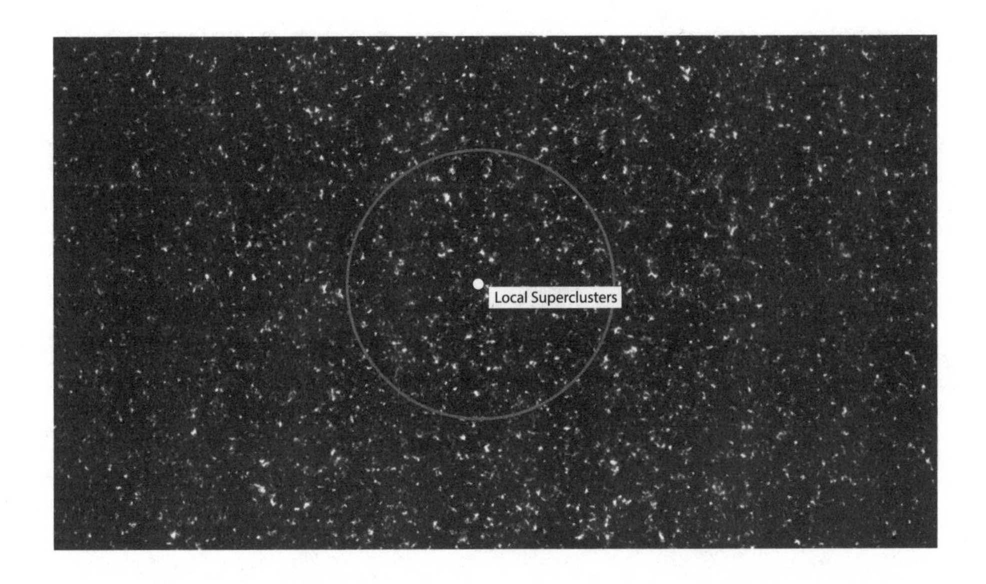

Figure 3.5: The Local Region of the Observable Universe That Contains the Outer and Inner Neighborhoods of Superclusters
The circle denotes the outer neighborhood of superclusters in which the Laniakea resides, and the white dot indicates the position of the inner neighborhood, or local superclusters. *Credit: Andrew Z. Colvin, Creative Commons Attribution*

imaging capacity, the brightness and sizes of galaxy superclusters and super-superclusters fade out the more distant they are from our neighborhood, but as visual artifacts only.

As figure 3.5 indicates, Laniakea's outer neighborhood includes some huge super-superclusters of galaxies, but only one appears in the inner neighborhood (at about 11 o'clock, just inside the circle indicating the boundary of the outer neighborhood). That one, as well as the largest super-superclusters of galaxies in and beyond the outer neighborhood, is located sufficiently distant from the Laniakea and its galaxies to pose no gravitational risk to the stability of their morphological structure and to not blast them with deadly radiation.

Laniakea Supercluster's Outer Neighborhood

Figure 3.6 zooms in to provide a closer view of the Laniakea's outer neighborhood. In this image the voids in the cosmic webs become evident. These voids

Figure 3.6: The Outer Neighborhood of the Local Superclusters
The white dot indicates the position of the inner neighborhood, or Local Superclusters, within its larger, outer neighborhood. *Credit: Andrew Z. Colvin, Creative Commons Attribution*

would appear to serve as safe havens for life. Several of the voids in this figure would seem adequate to house a galaxy safely distant from any dangerous super-superclusters or groupings of superclusters of galaxies. However, looks can be deceiving.

These voids lack the density of dwarf galaxies and of intergalactic gas required to sustain the structure of a large spiral galaxy. Advanced life is possible only in a large spiral galaxy (see chapters 6 and 7). Such a galaxy must steadily accrete (acquire through gravitational attraction) dwarf galaxies and intergalactic gas at a specific rate to sustain its structure long enough for development of the physical and chemical processes life requires. Voids also lack the diversity and quantities of heavy elements that life, especially advanced life, requires.

The Local Superclusters are located on the surface of a cosmic bubble within the cosmic web, sufficiently distant from super-superclusters (see figure 3.6). Above and slightly left of the Local Superclusters are five super-superclusters (in an upside-down V-like formation). Farther above and slightly to the left we see an even more enormous super-supercluster (much brighter and larger

Figure 3.7: Central Region of the Local Superclusters' Neighborhood
The white dot shows the position of the Local Superclusters. *Credit: Andrew Z. Colvin, Creative Commons Attribution*

than it appears, here, due to imaging challenges). Halfway between the Local Superclusters and the bottom edge of the figure is a long, shallow, arcing curve about half the width of the figure of ten super-superclusters. Another huge super-supercluster appears to the right, and two more to the far left, of the Local Superclusters. All these super-superclusters are far enough away to pose no risk to advanced life in the Local Superclusters.

Figure 3.7 provides a slightly closer view of the Laniakea's nearby neighborhood. Here, the voids and bubbles that comprise the cosmic web become more evident. Also, the safe distance from the super-superclusters of galaxies can be seen. Few such locations can be detected in all the vastness of the observable universe, because the farther away one observes, the lower the capability of detecting and measuring the properties of super-superclusters of galaxies and the farther back in time one sees the condition of the universe.

Laniakea's Near Neighbors: The Shapley Superclusters

Figure 3.8 zooms in on the nearest superclusters to the Laniakea Supercluster,

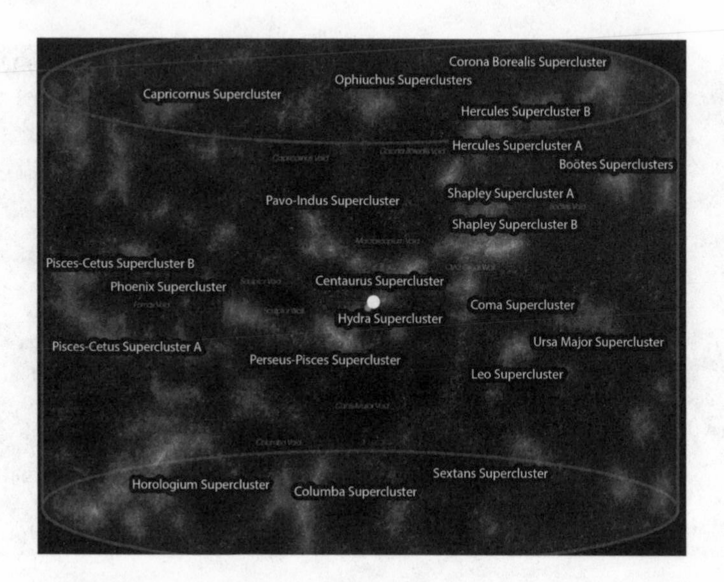

Figure 3.8: The Local Superclusters
The white dot indicates the position of the Local Group. *Credit: Andrew Z. Colvin, Creative Commons Attribution*

and figure 3.9 shows different details of the same area. The Laniakea Supercluster appears as an array of galaxy clusters that slightly resembles the numeral 7 at the middle of this image. The red dot near the center of the Laniakea Supercluster indicates the location of the Local Group within the (unlabeled) Virgo Cluster. (See figure 3.10 for a close-up.) This Local Group, a very small cluster of galaxies, is home to our MWG.

One way to highlight the uniqueness of the Laniakea is to describe the characteristics of typical superclusters, including our nearest neighbors. The differences are striking. To the right and slightly above the Laniakea Supercluster in figures 3.8 and 3.9, a glimpse of the gigantic *double* supercluster, Shapley Supercluster A and B, appears. To reveal the true massiveness of these superclusters would require telescopes stronger than those currently available. These images reveal only a fraction of the galaxies they contain. Even scientists have not differentiated with certainty whether to classify Shapley as one or two superclusters, which explains why the A and B designation is dropped in some cases. Both lie in a direction and an orientation partly obscured from view by

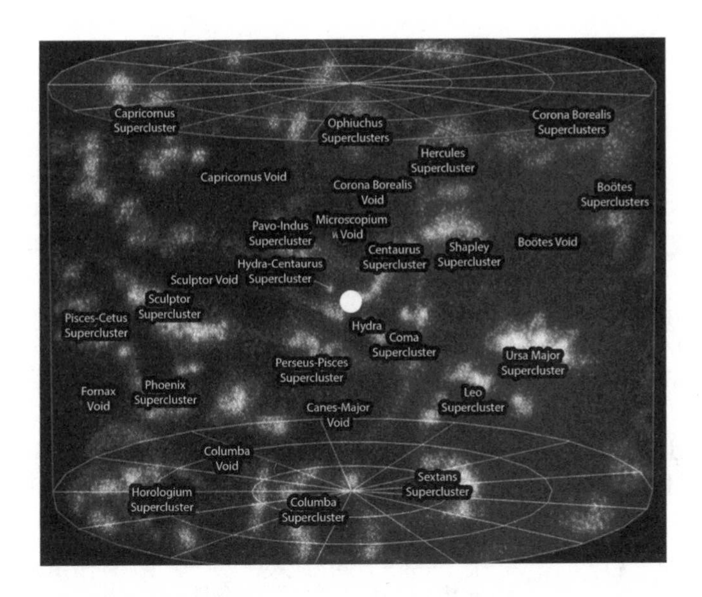

Figure 3.9: The Local Superclusters' Deep Exposure
The white dot indicates the position of the Local Group. *Credit: Andrew Z. Colvin, Creative Commons Attribution*

the intervening Virgo and Centaurus clusters of galaxies, as well as by intervening matter in our own MWG.

Nevertheless, figures 3.8 and 3.9 do show the general shape of the Shapley superclusters. They also hint at the density of galaxy clusters and galaxies within them. Both Shapley superclusters, roughly football shaped, are among the largest and densest concentrations of matter in the local region of the universe.[10] Their galaxy clusters and galaxies are closely surrounded by galaxy clusters and galaxies.

To date, astronomers have identified 122 galaxy clusters in the two Shapley superclusters.[11] Together, Shapley Supercluster A and B fill a volume equivalent to a 160-million-light-year-diameter sphere.[12] All their galaxy clusters are connected to each other by coherent sheets of galaxies, with no gaps.[13]

The galaxy clusters and galaxies are especially crowded near the cores of the Shapley superclusters. A spectroscopic survey by the Anglo-Australian Telescope showed that large and giant galaxies dominate the Shapley superclusters' cores. Based on their research, a team of fourteen astronomers led by

INAF Capodimonte Astronomical Observatory's Paola Merluzzi determined that the stellar-mass density in the Shapley superclusters' cores exceeds that of galaxies in the Laniakea Supercluster by at least 40 times.[14]

As densely packed with galaxy clusters and galaxies as the Shapleys are, evidence tells us they will grow even more densely packed with time. Velocity measurements on thousands of galaxies within Shapley Supercluster A and Shapley Supercluster B show that "the entire structure is gravitationally bound and in the process of collapse."[15] Throughout the Shapley superclusters, galaxies and galaxy clusters are in the process of merging.

Few galaxies within the two Shapley superclusters are still producing stars. Even in those that are, the formation rate appears highly suppressed. A study by two astronomers from Taiwan revealed that the gas supply that fuels star formation has been removed by phenomena known as ram pressure stripping, strangulation, and harassment.[16]

X-ray emission from the Shapley superclusters indicates the presence of high-temperature gas (hotter than 10,000,000 kelvin) in the intragalaxy cluster medium.[17] As the galaxies and galaxy clusters within the Shapley superclusters continue to move relative to one another, they encounter a wind from this hot gas. In most cases, the wind is strong enough to overcome the galaxies' gravitational potential to hold on to their galactic gas reservoirs. This ram pressure stripping has removed so much galactic gas as to nearly halt all star formation within the Shapleys' galaxies.

Galaxy strangulation is another process by which galaxies in the Shapley superclusters are losing their gas. As gravity pulls galaxies toward the Shapley superclusters' cores, it produces tidal effects. These tidal forces yank gas from the galaxies and thrust it into the intracluster medium.

Galaxy harassment occurs when two or more galaxies are drawn close enough to one another by their mutual gravitational attraction that the gravitational potential of one galaxy pulls gas away from another galaxy. The combination of ram pressure stripping, strangulation, and harassment means that the star formation rate for galaxies in the Shapley superclusters is either very low or zero.

For these reasons alone, the Shapley superclusters and the many others like them are not viable candidates to host any kind of advanced life. Advanced life requires a large spiral galaxy, like our MWG, where the spiral structure remains undisturbed and symmetrical for many billions of years (see chapter 7). Spiral structural stability depends upon the continual consumption of sufficient gas to support ongoing star formation. As noted, the galaxies in the Shapley superclusters are much too gas-poor. Also, the high number and density of galaxies in the Shapley superclusters would generate gravitational disturbances disruptive to the symmetry and stability of the spiral arm structure for any resident large spiral galaxy.

Meanwhile, the high rate of galaxy mergers occurring in the Shapley superclusters produces giant galaxies harboring super-supermassive black holes in their nuclei. A super-supermassive black hole has a mass that exceeds one billion times the Sun's mass. Such black holes generate deadly radiation, often sufficient to sterilize an entire cluster of galaxies (see chapter 4).

Laniakea's Other Nearby Neighbors

Another look at figures 3.8 and 3.9 reveals that the Shapley superclusters are not the only supermassive and superdense superclusters in the Laniakea's neighborhood. The Pisces-Cetus superclusters are nearly as massive as the two Shapleys, but not quite as dense.

The Horologium Supercluster is the largest, in terms of volume, in the Laniakea's neighborhood. With a diameter of 500 million light-years, this supercluster is three times larger than either of the Shapley superclusters. Despite its vast expanse, the Horologium Supercluster is remarkably dense.[18] Its galaxies and galaxy clusters, like those in the Shapley superclusters, are experiencing dramatic gravitational disruptions, infalls, and mergers.[19]

Other supermassive, superdense neighbors to the Laniakea Supercluster include the Hercules superclusters, Corona Borealis Supercluster, Bootes superclusters, Ursa Major Supercluster, Columba Supercluster, Sculptor superclusters, Ophiuchus Supercluster, Sextans Supercluster, and Capricornus Supercluster. These superclusters manifest a variety of shapes—from spheroidal to ellipsoidal to sausage shaped—all of which mean that the galaxy clusters and galaxies in them are too crowded together and, thus, unstable and unsafe for any possibility of advanced life within them. Gravitational disturbances, mergers, ram pressure stripping, strangulation, harassment, and nearby super-supermassive black holes rule out the possible existence of a large galaxy that could support advanced life.

Figure 3.10 shows the *immediate* neighborhood of the Laniakea Supercluster. To the right is the Great Wall of galaxy clusters. To the upper right is a portion of the Shapley superclusters. To the lower left is the Perseus-Pisces Supercluster. In between these superclusters are great voids.

The Perseus-Pisces Supercluster is nearest to the Laniakea Supercluster (see figure 4.1). Unlike the stretched out, spindly-shaped Laniakea Supercluster, the

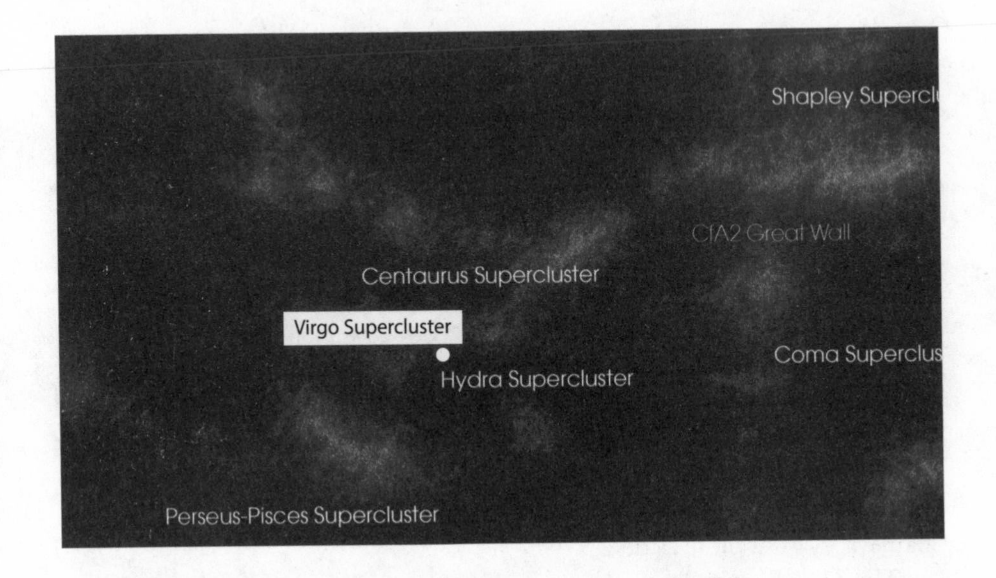

Figure 3.10: Laniakea Supercluster's Immediate Neighborhood
The white dot indicates the position of the Local Group. *Credit: Andrew Z. Colvin, Creative Commons Attribution*

Perseus-Pisces Supercluster has the shape of a fat sausage. In such a supercluster, the density of galaxy clusters and galaxies is far too great to permit the existence of anything resembling our Local Group. The same is true, of course, of galaxies within the Great Wall and the Shapley Supercluster. In the great voids between the nearest superclusters, the density of galaxies, gas, and dust is too low to sustain the spiral structure of a galaxy like the MWG (see chapter 6).

Within the region of local superclusters, the Laniakea Supercluster stands apart. Its unusual structure yields regions of low (but not too low) galaxy densities deep within its interior (see more in chapter 4), exactly what advanced life needs. A three-dimensional, 17.5-minute cosmographic tour of local superclusters, produced by University of Lyon's Hélène Courtois and her team,[20] can be seen here: Cosmography of the Local Universe (May 21, 2013), vimeo.com/pomarede/cosmography.

Obscured View

As wonderfully revealing as maps and cosmographic tours may be, our recognition and understanding of design in galaxy superclusters has long been at least partly obscured. A small fraction of the celestial sphere is obscured as we look out through the disk of our own MWG. Astronomers refer to this region of obscured view as the Zone of Avoidance.

For years, astronomers avoided observational studies of supergalaxy clusters, galaxy clusters, and galaxies seen (but only vaguely) behind the disk of the MWG. They knew they could not get a clear view. However, the situation changed dramatically when they began to make observations of a different kind. While our view is mostly obscured at optical (visible) wavelengths, at radio and x-ray wavelengths the MWG's disk becomes nearly transparent. Radio and x-ray astronomy observations now clearly show that certain well-known cosmic structures in the Zone of Avoidance are much more massive than anyone previously realized—and more significant for our existence.

These massive cosmic structures not only divulge evidence of what's unique about our location in the universe, but they also explain what has long been a mysterious anomaly in maps of the CMBR, remnants of radiation from the cosmic origin event.

The Great Attractors and Their Roles

We've long known that the MWG and the Laniakea galaxy cluster are moving, along with all the other bodies in the universe, in the direction of the generalized expansion of the universe. However, we can now discern a second source of movement, one relative to other astronomical bodies. We are being pulled along, locally, by the gravitational influence of these relatively nearby massive superclusters of galaxies called the "Great Attractors."

This second source of movement became detectable as we saw what appeared to be a dipole feature in the CMBR. The CMBR measured about 0.07% hotter on one side of the sky than on the other (see figure 3.11). It looked cooler in the direction of the constellation Aquarius and warmer in the direction of the constellation Leo. This difference results from the movement of the galaxy group that includes the MWG at a rate of 627 ± 22 kilometers/second relative to the CMBR frame of reference.[21]

This apparent dipole feature of the CMBR results from this movement of our galaxy with respect to the CMBR. It reveals the motion of the MWG in the direction of the Great Attractors. As we are being pulled, one portion of the CMBR grows slightly more distant, thus cooler, while the other grows nearer, and thus appears warmer.

Initially, astronomers had difficulty affirming this interpretation, a hint of

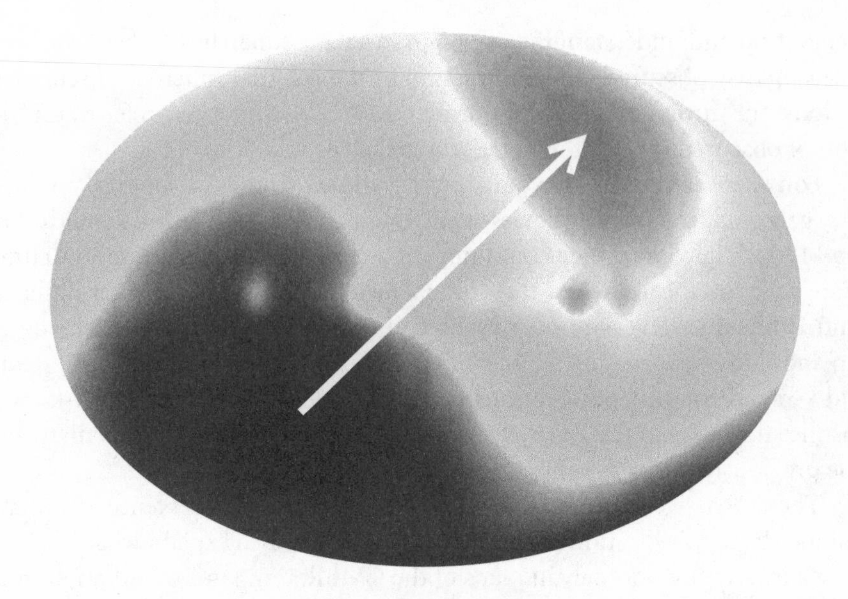

Figure 3.11: Dipole Anisotropy in the Cosmic Microwave Background Radiation
The colors represent temperature relative to the average temperature. Temperatures rise from the darkest blue, lower left (-0.0035 kelvin less than the average temperature), to the deepest orange, upper right (+0.0035 kelvin more than the average temperature). The arrow shows the direction of movement of our galaxy toward the Great Attractors. *Credit: NASA/WMAP*

our movement not just in sync with the expanding universe, but also in the direction the apparent dipole indicated.[22] This difficulty led to proposed alternate interpretations of the CMBR dipole anisotropy,[23] but these were later shown impossible.[24] The refutation of alternate interpretations led to renewed efforts to (1) affirm that the apparent dipole actually results from the Laniakea's (thus, our Local Group's and MWG's) motion toward the Great Attractors and (2) to learn more about the Great Attractors.

In 2004, three University of Hawaii astronomers produced the first all-sky catalog of x-ray-emitting galaxy clusters.[25] They found that the Local Group (the small galaxy cluster in which the MWG resides) is moving in a direction that aligns well with the CMBR anisotropy (see the directional arrow in figure 3.11). Furthermore, they determined that "most of the dipole signal at large distances can be attributed to the Shapley supercluster."[26]

In a follow-up study published in 2006, two of the University of Hawaii astronomers showed that the movement of the Local Group in this direction comprises three factors.[27] The Local Group is being gravitationally drawn toward the large, dense Norma and Pavo II galaxy clusters about 200 million light-years away.[28] A slightly stronger gravitational pull is exerted by the Shapley superclusters some 650 million light-years away and directly behind the Norma and Pavo II galaxy clusters.[29] Simultaneously, the Local Void has a repulsive effect on the Local Group. The Local Void is a region centered about 80 million light-years away on the side opposite to the Norma and Pavo II galaxy clusters and the Shapley superclusters.[30] The low density of galaxy superclusters, galaxy clusters, and galaxies in the Local Void means a diminished gravitational attraction there, easily overpowered by the draw of the Great Attractors.

Great Attractors' Orientation

Because the MWG's disk lines up with and intervenes between us and the Great Attractors, life benefits in at least two ways. For one, the disk receives the least gravitational distortion from the Great Attractors, given their distances and orientation. For another, the huge quantity of gas and dust in the disk of the MWG shields us from the radiation output from the Great Attractors as well as that of all the other galaxy clusters between us and the Great Attractors.

A remarkable feature of the Laniakea's neighborhood of superclusters, a feature that has major implications for the possibility of life within it, can be seen in figure 3.8. Many of the superclusters, especially the denser and more massive superclusters, are strung out in a row that aligns with the plane of the MWG.

Dearth of Deadly Radiators

One especially life-favoring feature of the Laniakea Supercluster is that it contains only one "active" super-supermassive black hole (see sidebar, "Active vs. Inactive Black Holes") Also, this one, a super-supermassive black hole (SSMBH) in the Virgo supergiant galaxy M87, is by no means among the largest in the observable universe.

The most massive and active SSMBH discovered to date resides in the core of the quasar TON 618. Its mass equals an astounding 66 billion solar masses,[32] exceeding that of most galaxies in the universe. It spews out an enormous amount of deadly radiation. However, it is so far away, some 10.8 billion light-years, that it poses no threat to the possibility of advanced life in the Local Group.

Active vs. Inactive Black Holes

A black hole is a physical body of enormous mass and density. Its gravitational force is so powerful that nothing—not even light—can escape once caught inside its "event horizon" (a specific distance from the black hole's core).

A large fraction of any gas, dust, asteroid, planet, or star that approaches a black hole's event horizon will be converted into energy. Based on Einstein's famous equation $E = mc^2$, physicists Jeffrey McClintock and Ronald Remillard calculated that a rapidly rotating black hole, as most black holes and especially the more massive ones are, will convert up to 42% of nearby matter (matter just outside the event horizon) into energy.[31] Even a nonrotating black hole will convert 5.7% of any nearby mass into energy. For comparison, the nuclear fusion furnace in the Sun's core converts just 0.07% of mass into energy.

Black holes in the process of accreting a huge quantity of matter rank as the deadliest objects in the universe. Astronomers call such black holes "active." An "inactive" black hole is one that accretes so little matter that the radiation emitted from just beyond its event horizon poses little or no risk to life located far away from the black hole.

The same team of astronomers who found the 66-billion-solar-mass black hole discovered six additional black holes more massive than the one in M87.[33] All six are active, but also more distant than 10 billion light-years from us.[34]

A different team of astronomers found several more SSMBHs in the mass range of 20–40 billion solar masses.[35] In each case, the SSMBH was more than 3 billion light-years away, again too far away to pose a threat to life in the Local Group.

Many giant galaxies possess two SMBHs in proximity to one another because of merger events. For some, the combined mass of the two SMBHs (or binaries) exceeds 15 billion solar masses.[36] The nearest such massive SMBH binary is 750 million light-years away, sufficiently distant to present no danger.

Within 100 megaparsecs (326 million light-years) of Earth, astronomers have detected 25 SSMBHs.[37] This number most likely represents just a fraction

Table 3.1: Relatively Nearby Super-Supermassive Black Holes

host galaxy	**distance** (millions of light-years)	**black hole mass** (billions of solar masses)
NGC 5419	183	7.24
NGC 1600	209	17.00
NGC 1277	238	17.00
NGC 3842	300	9.70
NGC 4889	307	20.90

of the actual number. Quiet SSMBHs typically go undetected. Another unusual feature of the Laniakea Supercluster is that most of its SSMBHs are in a dormant phase.

Table 3.1 lists the masses and distances of the 5 "nearby" SSMBHs larger than M87's. The especially big ones are all more than 200 million light-years away, outside the boundaries of the Laniakea Supercluster. None poses a hazard to life in our galaxy.

The unusual population and characteristic features of SSMBHs within the Laniakea Supercluster, as well as in regions just beyond it, mean that at this time in cosmic history, advanced life can exist and potentially thrive within it. The spindly, stretched-out shape of the Laniakea Supercluster, mentioned previously, also contributes to the possibility of a safe location.

The Laniakea's neighborhood of superclusters indeed manifests extraordinary characteristics, all of them advantageous for the possible existence of life somewhere within. Astronomers see no other configuration of superclusters remotely like it. The following chapter explores ways in which the structure of the Laniakea Supercluster, not just its location, stands apart from all others. It will zoom into the Laniakea's interior to examine the Virgo Cluster and what features make it a prospective haven for life.

Chapter 4

The Laniakea Supercluster

Chapter summary: *Our Laniakea Supercluster manifests several unique features that support the possibility for advanced life to exist and endure within it. Three examples are its distinct shape, its spatial distribution of supermassive black holes, and its paucity of active super-supermassive black holes.*

As astronomers survey the large-scale features of the observable universe as it has unfolded throughout time, the Laniakea Supercluster stands out. Its uniqueness is distinct from the mere fact that our home resides within it. Certain characteristics reveal it as a marvel of hospitality. Because of its proximity and well-defined boundaries, the Laniakea Supercluster gives astronomers access to detailed study. Observations continue to reveal specific ways in which the Laniakea Supercluster differs from all others.

The Laniakea's most obvious and most significant-for-life distinctions include its shape and its number and distribution of black holes, *active* black holes (see sidebar, Active vs. Inactive Black Holes, in chapter 3) in particular. For review purposes, here are the structures to consider and compare in this and subsequent chapters, starting with the largest:

- Galaxy super-supercluster—a grouping of galaxy superclusters.
- Galaxy supercluster—a clump of ten to a hundred galaxy clusters and galaxy groups.
- Galaxy cluster—a gravitationally bound collection of a few hundred to 5,000 or more medium-sized, large, and giant galaxies.
- Galaxy group—a gravitationally bound aggregate of five to a hundred

Figure 4.1: Map of the Galaxy Clusters Comprising the Laniakea Supercluster
Credit: Andrew Z. Colvin, Creative Commons Attribution

medium-sized, large, and giant galaxies.

- Galaxy—a gravitationally bound system of stars, stellar remnants, planets, gas, dust, and dark matter containing over 100 million stars. The largest known galaxy contains nearly 100 trillion stars.[1]

Distinct Shape

Figure 4.1 shows the positions of the galaxy clusters that comprise the Laniakea Supercluster. The three dominant galaxy clusters are the Virgo, Centaurus, and Hydra clusters. Because these three are so much more massive than all the other galaxy clusters in the Laniakea, they may be labeled (mislabeled) on some astronomical maps as superclusters. (According to the definition established by Tully's team in the Cosmicflows-3 galaxy catalog, they are clusters, not superclusters.)

The Virgo, Centaurus, and Hydra clusters account for roughly 90% of the mass of the Laniakea Supercluster. As figure 4.1 shows, these three clusters all reside to one side of the Laniakea Supercluster's spatial center. In this respect, the Laniakea Supercluster is severely lopsided. The remaining thirty galaxy clusters and galaxy groups are spread out along large sheets and filaments radiating outward, away from one another.

No other supercluster among all those yet observed resembles the Laniakea Supercluster in its shape. As noted in chapter 3, nearly all superclusters in the observable universe are either spheroidal or ellipsoidal, with their member galaxy clusters and galaxy groups jammed tightly together. To some observers, the shape of the Laniakea Supercluster resembles that of a stick insect or a praying mantis.

The Laniakea's long, thin, spindly filaments prove crucial to its potential for hosting advanced life. The filaments provide just enough density of matter (in the form of dwarf galaxies and intergalactic gas) to fuel and sustain the structure of a certain rare galaxy type—a large, symmetrical spiral galaxy—for several billion years. (Chapters 6 and 7 explain the significance of this galaxy type for life.) Because the Laniakea Supercluster's filaments are long and well-spaced, it is possible for a galaxy within one of its filaments to avoid the distorting and other disturbing effects of gravity from the massive Virgo, Centaurus, and Hydra clusters.

Paucity of Supermassive Black Holes Near the Milky Way Galaxy

A significant proportion of all galaxies' total masses resides in their cores. For example, half the Milky Way Galaxy's (MWG's) mass resides in its core. The number and density of stars, gases, and debris clouds in a galaxy's central region virtually guarantees the development of a very large black hole there. However, black holes form elsewhere, too.

A black hole forms when a massive star (typically 10–30 solar masses) collapses following the exhaustion of its nuclear fuel. After a black hole forms, it can continue to grow by absorbing gas, dust, comets, asteroids, and occasionally even another star in its immediate vicinity—if such matter is there. Such stellar-mass black holes are found throughout galaxies, but in galactic cores, the density of these black holes is so high that their mergers are inevitable. Over time, such merging events result in the development of a very massive black hole in the central zone of every galaxy.

As a very massive black hole in the center of a galaxy accretes more and more gas, dust, debris, and stars, it may eventually grow massive enough to become a supermassive black hole (SMBH), with a mass exceeding one million times the Sun's mass. A black hole more massive than one *billion* times the Sun's mass is considered a super-SMBH (SSMBH).

An SMBH resides at the core of every medium, large, and giant galaxy. Some dwarf galaxies and globular clusters (a globular cluster contains 10,000–10,000,000 stars within a diameter of 10–150 light-years) also possess massive black holes in their cores. However, no known globular clusters and only a few dwarf galaxies have SMBHs. All black holes manifest what's known as an "event horizon," the distance from the black hole's center from which nothing can escape the black hole's gravitational grip, not even light. The greater the mass of a black hole, the more distant (from the center) its event horizon. From an outside observer's perspective, everything inside a black hole's event horizon appears black (hence the appellation).

The area just outside a black hole's event horizon is its extreme danger zone, with respect to life. When gas, dust, debris, asteroids, comets, planets, or stars approach a black hole's event horizon, this matter gets converted into energy. In proportion to their rotation rates, black holes will convert 6%–42% of the matter just outside their event horizon into energy (see chapter 3).

SMBHs rotate, and most rotate at very high velocities, because the matter they accrete while becoming a black hole possesses angular momentum. The collapse of such matter into a black hole speeds up the hole's rotation.

Astronomers have developed a technique for measuring the rotation rate of SMBHs (by observing gravitational redshifts in SMBH x-ray spectra). These measurements show that for SMBHs greater than 100 million solar masses, rotation speeds range from 25%–50% the velocity of light.[2] For SMBHs less massive than 30 million solar masses, rotation speeds exceed 80% the velocity of light.[3]

The rapid rotation speeds of SMBHs imply that, just outside their event horizons, they are converting matter into energy with 20%–40% efficiency. Such efficiency equals 290–580 times that with which the nuclear furnace in the Sun's core converts matter into energy. This extremely high conversion rate of matter into energy explains why the regions just outside the event horizons of SMBHs rank as the most radiant and, thus, most deadly locations in the universe.

In 2019, astronomers captured the first ever image of a black hole's event horizon (see figure 4.2).[4] This particular black hole resides in the center of M87, a supergiant galaxy that resides in the core of the Virgo Cluster. Located some 53.7 million light-years away from our solar system, M87 is the nearest galaxy with an SMBH so massive (greater than one billion solar masses) as to be designated an SSMBH. In fact, the mass of the SSMBH in M87 equals 6.5 billion solar masses.[5]

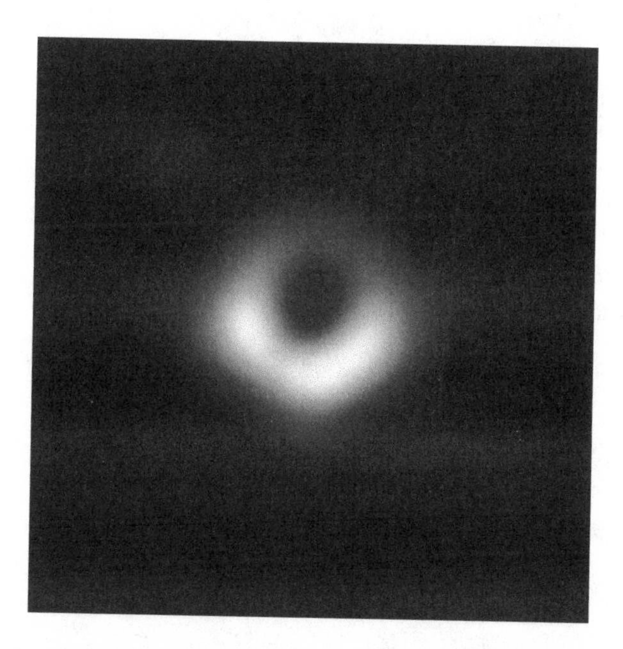

Figure 4.2: Event Horizon of M87's Super-Supermassive Black Hole
Credit: Event Horizon Telescope Team

If the MWG were located any closer to M87, the intense and erratic radiation emanating from just outside M87's SSMBH would mean no possibility for advanced life anywhere within the MWG, much less in any of the other galaxies in the vicinity of M87.[6] And yet, that's not the only danger M87 poses (see figure 4.3). Note the distinct radiation jet pouring out in a particular direction.

Since 1962, astronomers have been observing ultrahigh-energy cosmic rays (UHECRs).[7] Astronomers define UHECRs as cosmic rays (charged particles moving through space at high velocities) with energy levels above 5.7 x 10^{19} electron volts (eV) for protons and above 2.8 x 10^{21} eV for iron nuclei. These energy levels imply that the cosmic rays must come from sources closer to us than 160 million light-years.[8] If they were at greater distances, these highly energetic cosmic rays would have lost some (or much) of their energy due to interaction with photons in the cosmic microwave background radiation (CMBR).

Since 2008, the Pierre Auger Observatory in Argentina and the Telescope Array in Utah together have been detecting a new UHECR about once every

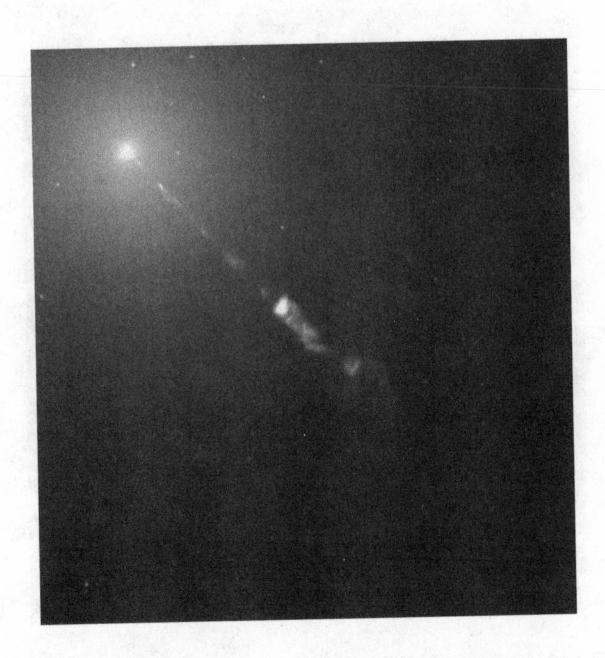

Figure 4.3: Nucleus of the M87 Galaxy Showing the Relativistic Jet Blasting Out from just outside of M87's Super-Supermassive Black Hole
The jet, 4,400 light-years long, is comprised of matter ejected at relativistic velocities by the supermassive black hole. *Credit: NASA/Hubble Heritage Team (STScI/AURA)*

four weeks.[9] The most energetic cosmic ray detected to date had a kinetic energy equal to 3.2 x 10^{20} electron volts,[10] roughly equal to the kinetic energy of a baseball moving at 100 kilometers per hour (60 mph) packed into a single particle! This energy level is about 30 million times greater than the maximum particle energy achieved at CERN's Large Hadron Collider, and several trillion times greater—thus, more deadly—than the cosmic rays that commonly strike Earth.

For more than two decades, astronomers have recognized that UHECRs must originate from beyond our MWG. UHECRs cannot be confined by our galaxy's relatively weak magnetic field, nor can they be accelerated within our galaxy. In 2017, the Pierre Auger Collaboration reported their observations of a slightly dipolar distribution of UHECRs, observations that confirmed UHECRs must arrive from outside our galaxy.[11]

In 2019, a team of Korean astronomers completed an analysis of five years' data from the Telescope Array. This data indicated that UHECRs are arriving from a hot spot centered on the Virgo Cluster.[12] Further, they reported "a new finding that there are filaments of galaxies connected to the Virgo Cluster around the hotspot."[13] Together with other astronomers, they noted six distinct filaments, each with galaxies falling inward toward the core of the Virgo Cluster, indicating that these filaments are dynamically connected to the cluster.[14] The original team deduced that the UHECRs detected by the Telescope Array are "produced at sources in the Virgo Cluster, and escape to and propagate along filaments, before they are scattered toward us."[15]

This team considered three possible Virgo Cluster sources of the observed UHECRs: (1) one or more powerful radio galaxies, (2) transient gamma-ray bursts, and (3) cluster-scale shock waves. Their assessment of the data led to an overwhelming favorite among these candidates. It turned out to be the first, the exceptionally powerful radio supergiant galaxy M87.

As figure 4.3 shows, a jet of radiation blasts out from the region just outside of M87's SSMBH event horizon. It is exploding outward at velocities nearing the speed of light. Evidently, nothing less than the jet blast's extremely high velocities and extreme energy density can adequately account for the characteristics of the observed UHECRs.

Thanks to the spindly, elongated structure of the Laniakea Supercluster, the MWG's Local Group resides at a sufficient distance from the Virgo Cluster to avoid heavy bombardment by the UHECRs emitted by M87's jet. What's more, M87's relativistic jet currently points away from us. Observations also indicate that M87's SSMBH and jet are less deadly today than in the past.[16]

Paucity of Active Super-Supermassive Black Holes

M87 is not the only supergiant galaxy in the Laniakea Supercluster. In our own Virgo Cluster alone, M87 is joined by four additional supergiant galaxies: M49, M60, M84, and M86. None of their SSMBHs are strong x-ray emitters.[17] M60's huge SSMBH[18] is currently inactive, and M49, M84, and M86's SSMBHs are smaller than M60's[19] and are relatively quiet.

Another cluster within Laniakea, the Fornax, contains one supergiant galaxy, NGC 1399. Its SMBH weighs in at 510 million solar masses,[20] but NGC 1399 poses no danger in that it resides 66 million light-years away. Both the Centaurus and Hydra clusters also contain supergiant galaxies, and these, too, reside at such great distances (170 and 190 million light-years away, respectively) that their SMBHs are not a threat to life in our galaxy.

Multiple unusual characteristics of the Laniakea Supercluster's interior, from its spindly, stretched-out shape to the population, location, and distinct features of its supermassive black holes, play a significant role for the possibility of advanced life to exist and thrive within it at this time in cosmic history. Given the vastness of the universe, it may seem strange that a conceivably safe time and place for advanced life would be so incredibly rare, but it appears to be so. The next chapter takes us deeper inside the Laniakea Supercluster to examine the interior of the Virgo Cluster. What features of this massive galaxy cluster make it a haven for our Local Group of galaxies?

Chapter 5

The Virgo Cluster Interior

Chapter summary: *As in the case of the Laniakea Supercluster, some unusual characteristics of our Virgo Cluster of galaxies set it apart. Its core, unlike the typical cluster core, is disk-shaped rather than spheroidal, and the density of galaxies there measures much lower, compared with other large galaxy clusters. The Virgo Cluster's uniqueness can be seen most distinctly in its filamentary structure. This structure makes the existence of our similarly unusual Local Group of galaxies possible. Though situated along one of the Virgo Cluster's sub-subfilaments, our Local Group sits well apart from other galaxy groups. Its location and neighborhood significantly impact its capacity to host a potential galactic site for advanced life.*

In the astronomical research literature, the Virgo Cluster refers to the dense conglomeration of large and giant galaxies surrounding the M87 galaxy. The Virgo Supercluster refers to this dense conglomeration plus the many filaments of galaxy groups that radiate out from the dense conglomeration. This terminology was adopted before astronomers developed observational methods for determining the boundaries of superclusters of galaxies (see chapter 3). For the purposes of this chapter, what is referred to in the astronomical literature as the Virgo Cluster will be called the Virgo Cluster core, and what is referred to as the Virgo Supercluster will be called the Virgo Cluster. For comparison, the Virgo Supercluster referred to in the astronomical literature is roughly half the size of the Laniakea Supercluster.

The Virgo Cluster's diameter reaches across 110 million light-years. Figure 5.1 attempts to illustrate its extent. However, as a two-dimensional projection of a three-dimensional map, it may seem confusing.

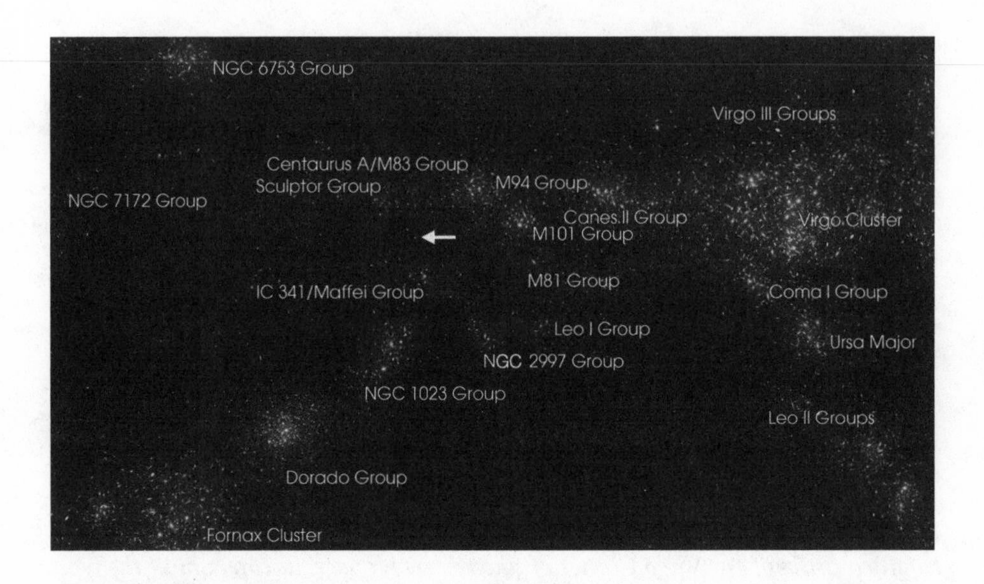

Figure 5.1: Full Extent of the Virgo Cluster
The arrow shows the location of the MWG. The nearest white dot above and left of the MWG is the other large galaxy in the Local Group, the Andromeda Galaxy. *Credit: Andrew Z. Colvin, Creative Commons Attribution*

The spatial separation of the various galaxy clusters and groups is greater for some and lesser for others than the figure seems to indicate. For example, the Local Group to which our Milky Way Galaxy (MWG) belongs appears closer to the Dorado Group than to the dense core of the Virgo Cluster, but it is not. The actual distance to the Dorado Group is 62 million light-years,[1] and the distance to the Virgo Cluster core is 54 million light-years.[2]

Virgo Cluster Structure

Most large galaxy clusters are dominated by a spheroidal core densely populated by a conglomeration of thousands of giant, large, and medium-sized galaxies, and surrounded by a less-dense halo of medium-sized and small galaxies. While the Virgo Cluster possesses a similar conglomeration, its core takes the shape of a disk and is much less densely populated.

The shape of the Virgo Cluster is likewise distinct. Large galaxy clusters typically manifest a spheroidal shape. The Virgo Cluster's shape resembles a flattened ellipsoid.

The most striking difference between the Virgo Cluster and other large galaxy clusters is twofold: the extent to which long filaments of small galaxy groups radiate from the core and the asymmetry in dispersion of these long filaments.

Figure 5.1 shows three primary filaments that radiate outward from the Virgo Cluster core, two with a simple structure and one with a highly complex structure. The filament labeled Virgo III is one of the simple-structured filaments (seen above the Virgo Cluster core). The Coma I, Ursa Major, and Leo II groups comprise the other simple-structured filament (seen radiating downward and to the right from the Virgo Cluster core).

The longest and most complex of the Virgo Cluster filaments radiates outward to the left of the core (in this image) and then branches into four subfilaments. The first subfilament, comprised of the M101, M81, Leo I, and NGC 2997 groups, can be seen extending downward to the right and curling back toward the left.

The nexus of the other three subfilaments resides near to the location of the Local Group. The most dominant of the three, comprised of the Maffei, NGC 1023, and Dorado groups, branches toward the lower left, toward the Fornax Cluster. The second of these three, made up of the Sculptor and NGC 7172 groups, branches toward the left. The third one branches toward the upper left in this figure and includes the NGC 6753 group.

Local Group's General Neighborhood

One extraordinary feature of the longest and most complex of the Virgo Cluster filaments, as seen in figure 5.1, is the region where it branches into three subfilaments. This region hosts an exceptionally low density of galaxies, especially of large galaxies. This zone of low galaxy density along a "wimpy" little subsubfilament branching off from the Virgo Cluster's main filament provides an ideal locale (for the possibility of advanced life) for the Local Group.

Filament regions with a low density of giant and large galaxies possess a greater supply of available gas (a supply that has not been gobbled up by large and giant galaxies). Its position along one of the Virgo Cluster filaments means that the Local Group possesses a sufficient supply of gas to sustain ongoing star formation. This greater gas supply means that star formation in the galaxies located within the group can be sustained for several billion years or more. The importance of this sustenance becomes clear in the chapter describing our MWG (see chapter 7).

The Local Group's position along the Virgo Cluster's longest and largest filament explains its low population of dwarf elliptical galaxies, especially of the larger dwarf elliptical galaxies. Several studies and observational programs show that most large spiral galaxies are being gravitationally torn apart when located among a high-density population of giant and large galaxies.[3] Most large, luminous dwarf elliptical galaxies appear to be the remnants of torn up spiral galaxies.

The Local Group possesses no giant galaxies and only two well-separated large galaxies (see chapter 6), and hosts only a few dwarf elliptical galaxies, none of which are large. The paucity and relatively low mass of such galaxies in the Local Group and its immediate neighborhood allows for structural longevity among the Local Group's spiral galaxies.

Local Group's Immediate Neighbors

Figure 5.2 gives a closer look at the immediate vicinity of the Local Group. It reveals more clearly that the Local Group is situated along a sub-subfilament of the Virgo Cluster, in a region that is sparsely populated by large galaxies.

The Local Group enjoys a good position in the neighborhood. The galaxy groups in the Local Group's immediate neighborhood are all much closer to their adjacent galaxy groups than the Local Group is to its nearest galaxy groups. Furthermore, the galaxy groups closest the Local Group, the Maffei Group (seen below it) and the Sculptor Group (seen above it and to the left), are the least massive and densely populated of the galaxy groups in the Local Group's vicinity.

The Maffei Group consists of three large galaxies (Maffei 1, Maffei 2, IC 342), thirteen medium-sized galaxies, and an estimated ten (or more) times as many dwarf galaxies. Dwarf galaxies in the Maffei Group are difficult to detect, and the general morphology (structure and shape) of the Maffei Group is challenging to determine since the Maffei Group lies in the zone of avoidance, where dust from the plane of the MWG obscures light.

A team of four astronomers measured the distance from the Local Group to Maffei 2 at 18.7 ± 1.3 million light-years.[4] This distance makes it "highly unlikely that the [Maffei Group] galaxies [have] interacted with the Local Group since the big bang."[5] Two Russian astronomers used a light extinction measurement technique to suggest that the Maffei Group may be three million light-years more distant than previous measurements indicate. They also proposed that the Maffei Group may consist of two distinct galaxy groups, one associated with Maffei 1 and 2 and the other with IC 342.[6]

The Sculptor Group is an even looser group of galaxies than the Maffei

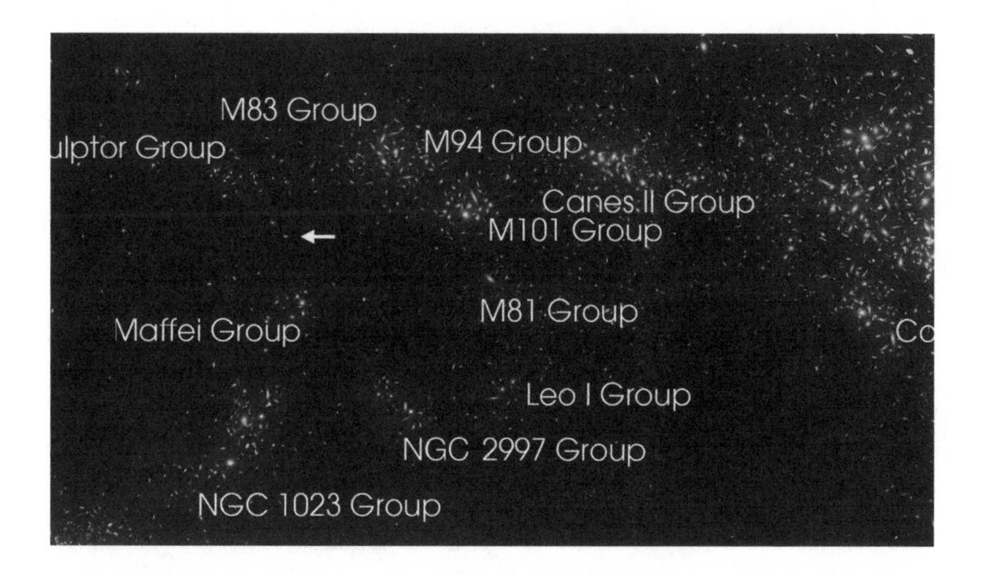

Figure 5.2: Galaxy Groups in the Local Group's Neighborhood
The arrow shows the MWG's location. The galaxy just left and above the MWG is the Andromeda Galaxy. The faint galaxy immediately to the left of the Andromeda Galaxy is the Triangulum Galaxy. The separation of the MWG and the Triangulum Galaxy approximates the diameter of the Local Group. The MWG, Andromeda Galaxy, and Triangulum Galaxy define the spatial extent of the Local Group in this figure. *Credit: Andrew Z. Colvin, Creative Commons Attribution*

Group(s). Within its elongated shape, astronomers have identified one large, ten medium-sized, and an unspecified number of dwarf galaxies. Most of the Sculptor Group galaxies are concentrated in three spatially separated clumps around NGC 300, NGC 253, and NGC 7793, which are at distances of 6.5,[7] 12.9,[8] and 12.8[9] million light-years (from Earth), respectively.

NGC 300 is the closest medium-sized galaxy in the Sculptor Group. Many astronomers believe NGC 300 is a lone galaxy residing between the Local Group and the two main clumps of galaxies in the Sculptor Group. The largest of the Sculptor Group galaxies are far less massive than the largest Maffei Group galaxies. The Sculptor Group galaxies are also widely dispersed. Thus, the Sculptor Group bears even less impact on the dynamics and structure of the Local Group than the Maffei Group.

Galaxies that dominate the remaining nearby groups—NGC 5128

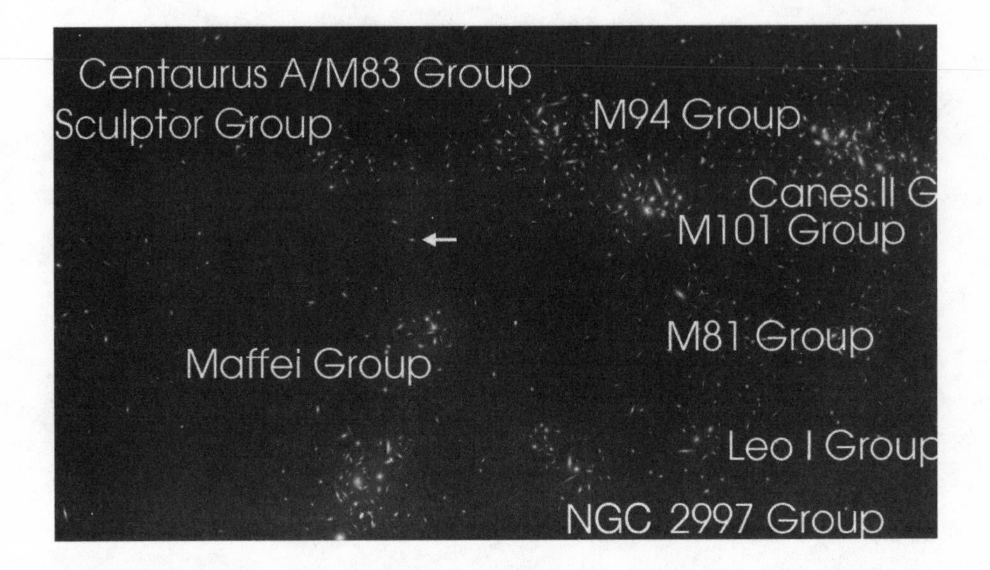

Figure 5.3: Galaxies and Galaxy Groups Near the Local Group
The arrow shows the MWG's location. The nearest white dot above and left of the MWG is the Andromeda Galaxy. The faint dot just left and below the Andromeda Galaxy is the Triangulum Galaxy, a dwarf spiral galaxy that is third largest in size in the Local Group. The Local Group extends from the MWG to the Triangulum Galaxy. *Credit: Andrew Z. Colvin, Creative Commons Attribution*

(Centaurus A), M81, M83, M94, and M101—reside at distances of 12.4,[10] 11.9,[11] 14.7,[12] 17.0 ± 1.4,[13] and 20.9 ± 0.6[14] million light-years, respectively. (Most astronomers now consider the NGC 5128 and M83 groups to be subgroups of a single galaxy group.) None of these nearest groups have gravitationally disturbed either the structure or dynamics of the Local Group.

Figure 5.3 zooms in on the Local Group (all but imperceptible as a "group") and its immediate neighbors. It shows how sparsely populated the Local Group is, with two large galaxies and multiple dwarf galaxies (too faint to be seen in this image), in comparison with its six nearest galaxy groups. The figure also reveals that the Local Group, though firmly situated on one of the Virgo Cluster's sub-subfilaments, resides at a considerable distance from all other galaxy groups in the filament.

This relative isolation is a unique feature of the Local Group. The Virgo

Cluster's other galaxy groups are much more populous and much closer to neighboring groups. As the next chapter describes, the Local Group also possesses several interior features that make it unique among all the Virgo Cluster galaxy groups and perhaps even unique among all the observable universe's galaxy groups.

Chapter 6

The Local Group Interior

Chapter summary: *Our Local Group has the same diameter as the Virgo Cluster core but contains about fifty times fewer galaxies. It has no giant galaxies, only two large galaxies, just five large dwarf galaxies, and over a hundred small dwarf galaxies. The subgroup of the Milky Way Galaxy (MWG) and Large and Small Magellanic Clouds is unique among known galaxy subgroups. The Magellanic Clouds' masses, structures, and locations are optimized for shepherding small dwarf galaxies and gas streams into the MWG at a just-right rate to maintain the symmetry of the MWG's spiral structure, a structure significant to the needs of advanced life. The supermassive black hole population in the Local Group is unlike that of any other known galaxy group, a population that allows for advanced life in the MWG.*

Our home group of galaxies, unimaginatively named the Local Group, is large in terms of extent. Its diameter is as large as, or larger than, other galaxy groups in the Virgo Cluster and about the same size as the Virgo Cluster core. However, by contrast with the Virgo Cluster core, it's a lightweight with fifty times fewer galaxies. While the Virgo Cluster core contains several giant galaxies, the Local Group contains none. The Virgo Cluster core contains dozens of large galaxies, while the Local Group contains only two. The Virgo Cluster's core population of large galaxies includes elliptical, spheroidal, barred spiral, and unbarred spiral galaxies, whereas the Local Group includes only two, both barred spirals. While the Virgo Cluster core contains hundreds of medium-sized galaxies, the Local Group hosts just one, the Triangulum Galaxy, and it's medium-sized only in spatial extent. Its mass drops it into the large dwarf category.

Among the nearby galaxy groups—M81, Centaurus A/M83, Maffei, Sculptor Group, and Canes Venatici II Group—the Local Group has the lowest total mass (although Sculptor may be nearly as low).[1] But its most striking feature is its center. The Local Group's dynamical core is *empty*. Unlike the cores of all other known galaxy groups, it has no giant, large, medium-sized, or large dwarf galaxies in or near its center. This unique core structure may explain why no ultracompact dwarf galaxies exist in the Local Group, along with their accompanying supermassive black holes.

These ultracompact dwarf galaxies, abundant in the Virgo Cluster core and common in Virgo Cluster (and similarly large cluster) galaxy groups are about 200 light-years in diameter, packed with an extremely high density of stars—a hundred million or more. Such features indicate that these galaxies are most likely the tidally stripped remnants of what were once much larger galaxies.[2] The extremely high density of stars in ultracompact dwarf galaxies produces black holes in their cores—black holes at least as massive as a million times the Sun's mass and as great as 30 million solar masses.[3] (For comparison, the mass of the black hole at the core of our MWG, with its several hundred billion stars, has a mass equal to only 4 million solar masses.)

Unusual Distribution of the Group's Bigger Galaxies

What especially sets apart the Local Group from other galaxy groups is the position of its galaxies. In the absence of a core, the group's two large galaxies reside relatively far from one another, and its large dwarf galaxies number only five. Figure 6.1 shows a map of the Local Group's larger galaxies.

The MWG (lower right in figure 6.1) and the Andromeda Galaxy (upper left in the figure) are similar in mass. The MWG's total mass (ordinary matter plus dark matter) equals 1.2 ± 0.2 trillion solar masses.[4] The Andromeda Galaxy's total mass is 1.3 ± 0.2 trillion solar masses.[5] How the mass is distributed within each galaxy, however, is starkly different (see chapter 7). This difference in mass distribution holds significance for both the gravitational stability and the radiation intensity within each galaxy. It also impacts the positions, velocities, and interactions of the other galaxies in the Local Group.

Two of the five large dwarf galaxies sit at the high end of the large dwarf galaxy mass spectrum. The Triangulum Galaxy (to the extreme left in figure 6.1) has a total mass of just under 100 billion solar masses.[6] The Large Magellanic Cloud (below and slightly left of the MWG in figure 6.1) has a diameter (14,000 light-years) some 4.3 times smaller than the Triangulum Galaxy. However, its diminutive size belies its mass.

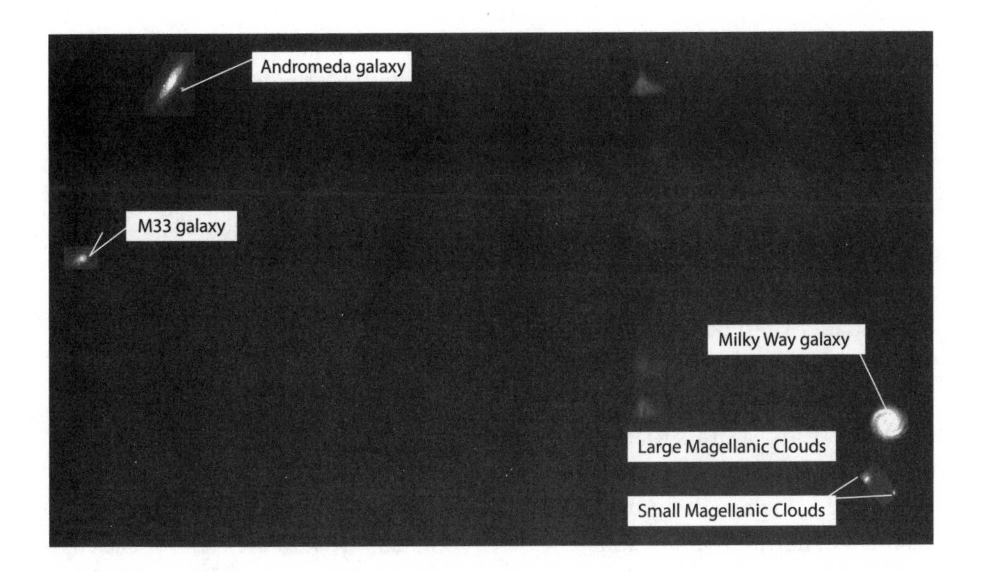

Figure 6.1: Map of the Largest Galaxies in the Local Group
The sizes and separations of the galaxies are to scale. *Galaxy image credits: NASA/ESA/ESO/JPL-Caltech (R. Hurt); Map credit: Hugh Ross*

Astronomy teams have used several methods to determine the mass of the Large Magellanic Cloud (LMC). Based on the LMC's gravitational effects on the Orphan Stream (a twisted tidal stream of gas and stars between the MWG and the LMC), an international team of astronomers provisionally measured that the mass of the LMC is 138 ± 25 billion solar masses.[7] Another team of astronomers, using measurements of the degree to which the LMC influences the motion between the Andromeda and Milky Way galaxies, determined the mass of the LMC may be much larger, at 250 ± 85 billion solar masses.[8] Recognizing that the mass and inward motion of the LMC are likely responsible for the slight warp in the MWG's disk, another team of astronomers determined that the mass of the LMC is 250 billion solar masses.[9] Using an orbit evolution model to trace the infall orbit of the LMC toward the MWG, yet another team of astronomers calculated that the LMC's total mass is 300 ± 70 billion solar masses.[10]

By studying relationships between stellar mass and dark matter halo mass for a wide range of galaxy types, astronomers developed a fresh approach to measuring galaxy mass.[11] With this approach applied, the mass of the LMC is at least 200 billion solar masses. One more discovery, the finding that the LMC possesses a system of small dwarf galaxies in its gravitational grip, also implies its total mass equals ~200 billion solar masses.[12] These measurements move the LMC into third place among the Local Group's most massive galaxies, displacing the Triangulum Galaxy by a factor of two.

The other three large dwarf galaxies in the Local Group are considerably smaller than both the LMC and Triangulum. The total mass of the Small Magellanic Cloud (SMC, seen to the right and below the LMC in figure 6.1) equals 7.5 billion solar masses.[13] At one time, however, before the LMC robbed the SMC of most of its mass, it weighed in at about 50 billion solar masses.[14]

M32 (the tiny white dot immediately to the left of the core bulge of the Andromeda Galaxy in figure 6.1) is a dwarf compact elliptical galaxy with a total mass of about 3 billion solar masses.[15] NGC 205 (just to the right of the core bulge of the Andromeda Galaxy in figure 6.1) is also a dwarf elliptical galaxy, but it differs radically from M32. While the mass of M32 likely resides primarily in its stars,[16] the mass in NGC 205 resides primarily in its gas and especially in its dark matter. NGC 205's total mass is 13 billion solar masses, with only 0.4 billion solar masses in the form of stars.[17]

Distribution of the Smaller Galaxies

Most galaxies in the Local Group are low-mass dwarf galaxies. With telescope technology available in 1998, the total number of low-mass dwarf galaxies added up to 35.[18] By 2006, the list had grown to 46.[19] In 2007, astronomers used the Keck telescopes to discover 8 more ultrafaint dwarf galaxies,[20] all of which proved to be satellites of the MWG.

In 2012, astronomer Alan McConnachie published a list of 79 low-mass dwarf galaxies in the Local Group, along with some information on their characteristics.[21] Of these, 23 surrounded the MWG and 18 were seen to be satellites of Andromeda. The remaining 38 were isolated Local Group galaxies. Later, in just one year alone, 2015, the Dark Energy Survey and Pan-STARRS nearly doubled the list of known low-mass dwarf galaxies surrounding the MWG.[22]

Low-mass dwarf galaxies in the Local Group are the oldest, least chemically enriched, and most dark-matter-dominated stellar systems yet known. In other words, they are unlikely candidates to host life. Astronomers observe a strong inverse correlation between the total mass of dwarf galaxies and the percentage of their total mass comprised of stars. They see an especially steep decline in star content with respect to total mass in the case of dwarf galaxies measuring less massive than 100 million solar masses.

If a low-mass dwarf galaxy manages to avoid the tidal consequences—ram pressure stripping, harassment, or strangulation (see chapter 3)—due to close encounters with a large dwarf or larger galaxy, favorable conditions can result. It can remain rich in both baryonic gas (gas made up of protons, neutrons, and electrons) and dark matter (gas made up of particles that either do not or only weakly interact with photons). Both ingredients are needed to sustain advanced life in a large spiral galaxy.

As it turns out, most, though not all,[23] of the Local Group's dwarf galaxies *have* avoided tidal consequences and, thus, remain richly endowed with baryonic gas and dark matter. The significance of this endowment requires some additional background.

Despite the Local Group's proximity to its neighbors, astronomers have yet to detect most of its low-mass dwarf galaxies. After all, the smallest dwarf galaxies are exceptionally faint, and many of the low-mass dwarf galaxies in the Local Group are ultradiffuse in that their stars are spread far apart from one another.[24] Meanwhile, the most successful of the big bang origin models—the ΛCDM model (a universe at later cosmic epochs dominated first by dark energy and secondarily by cold dark matter)—predicts that the vast majority of galaxies will be low-mass dwarf galaxies, with the population increasing inversely with mass.[25]

This awareness that most of the Local Group's smaller dwarf galaxies remain undetected has launched intense searches for nearby faint dwarf galaxies using integrated-light photometric surveys. One such survey currently underway is the Smallest Scale of Hierarchy (SSH) survey using the Large Binocular Telescope.[26] That survey aims to detect satellite dwarf galaxies of known low-mass dwarf galaxies within the Local Group. Future surveys will likely be able to detect galaxies with total stellar mass as low as the equivalent of 10,000 solar masses.[27]

Even what is known to date about dwarf galaxies of the Local Group reveals several unusual features. For example, about 30% of the larger dwarf galaxies revolving around the Milky Way and Andromeda galaxies are gravitationally connected pairs.[28] For other galaxy groups similar in size to our Local Group, only 4% of the larger dwarf galaxies likely exist as pairs. The high percentage of dwarf galaxy pairing indicates the subclustering of dwarf galaxies within the Local Group, an outcome that suggests interaction of Local Group dwarf galaxies with the fine structure of the cosmic web.[29]

Additional evidence of this interaction between Local Group dwarf galaxies and the fine structure of the cosmic web arises from discovery that five Local Group dwarfs, NGC 3109, Antlia, Sextans A, Sextans B, and Leo P, are highly ordered in both space and velocity.[30] In other words, they are lined up in a row. This elongated positioning implies that they were accreted as a filamentary substructure.

A study by astronomers Alis Deason, Andrew Wetzel, and Shea Garrison-Kimmel has shown that, despite the Local Group's low density of large and medium-sized galaxies, the Local Group's dwarf galaxies have experienced an unusually high number of dwarf-dwarf merger events.[31] Understandably, the higher-mass dwarf galaxies experienced a higher rate of merger events than the lower-mass dwarf galaxies. Most unusual, however, is the finding that the dwarf galaxies most distant from the Milky Way and Andromeda galaxies are twice as likely to have experienced merger events than dwarf galaxies gravitationally connected (as satellites) to the Milky Way and Andromeda galaxies. Because of these merger events, the Local Group is littered with merger "leftovers," including streams and small clouds of dark matter, gas, and stars.

The association of many Local Group dwarf galaxies with the fine structure of the cosmic web, in addition to the high number of dwarf-dwarf merger events, impacts both the gas content and relative abundance of elements in the Local Group's dwarf galaxies. The precise gas content of the Local Group, the relative abundance of elements in the group's dwarf galaxies, the unique population, demographics, and spatial distribution of the larger and smaller dwarf galaxies, and remnant streams and clouds *all* factor into the MWG's capacity to host advanced life. Another major determining factor is how two of the Local Group galaxies funnel essential ingredients into the MWG.

Shepherd Galaxies

The proverb "You are what you eat" has motivated many of us to eat healthier. If we want to live long and enjoy an active lifestyle, we must be disciplined and mindful of what we consume. Some people are wealthy enough to employ a trained dietician who not only instructs them in what to eat but also provides the just-right food, prepared in the just-right way, in the just-right amounts, at just-right times for optimal benefit.

What is true for the human body is also true for spiral galaxies. For a variety of reasons (see chapter 7), advanced life as we know it requires a just-right-sized large spiral galaxy that maintains highly symmetrical spiral arms for billions of years. To maintain the spiral structure of such a galaxy, it must receive

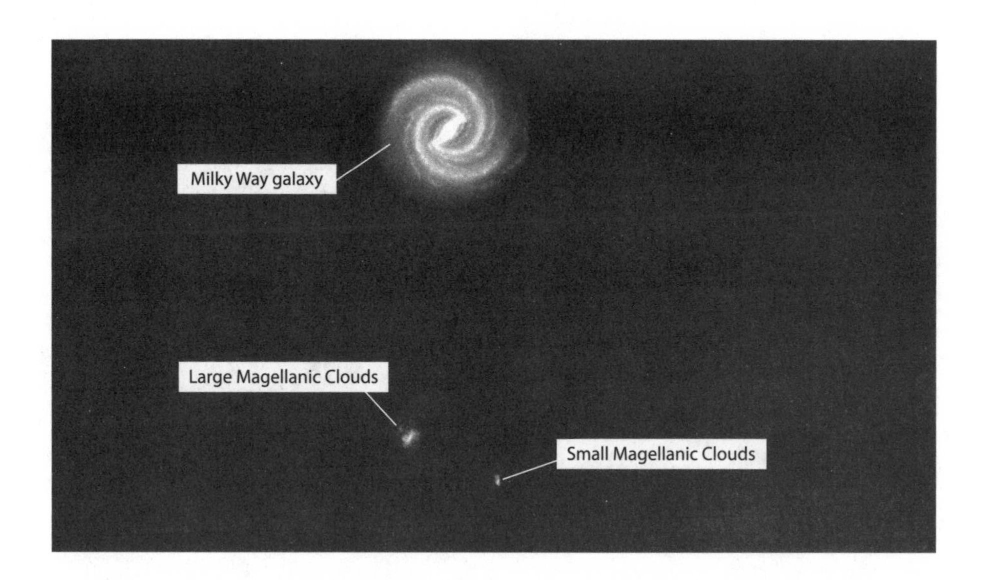

Figure 6.2: Map of the Milky Way Galaxy and the Large and Small Magellanic Clouds
The visual sizes and separations of the galaxies are to scale. *Credits for the individual galaxies: NASA/ESO/JPL-Caltech (R. Hurt)*

frequent infusions of just-right quantities of gas of a highly fine-tuned composition and dark matter at just-right times. These gas and dark matter infusions come from low-mass dwarf galaxies and the remnant streams and clouds from past dwarf galaxy merger events, and they are delivered to the MWG by a pair of cosmic dieticians: the LMC and SMC.

A Rare Find/Configuration

The configuration of the MWG and the LMC and SMC (see figure 6.2) is rare and possibly unique in the universe. In 2011, a team of five astronomers led by Lulu Liu scoured the seventh data release of the Sloan Digital Sky Survey for galaxies roughly analogous to the MWG.[32] They found 22,581 isolated MWG analogues. Their definition of isolated was broad. They defined an isolated MWG analogue as any galaxy, not necessarily a spiral galaxy, of the same approximate luminosity as the MWG that "is not itself a satellite of a more massive system."[33] Of these 22,581 galaxies, 81% lacked an orbiting galaxy as

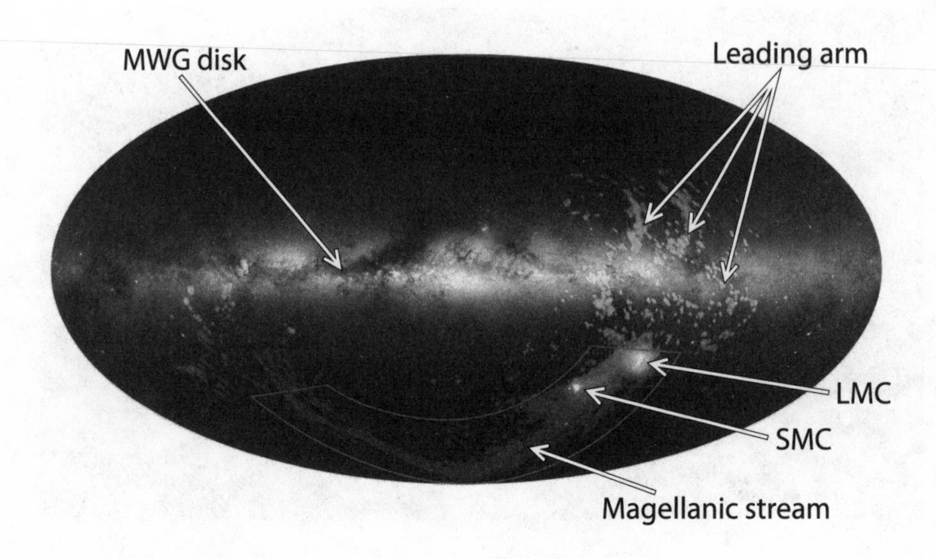

Figure 6.3: Map of the Magellanic Stream, Leading Arm, Milky Way Galaxy Disk, and Large and Small Magellanic Clouds
Credits: NRAO/AUI/NSF/LAB Survey

large as the SMC within 500,000 light-years distance. For comparison, the LMC is only 161,700 light-years away.[34] Only 3.5% possessed two satellites as large as, or larger than, the SMC within 500,000 light-years.

In 2012, a team of sixteen astronomers led by Aaron Robotham narrowed the field when they analyzed the Galaxy and Mass Assembly survey in search of analogues to the MWG–Magellanic Clouds system.[35] Among star-forming galaxies that come within a factor of two of the stellar mass of the MWG, they found that only 0.4% possessed two close (within 230 thousand light-years compared to 162 and 203[36] thousand light-years for the SMC and LMC, respectively) companion star-forming dwarf galaxies at least as massive as the SMC.

In 2017, astronomers Sanjaya Paudel and Chandreyee Sengupta discovered in the constellation Hydra the closest analogue to date of the MWG–Magellanic Clouds system: the interacting pair of dwarf galaxies, UGC 4703, located 264 thousand light-years away from NGC 2718, an isolated spiral galaxy with the same approximate stellar mass as the MWG.[37] The stellar mass of the smaller of the UGC 4703 pair is nearly the same as that of the SMC, and the stellar mass for the larger of the UGC 4703 pair is about 30% less than that of the LMC.

Yet, in the analyses published before 2013, astronomers had not realized the immensity of the total masses of both the LMC and the MWG. Paudel and Sengupta hinted at the anomalously high quantity of dark matter in both the LMC and the MWG when pointing out that no extended neutral hydrogen stream connects NGC 2718 to the UGC 4703 pair as the Magellanic Stream and its Leading Arm (see figure 6.3) connect the LMC and SMC to the MWG.

At 161.7 ± 1.8 thousand light-years,[38] the LMC is 63% closer to the MWG than UGC 4703 is to NGC 2718. The closer proximity and greater mass of the LMC and MWG compared to UGC 4703 and NGC 2718 imply a much stronger gravitational interaction. The mass distribution and configuration of the MWG, LMC, and SMC may well be unique among MWG analogues.

Timing of Development

This unique distribution and configuration of our galaxy and its satellites is apparently a relatively recent development. A team of Australian and Japanese astronomers noted that while most of the LMC's globular clusters measure about 13 billion years old, a few appear to be only about 3 billion years old.[39] The team performed the most detailed calculations to date of the past orbits of the LMC and SMC around the MWG. They demonstrated that the LMC and SMC have been dynamically coupled only for the past 4 billion years and that 3.6 billion years ago they experienced a very close tidal encounter. This encounter induced the rich gas reservoirs in the LMC and SMC to undergo dramatic condensation events, leading to the birth of additional globular clusters. Because it is so much more massive than the SMC, the LMC ended up with all the new globular clusters.

In 2011, astronomers Jonathan Diaz and Kenji Bekki produced a tidal model for the MGW–LMC/SMC system to explain the observed properties of the Magellanic Stream and its Leading Arm.[40] Their model showed that the LMC became gravitationally connected to the MWG just 4–5 billion years ago, and only later did the LMC and SMC become gravitationally bound to one another.

The discovery in 2015 of nine ultrafaint dwarf galaxies near the LMC[41] implies that a quarter to a half of these galaxies were likely members of an LMC-dominated group of dwarf galaxies. Based on this finding, a team of four astronomers led by Alis Deason determined that the LMC fell into the gravitational grip of the MWG only about 2 billion years ago.[42]

Diet and Stability

The mass distribution and configuration of the LMC and SMC relative to the MWG explains to a large degree the MWG's just-right diet. Low-mass dwarf galaxies that have escaped tidal stripping, unlike their larger cousins, are extremely gas rich. Thus, if the gravitational pull of a spiral galaxy is strong enough to draw such dwarf galaxies into its bulge (its central core), it will receive the gas it needs to sustain its spiral structure. However, if the spiral galaxy draws in one of the larger of these dwarf galaxies, or several smaller dwarf galaxies all at once, it will receive so much gas as to produce a "burp."

If consumed by a spiral galaxy, a large dwarf galaxy or set of smaller galaxies would gravitationally distort the structure of spiral arms, destabilizing their structure to a degree intolerable for advanced life, as chapter 7 explains. What's more, the infusion of gas would generate such an aggressive burst of star formation as to shower the region with deadly radiation and cause additional gravitational disturbances.

A team of astronomers from China, Germany, Russia, and Ukraine studied what would happen if a galaxy like ours were to merge with dwarf galaxies ranging in size from one-eighth to one-seventieth the mass of the MWG and then created a computerized reenactment.[43] The team's primary goal was to determine changes in the spiral galaxy's metallicity gradient—its abundance of elements heavier than helium with respect to distance from the galaxy's center—when induced by a merger with a large dwarf galaxy. Secondarily, their study sought to reveal spiral disk perturbations resulting from the merger.

The team's computer simulations showed first that the MWG's central bar (the bar-like structure that surrounds the central core, see figure 7.2) is not a perturbation or a short-lived phenomenon. As long as our galaxy consumes a dwarf galaxy no larger than one-seventieth its mass at a just-right rate, its central bar remains a stable feature of its bulge. Second, the team demonstrated that if our galaxy had consumed dwarf galaxies significantly larger than one-seventieth its mass throughout the past 10 billion years, its metallicity gradient would have changed substantially and its spiral arm structure and disk shape would have suffered one or more severe distortions.

The unusual characteristics and history of our Local Group have allowed for the MWG to maintain its central bar and highly symmetrical spiral arms, with only a few spurs and feathers between them, throughout the past 10 billion years.[44] The new study shows that the stability of this spiral structure has been maintained for many billions of years primarily because our galaxy has maintained a strict diet. It has consumed dwarf galaxies of the just-right

Future Collision between the Milky Way Galaxy and the Magellanic Clouds

The collision between the MWG and the Magellanic Clouds is not imminent. The merger of the LMC and SMC with the MWG will take another two and a half billion years, but when it does occur, it will substantially augment the mass of the MWG's central supermassive black hole. Its present minuscule 4 million solar masses (see chapter 7) will increase to as much as 32 million solar masses.[48] The accretion of up to 28 million solar masses of material into the MWG's supermassive black hole will shower the entire MWG with deadly radiation. The merger will also eject an enormous number of disk stars to the halo. It is unlikely that the solar system's orbit about the MWG core will remain undisturbed.

elemental composition and just-right mass at a just-right rate.

In their published paper, the research team did not speculate as to why the MWG attained and retained such an extraordinarily stable spiral structure. Other research teams, however, have offered some ideas. They point out that the MWG's unique environment likely plays a significant role.[45] In particular, the proximity of the LMC and SMC, as well as their large combined mass and high gas content, allows the tidal forces of the MWG to draw from them a nearly steady stream of gas.[46]

The Shepherd Role

The Magellanic Clouds are massive enough, sufficiently close together, and positioned at the just-right distance from the MWG as to funnel a steady supply of the Local Group's gas-rich, low-mass dwarf galaxies into the MWG's core.[47] The Magellanic Stream and its Leading Arm exemplify a shepherding role—provisional and protective. This steady, gradual supply of gas has sustained our galaxy's spiral structure throughout the past several billion years without disturbing its overall symmetry and morphology.

Disturbance will occur in the future, however. The LMC and SMC are on a collision trajectory with our MWG (see sidebar, "Future Collision between the Milky Way Galaxy and the Magellanic Clouds").

It took the approach of the LMC and the SMC toward the MWG and the precise characteristics of the LMC and the SMC to endow our MWG with the just-right spiral arm structure at the just-right time so that advanced life could exist and thrive at a specific location within the MWG. The specific configurations and dynamics of the LMC, SMC, and MWG made possible a temporary home for human civilization at the just-right moment in cosmic history.

Extraordinary Supermassive Black Holes

One more significant-for-life interior feature of our Local Group is its unique population of massive black holes in the central cores of its galaxies, all of which are either smaller than expected or inactive. A supermassive black hole (SMBH) is a black hole with a mass greater than one million solar masses. As stated in chapter 4, all medium, large, and giant galaxies possess an SMBH in their central core region. The LMC may be the lone exception. With a mass now determined to be greater than 200 billion solar masses, the LMC is firmly in the medium-sized galaxy category. Although it does have a black hole in its core, it is unlikely a supermassive one.

The kick velocity of the star HE 0437-5439 (aka HVS3) as it is being ejected from the center or very near the center of the LMC requires the presence there of a black hole with a minimum mass of 4,000 solar masses.[49] Measurements of the velocities of more than a hundred thousand stars within 820 light-years of the LMC's central black hole establish a 2-standard-deviation upper limit for that black hole's mass. Its mass must be much less than 2,500,000 solar masses.[50]

Astronomers' inability to detect any radiation emission from the region just outside the event horizon of the LMC's central black hole implies one of two possibilities: either this black hole's mass is close to the measured lower limit of 4,000 solar masses, or this black hole presently is accreting little or no gas and no objects more massive than one of the smaller moons in our solar system. Whatever the case, the LMC's central black hole currently poses no radiation risk.

Astronomers have been unsuccessful in their attempts to detect a central black hole in the SMC. Neither have they observed any significant x-ray radiation from the SMC's central region. Thus, neither the LMC nor SMC emits radiation so deadly as to pose a risk to advanced life in the MWG.

The Andromeda Galaxy (AG) is home to the Local Group's largest SMBH. Measuring the AG's SMBH mass is complicated by the presence of three distinct stellar nuclei in the AG's core—three compact disks of stars colorfully labeled by astronomers as P1, P2, and P3. Astronomers Robert Salow and

Thomas Statler analyzed the dynamics of P1 and P2 and on that basis calculated the mass of the SMBH to be 56.2 ± 6.6 million solar masses.[51] Measurements of the dynamics of a hydrogen gas disk orbiting the SMBH seemed to affirm this value.[52] However, an analysis of the dynamics of P1, P2, and P3 by a team of fifteen astronomers led by Ralf Bender showed that the SMBH's mass is 140 million solar masses.[53] Taking into account all conceivable random and systematic errors in their analysis, they set a range for the mass of the AG's SMBH. It must be equal to no less than 110 million solar masses and no more than 230 million solar masses. The earlier, lower-mass determinations for the SMBH were due, they explained, to an overestimate of the distance of P3 relative to the AG's central bulge.

With the AG residing only 2.5 million light-years away from the MWG, its SMBH mass would appear to pose a deadly threat to any potential advanced life in the vicinity of the MWG. If it were to accrete anything as massive as a planet, let alone a star, the region just outside the AG's SMBH event horizon would emit intense, highly energetic radiation throughout the Local Group. As it is, astronomers have been surprised by how little deadly radiation output in the group can be attributed to the region just outside the AG's SMBH.

In a paper entitled "The Murmur of the Hidden Monster," a team of eight astronomers reported on their Chandra X-Ray Observatory measurements of the x-ray radiation attributable to the AG's SMBH.[54] From 1999 to 2005, such radiation measured less than or equal to 10^{36} ergs/second—less than a ten-billionth of its maximum possible output. In the six years after that study, astronomers observed an average x-ray flux of only 4.8 x 10^{36} ergs/second, and that included one brief outburst of 4.3 x 10^{37} ergs/second. This very low x-ray flux resulting from AG's SMBH motivated the team of astronomers to describe the SMBH as "remarkable" for its "extreme radiative quiescence."[55]

While astronomers have been surprised by how tiny the LMC's central black hole apparently is, given the LMC's high mass, they have been equally astonished at how massive the central black hole is in M32, an AG satellite dwarf galaxy, given M32's low mass. A combination of Hubble Space Telescope (HST) and ground-based telescope measurements of the velocities of stars in M32's core reveal that M32's SMBH equals 3.4 million solar masses.[56]

Though M32 has only 0.25% of the MWG's mass, its SMBH is 85% as massive as the MWG's SMBH. The very weak x-ray and radio radiation from M32's core indicates that M32's SMBH must be fuel-starved.[57] Its accretion rate must be less than a ten-billionth of a solar mass per year (that's less than the mass of the asteroid Vesta).[58] The known history of M32 tells us that the accretion rate of its SMBH has remained low throughout the past 200 million years.[59] During that time, M32's SMBH has posed no threat to life in the MWG.

The other large dwarf galaxies in the AG's vicinity, M33 and NGC 205, both lack an SMBH. Observations made with the Hubble Space Telescope Imaging Spectrograph establish that M33's central black hole cannot be any more massive than 1,500 solar masses.[60] Likewise, HST images and spectra show that NGC 205's central black hole must be less massive than 38,000 solar masses.[61] The central black holes in M33 and NGC 205 likewise pose no threat to life in the MWG.

All the remaining dwarf galaxies in the Local Group possess central black holes less massive than 10,000 solar masses. At about double the distance from the Local Group's outer boundary, the dwarf galaxy NGC 404 has a central black hole roughly 100,000 times as massive as the Sun.[62] But it is sufficiently distant to pose no threat.

The nearest *active* SMBH to the Local Group is the one in the nucleus of Centaurus A, aka NGC 5128. Centaurus A is a large elliptical galaxy with a superimposed dust lane likely resulting from a relatively recent merger event with a somewhat smaller galaxy. A team of astronomers measured Centaurus A's SMBH at 45 million solar masses.[63] Astronomer Marina Rejkuba measured the distance to Centaurus A, 12.5 ± 1.1 million light-years.[64] At that distance, there is no threat to life in the MWG from Centaurus A's SMBH.

The Local Group is a galaxy group like no other in spaciousness, sparseness, configuration, stability, and radiation quiescence. Perhaps it's no wonder, then, that it hosts a galaxy like no other. The next chapter takes you inside the galaxy we humans call home, the Milky Way Galaxy.

Chapter 7

The Milky Way Galaxy Interior

Chapter summary: *Our Milky Way Galaxy (MWG) possesses dozens of unusual and unique features important for advanced life, characteristics observed in no other galaxy among all those carefully studied by astronomers. The most important of these include its mass distribution, stellar populations, halos, disks, spiral arms, feathers and spurs, catalog of elements, merger history, and supermassive black hole. Even the galaxies considered most similar to the MWG prove starkly different.*

People who live in China know it as the Silver River. People living in or around Africa's Kalahari Desert know it as Backbone of the Night. People in most of the rest of the world know it as the Milky Way, thanks to an ancient Greek myth about Hera and Zeus. Whatever it's called, the MWG is home to Earth's solar system, and it is a marvel to behold on a dark, clear night away from city lights.

Although no one can take a photograph of the whole of it, astronomers can illustrate its large spiral structure. As noted in the previous chapter, the MWG and the Andromeda Galaxy together dominate the Local Group of galaxies within the Virgo Cluster. Each of the two galaxies possesses approximately the same total mass of ordinary matter plus dark matter totaling 1.2 ± 0.2 trillion solar masses.[1] However, their similarity mostly ends there.

MWG's Mass Distribution

By nature, spiral galaxies possess a low ratio of stellar mass to total mass. In the case of the MWG, that ratio is exceptionally low. Its total mass in the form of

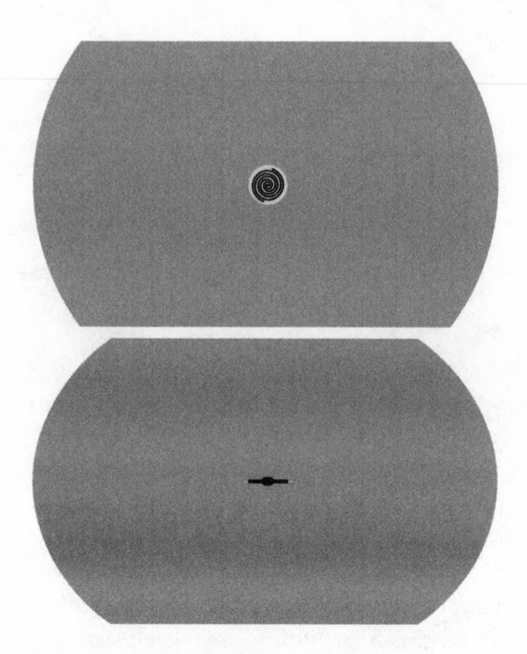

Figure 7.1: Major Components of the Milky Way Galaxy
Top: plan view of the MWG components
Bottom: side view of the MWG components
The central stellar bulge and the stellar disk are shown in black. The thin disk of gas appears in light gray. The much larger dark gray area depicts the dark matter halo, not all of which shows up in the plan view. The dark matter halo would be circular. *Diagram credit: Hugh Ross*

stars is 54.3 ± 5.7 billion solar masses, only 4.5% of its total mass.[2] The MWG's sister galaxy, the Andromeda, has double the stellar mass of the MWG.[3]

This difference results from the different way the two galaxies interact with the matter around them. The MWG has been stripping matter from low-mass dwarf galaxies, matter that falls into its halo. An analysis of this matter reveals that the MWG has robbed up to 30% of its stars from neighboring low-mass dwarf galaxies.[4] These stars were drawn into MWG's inner halo. Meanwhile, the MWG also acquired up to 80% of its dark matter from these galaxies, and this matter ended up nearly evenly distributed throughout the whole of the MWG's halo.

Figure 7.1 shows the three major parts of the MWG's structure. The most familiar part is the smallest component, the stellar disk. This pancake-shaped disk has a diameter of about 130,000 light-years,[5] but its star density falls off rapidly at distances beyond 50,000 light-years from the galactic center. Only a few stars belonging to the stellar disk have been detected at distances as far as 85,000 light-years from the galactic center.[6]

The MWG's stellar disk is embedded in a somewhat larger but thinner disk of gas, measuring at least 165,000 light-years across.[7] Much of the gas in this disk results from the ongoing interaction of the MWG with the nearest low-mass dwarf galaxies. Both disks are embedded within a much larger halo of dark matter. This dark matter halo has the shape of a mildly oblate spheroid,[8] a slightly flattened beachball. In other words, the MWG contains a nearly flat disk inside a much larger, nearly (but not quite) round ball, difficult to depict in a two-dimensional figure.

The dark matter halo is comprised of exotic particles, particles that very weakly, if at all, interact with photons (light). Since this halo emits no light, its diameter is very difficult for astronomers to measure. However, computer simulations show that just beyond the edge of a large spiral galaxy's dark matter halo the velocities of nearby low-mass dwarf galaxies drop sharply. A team of astronomers led by Alis Deason detected a sudden drop in the velocities of low-mass dwarf galaxies about 950,000 light-years from the MWG's center.[9] On the basis of this radius measurement, they determined the diameter of MWG's dark matter halo in the plane of its disk: 1.9 million light-years.

This configuration itself plays a huge role in stabilizing the features of the MWG's stellar disk. The MWG is exceptional among spiral galaxies in its composition of ordinary matter, matter made up of protons and neutrons, also known as baryons. These baryons comprise only 4.2% of the MWG's total mass.[10] The cosmic average for galaxies is 15.7%.[11] The predominance of the MWG's dark matter halo, with its shape and distribution, plays a significant role in maintaining the exceptional symmetry and stability of the MWG's spiral arm structure. This structure, in turn, plays a major role in the galaxy's possible role as a home for advanced life.

MWG's Stellar Distribution

The MWG stars are distributed among five locations: the central core, the bar, the thin disk, the thick disk, and the halo. The central core and bar are often collectively referred to as the bulge. Figure 7.2 provides a face-on view of the MWG's stellar distribution constructed from MWG images across a broad range of wavelengths.

Figure 7.2: Constructed Face-On Map of the Milky Way Galaxy
The large dot indicates the position of Earth's solar system. *Credit: NASA/JPL-Caltech (R. Hurt)*

The MWG's bulge has a nearly boxy, rectangular shape, roughly 11,000 light-years long from end to end.[12] This bulge measures about three times as thick as the MWG's disk. Astronomer Matthieu Portail led a team of astronomers in measuring the total mass of stars in the bar-bulge and found it equals 18.8 ± 1.2 billion solar masses,[13] a measurement affirmed via an independent measuring method used by another team of astronomers led by Elena Valenti.[14]

When astronomer Paul McMillan reviewed updated mass measurements and mass models of the MWG, he determined that the total stellar mass of the MWG's disk, which does not include the MWG's bulge but includes both a thin disk and a thick disk, equals 64.3 ± 6.3 billion solar masses.[15] More than 90% of these stars reside in the thin disk.[16]

The inner portion of this thin disk is composed of stars relatively rich in elements heavier than hydrogen and helium, stars astronomers refer to as metal-rich. Metal-poor stars reside in the outer portion of the thin disk. Our star, the

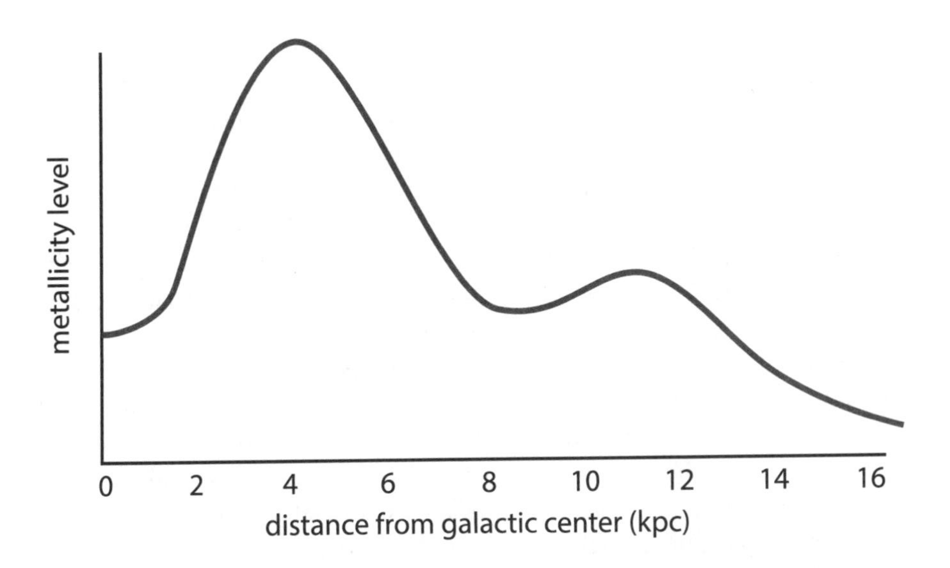

Figure 7.3: Thin Disk Metal Abundance Relative to Distance from the Milky Way Galaxy's Galactic Center
The curve shows the relative quantity of elements heavier than helium in the MWG's gas and dust with respect to distance from MWG's center. 1 kiloparsec (kpc) = 3,262 light-years. Data for the curve is from Yu. N. Mishurov, Jacques R. D. Lépine, and I. A. Acharova, "Corotation: Its Influence on the Chemical Abundance Pattern of the Galaxy," *Astrophysical Journal Letters* 571, no. 2 (June 1, 2002): L113–L115, doi:10.1086/341360.
Diagram credit: Hugh Ross

Sun, is located at the boundary between the inner portion and outer portion of the thin disk.

The average thickness of the thin disk equals ~1,000 light-years.[17] The average thickness of the thick disk is about three times greater, ~3,000 light-years.[18] Both disks extend out to nearly the same radial distance from the galactic center.[19] Although the two disks formed in parallel, they did so at much different rates.[20]

The thick disk formed quickly, on an accretion time scale of only 0.1 billion years, approximately 10 billion years ago.[21] By contrast, the thin disk (which formed at different rates) formed on an accretion time scale of 7 billion years in the vicinity of the Sun, and elsewhere on an accretion timescale of 10 billion years.[22]

The thick disk formed during a period when the MWG was experiencing high turbulence due to the gravitational collapse of gas-rich giant clumps.[23] This turbulence gave rise to a thick disk and briefly prevented the formation of a thin disk. The metal abundance of the gas and stars in the thick disk is low, relatively uniform, and shows no variation with respect to distance from the galactic center.[24] Such is not the case, however, for the thin disk. Figure 7.3 shows the variation in metal abundance of the gas and dust (the ingredients for star formation) in the thin disk relative to distance from the galactic center.

The best measurement to date of the Sun's distance from the galactic center is 8.178 ± 0.013 kiloparsecs (26,673 ± 42 light-years).[25] That distance places the Sun and its system of planets at the lowest point of the dip between the two peaks of metallicity level (see figure 7.3). This location also coincides with the boundary between the inner and outer portions of the thin disk and bears significance for advanced life that becomes apparent in later chapters.

A stellar halo much smaller than the dark matter halo surrounds on all sides and ends both the inner and outer disks. This stellar halo's mass is much smaller than that of the thin and thick disks. Two independent teams of astronomers analyzing two different star surveys determined that the mass of the stellar halo is 1.30 ± 0.25 billion solar masses, which amounts to just 2% of the MWG's total stellar mass.[26] The shape of the stellar halo may be described as a prolate spheroid, slightly more flattened than the much larger dark matter halo.[27] It appears to have a sharp boundary at a distance of 520,000 light-years from the galactic center.[28]

Last Big Merger

The elemental composition of the stars in the stellar halo measures the same as that of the thick disk stars.[29] Also, the stars that populate both the thick disk and the stellar halo all measure to be old, if one excludes the high-velocity runaway stars that escaped from the bulge and thin disk. These similarities imply that the stellar halo and the thick disk formed from the same event that occurred long ago in the MWG's history.

An analysis of the two major surveys of stellar populations, the APOGEE and Gaia DR2 surveys, reveals that the MWG experienced an unusually intense accretion event more than 10 billion years ago.[30] The most in-depth analysis of these surveys shows that 10–11 billion years ago, the MWG accreted either a medium-sized galaxy or a high-mass dwarf galaxy astronomers call the Gaia-Enceladus-Sausage (GES).[31] This accretion event goes a long way toward explaining the observed properties of MWG's stellar halo.[32]

A team of astronomers led by G. C. Myeong found evidence of a second ancient accretion event.[33] They showed that just before the MWG accreted GES it accreted a slightly smaller galaxy they named the Sequoia Galaxy.

These two ancient accretion events grew the MWG to a sufficient size that it could maintain its structure despite potential gravitational interactions with smaller galaxies. Currently, if the MWG were any smaller, its gravitational interaction with the Large Magellanic Cloud (LMC) would have so warped its spiral arm configuration as to render it unfit for advanced life.[34]

Galaxy Outlier

The uniqueness of the MWG shows up most clearly in contrast with other spiral galaxies of similar mass. Its sister galaxy, the Andromeda, reveals what is typical for such galaxies and, thus, serves as a helpful foil.

The ratio of the MWG's stellar mass to its total mass is lower, by a factor of 2, than is typical of other local spiral galaxies its size, including Andromeda (as noted above).[35] The angular momentum of the MWG disk (the product of the disk radius and the disk rotational velocity) is only 40% that of the Andromeda Galaxy (AG).[36] The angular momenta of the disks in other spiral galaxies of similar total mass average more than twice that of the MWG.[37]

The MWG has a much smaller disk scale length than is typical. (The disk scale length refers to a measure of a disk's mass distribution.[38]) The disk scale length for the MWG measures 3.00 ± 0.22 kiloparsecs (97,800 ± 700 light-years).[39] The disk scale length for the AG measures 6.08 ± 0.09 kiloparsecs (19,830 ± 290 light-years).[40] Likewise, other local spiral galaxies in the MWG's mass range possess disk scale lengths about double the MWG's.[41]

The MWG is also unique in that its stellar halo is clearly divided into two compositionally distinct regions: an inner and an outer halo. (A spiral galaxy's stellar halo refers to stars outside the galaxy's brightest regions—the bulge and the disk.) Stars in the MWG's outer stellar halo are unusually low in their abundance of elements heavier than helium, three times lower, in fact, than inner stellar halo stars.[42]

As part of a different stellar category, outskirt stars are those located 17,000–100,000 light-years from the galactic center. Stars in the MWG's outskirts possess a much lower abundance of elements heavier than helium, again three times lower, than outskirt stars of other local spiral galaxies of similar mass.[43]

Stars in the MWG's outskirts are also more uniform in their elemental abundance profiles, with no observed dependence on distance from the galactic center.[44] The AG halo stars, typical of the halo stars in other local spiral galaxies, show a sharp decline (by a factor of 8) in their abundance of heavier-than-helium elements moving outward from 30,000 to 330,000 light-years from the galactic center.[45] The trend in all local spiral galaxies shows increasing abundance of heavy elements (elements heavier than helium) with increasing disk rotation velocity—except in the MWG.[46]

Another unique feature of the MWG is that, unlike other local spiral galaxies, the MWG's outer halo stars show a sharp drop-off in stellar number density beyond 90,000 light-years from the galactic center.[47] This drop-off becomes even steeper at distances greater than 160,000 light-years from the galactic center.[48]

All these properties of the stars in the outskirts of the MWG imply that such stars have been dynamically undisturbed for a very long time. More than any other stars in a galaxy, outskirt stars are sensitive to the residual effects of past merger events, "with the outer regions of the halo being particularly information rich."[49]

The observed features of the MWG's outskirt stars indicate that over the past 10 billion years, the MWG has experienced no merger event with a galaxy as massive as, or more massive than, 1 billion solar masses.[50] The observed features of the MWG's disks likewise establish that the MWG has experienced no merger with another galaxy of that size in at least the past 4 billion years.[51] By contrast, the observed features of outskirt stars in other spiral galaxies of the same approximate mass as the MWG indicate they have experienced several major mergers during the past several billion years.[52]

In fact, throughout its past 10 billion years, the MWG has suffered no merger events of sufficient magnitude to alter its spiral structure in any life-threatening manner. Meanwhile, it has accreted sufficient streams of gas and a sufficient number and rate of low-mass dwarf galaxies to sustain its spiral structure. Unlike other known spiral galaxies, the MWG continuously "sips" rather than intermittently "gulps" available matter. This unique history helps explain why the MWG today has such remarkably symmetrical spiral arms (see figure 7.8), a spiral structure and stability essential to the possibility of hosting advanced life.

Spiral Arm Pitch Angle

Another rare interior feature of the MWG is the pitch angle of its spiral arms. For a spiral arm, the pitch angle is the angle between lines tangent to a circle and to the spiral arm at a given distance from the galactic center (see figure

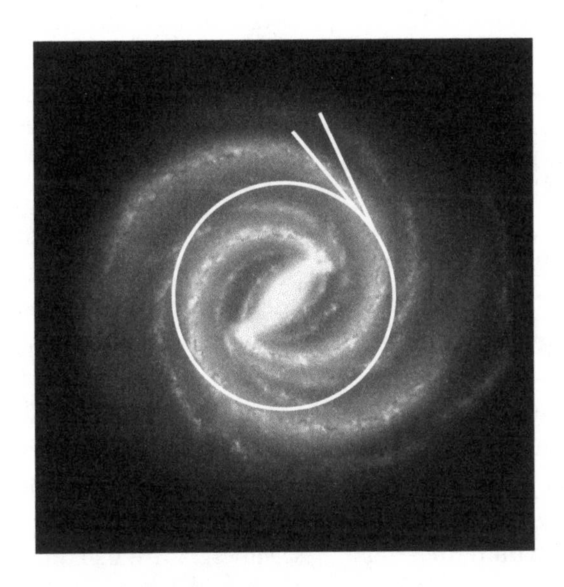

Figure 7.4: Spiral Arm Pitch Angle
The pitch angle is the angle between the two straight lines. *Image credit: NASA/JPL-Caltech (R. Hurt); Diagram credit: Hugh Ross*

7.4). The smaller the pitch angle, the more tightly wrapped the spiral arms will be.

Astronomers have accumulated an abundance of observational data showing that the spiral arm pitch angle correlates with other crucial-for-life galactic features. For example, the smaller the pitch angle, the larger the stellar mass in the bulge.[53] Unless the stellar mass in the bulge is sufficiently large, the spiral arms are susceptible to disturbance by close-passing galaxies or during accretion of gas streams and dwarf galaxies. In either case, the spiral arm structure cannot be sustained for a long time. However, if the stellar mass of the bulge is too large, it will produce an especially enormous supermassive black hole with accompanying deadly radiation.

An inverse correlation also exists between the size of the pitch angle and the mass of the galaxy's central black hole. The smaller the pitch angle, the more massive the central black hole.[54] A high-mass supermassive black hole in or near the galactic center will generate deadly radiation throughout its galaxy and beyond. Another inverse correlation exists between the pitch angle and that galaxy's dark matter content. The larger the pitch angle, the lower the galaxy's quantity of dark matter.[55] A high dark matter content is necessary for stabilizing spiral arm structure over a long time. The pitch angle must fall within a narrow range to avoid one pitfall and meet the other necessity for the possibility of advanced life.

Yet another strong correlation exists between the pitch angle and the proportion of a galaxy's total mass that exists in the form of stars. The smaller the pitch angle, the more that stars contribute to the total mass of a galaxy.[56] A higher stellar mass results in more deadly radiation sources, but insufficient stellar mass means the spiral structure will be more easily disturbed by close-passing galaxies and by the galaxy's accretion of gas streams and dwarf galaxies.

The pitch angle also relates to the number of a galaxy's spiral arms. The smaller the pitch angle, the greater the number of a spiral galaxy's arms.[57] The population of supergiant stars tends to be higher in two-arm spiral galaxies than in galaxies with more arms. These supergiant stars emit deadly, high-energy radiation.

The spiral arm pitch angle of the MWG—a four-arm structure, with two dominant and two subsidiary arms[58]—measures about 12° for the Sagittarius-Carina arm (inner to the Sun's orbital distance),[59] and 13.3° ± 1.3° for the Perseus arm (outer to the Sun's orbital distance).[60] As it is for human beings, so it is for spiral galaxies. To be either too tightly or too loosely wound up is not good.

When a galaxy's spiral arms are tightly wound, the arms will be close together. Any planet that exists between two of the spiral arms would be close to the powerful ultraviolet radiation emitted by the young giant stars in the spiral arms. Additionally, it would be subject to gravitational disturbances caused by giant molecular clouds that also reside in the spiral arms.

Tightly wound galaxy arms also generate an inordinate number of "spurs" and "feathers" that extend into the space between arms. These outcroppings expose any planets between spiral arms to more sources of deadly radiation and gravitational disturbances.

On the other hand, when a galaxy's spiral arms are loosely wound, the symmetry of their structure is easily disrupted. Such structure is prone to warping by nearby galaxies, even nearby dwarf galaxies, and by the galaxy's own internal inhomogeneities.

Benefits of a Large Spiral Galaxy

Galaxies without spiral arms may be considered noncandidates to host life

Figure 7.5: Blue and Red Population Spiral Galaxies
Credit: NGC 1309 (left) NASA/ESA/Hubble Legacy Archive; NGC 3190 (right) European Southern Observatory

due to the high density of stars in such galaxies. High star density leads to erratic planetary orbits and frequent bombardment by planetesimals, comets, asteroids, molecular clouds, and dust. Large armless galaxies grow especially large supermassive black holes, the kind that generate deadly radiation. Given that the existence of advanced life requires a long, continuous history of less-advanced life,[61] a galaxy that can possibly host advanced life must maintain its stable spiral structure for at least several billion years.

Dwarf galaxies, on the other hand, lack mass. The smaller the total mass of a galaxy, the higher the probability that it will suffer frequent and substantial gravitational disturbances due to the influence of other nearby galaxies. The MWG is barely massive enough to have avoided such disturbances over the past 4 billion years.

At the same time, the mass of the MWG is just small enough to avoid attracting other galaxies of sufficient mass to substantially disturb its structure. While the MWG is on a collision course with both the LMC and the AG, neither of these collisions will occur within the next 2.5 billion years, and the

MWG's structure appears stable enough for life's existence, here, for at least the next billion years.

Red, Green, or Blue

Nearly all galaxies are described by one of two colors. Young stars tend to be hot and, therefore, blue-colored. Old stars tend to be cooler and, therefore, red-colored. So, galaxies aggressively forming new stars manifest a blue color, while galaxies where star formation has ceased take on a reddish hue. Since astronomers developed the first galaxy catalogs a century ago, they categorized the galaxies of the universe as belonging to either the blue population or the red (see figure 7.5).[62]

The MWG stands out, however, in that it fits into neither the blue nor the red category. Rather, it appears green. While star formation has certainly subsided in the MWG, it has not yet ended. Thus, our galaxy contains both blue stars and stars sufficiently aged to be yellow, but not many that are red. Blended, these stars give the MWG galaxy its green hue.

Green galaxies are rare, but they are also exactly the kind required for the possible existence of advanced life. A galaxy dominated by blue stars will bathe any planets it contains with multiple intense flares and an abundance of ultraviolet and x-ray radiation. What's more, the aggressive star formation in a blue galaxy will inevitably cause major disturbances (warps, bends, spurs, and feathers) in its spiral structure.

A galaxy dominated by red stars will also bathe its planets with multiple, intense flares, but it will also expose them to deadly supernova and nova events. For example, within NGC 3190 (in figure 7.6) two supernova eruption events occurred in a single year.[63] Red galaxies also lack the necessary level of ongoing star formation to sustain their spiral structure over the long term. The MWG's spiral arms are stable, well separated, highly symmetrical, free of any significant warps or bends, and relatively free of spurs and feathers. These arm conditions are possible because our galaxy is dominated by yellow stars well complemented by significant populations of blue stars.

A team of Australian astronomers has labeled the MWG's current green hue as its "midlife crisis."[64] The label seems to fit in that its disk lacks a high number of both very old stars and newborn stars. It is experiencing a transition, a midlife change from a star-forming galaxy to a galaxy in which star formation has shut down. However, just as reaching midlife inspires people to reconsider and adjust their priorities, so, too, the MWG's midlife brought about an important transformation. The MWG's activity shifted from building the required components for advanced life (carbon, nitrogen, oxygen, phosphorus, calcium, iron, etc.) to supporting and sustaining advanced life.

The Australian team showed that the MWG has other unique features that favor the support of advanced life. For a galaxy of its size and mass it is "underluminous," thereby protecting Earth from radiation exposure.[65] This low luminosity also enables astronomers to explore the MWG and the universe beyond in much greater depth and detail. Discovery of many of the interior characteristics described in these pages is open to study, in large part, due to this lack of luminosity.

A Supermassive Black Hole Like No Other

As chapter 4 mentions, all medium, large, and giant galaxies host a supermassive black hole in their cores. Astronomers call any black hole in excess of one million solar masses supermassive. From just outside its event horizon, a supermassive black hole (SMBH) can generate radiation so deadly as to render advanced life impossible virtually everywhere within its galaxy. This radiation can be so powerful as to render advanced life impossible in multiple galaxies within the SMBH's vicinity.

In the case of the MWG, it surrounds an exceptionally low-mass SMBH, one that weighs in at only 4.152 ± 0.014 million solar masses.[66] This low mass limits the quantity of deadly radiation it can generate. Astronomers have determined that the MWG's SMBH's low mass is truly extraordinary and unexpected. It deviates by far from the otherwise strong and consistent correlations among multiple galaxy characteristics and the mass of those galaxies' SMBHs. Based on these seven features, astronomers would expect the MWG's SMBH to be significantly more massive than it is:

1. number of globular clusters orbiting the galaxy,[67]
2. mass of the galaxy's central bulge,[68]
3. luminosity of the galaxy's central bulge,[69]
4. luminosity of the galaxy,[70]
5. the pitch angle of the spiral arms,[71]
6. velocity dispersion (range of velocities) of stars in the central bulge,[72] and
7. total stellar mass.[73]

In a galaxy's central bulge, the density of stars is nearly equal to that in a globular cluster, a tight grouping of 50,000–10,000,000 stars (see figure 7.6).

Figure 7.6: NGC 362, a Typical Globular Cluster
Credit: NASA/ESA/Hubble WFC3

The velocity of gas in a galaxy's central bulge is directly proportional to the mass of its SMBH. This gas velocity can be difficult to measure. Fortunately, the velocity dispersion of stars in a central bulge is easier to measure, and astronomers have demonstrated that it correlates tightly with the gas velocity.

These correlations apply to all galaxies, but with slight variation, depending on the type of galaxy hosting the SMBH.[74] In a galaxy with an active galactic nucleus (one releasing a copious amount of intense radiation), astronomers must first correct for the vision-dimming effect of intervening dust.[75] In supergiant elliptical galaxies within the cores of large galaxy clusters, SMBHs tend to be more massive than those in elliptical field galaxies residing either outside or on the fringes of galaxy clusters and galaxy groups.[76] These correlations also indicate higher SMBH mass for elliptical field galaxies than for spiral galaxies.[77] Among spiral galaxies, those with a central bar structure tend to possess slightly less massive SMBHs than spiral galaxies without such a structure.[78]

Given that the MWG is a spiral galaxy with a central bar (see figure 7.2), astronomers would expect its SMBH to be slightly less massive than the six or seven correlations would indicate, based on the average properties of the known population of galaxies. However, the mass of our galaxy's SMBH falls far below what this small adjustment would predict.

While the total mass of the AG is equal to the mass of our galaxy, and both galaxies are barred spirals,[79] only the mass of the AG's SMBH aligns with all these correlations. The MWG's SMBH measures about 35 times less massive. This difference in mass means that our galaxy's SMBH holds 35 times less potential to emit deadly radiation from regions just outside its event horizon. This much lower potential—by a factor of 35—makes a significant difference to the possibility of advanced life's existence and survival in the MWG.

Just as importantly, if not more so, our own galaxy's SMBH has remained unusually quiet for at least the past hundred thousand years. It emits a relatively low level of radiation. This implies that it is currently drawing a low quantity of gas, dust, comets, asteroids, planets, and/or stars toward its event horizon.

SMBHs in nearby galaxies consume a star of the Sun's mass or greater about once every 100,000 years, on average.[80] When this consumption happens, a bright flare lasting several months or longer blasts deadly radiation throughout the galaxy. Stars smaller than the Sun are consumed about once every 10,000 years, causing deadly radiation to emit for days to weeks. Molecular gas clouds get consumed at a rate anywhere from one per century to one every few millennia. These events likewise pour out deadly radiation lasting days to weeks.

The MWG's SMBH has entered a phase of minimal consumption, comparable to light snacking. Its intake produces tiny flares that last only hours on an almost daily basis.[81] In 2012, a team of astronomers demonstrated that SMBHs in galaxies with active nuclei maintain near-continual consumption of large asteroids and comets, leading to continual emission of high energy radiation from the region just outside the SMBH's event horizon.[82] It would appear that giant asteroid-comet clouds surround most, if not all, SMBHs.[83] Here again, the MWG is different. Its SMBH is relatively small, and its diffuse asteroid-comet cloud leads to frequent but tiny flares.[84] As a team of astronomers led by Lia Corrales wrote, "The supermassive black hole at the center of our galaxy, Sgr A*, is surprisingly under-luminous."[85]

A high-resolution cosmological hydrodynamic simulation of Milky-Way-type galaxies indicates that past merger events with high-mass dwarf galaxies efficiently feeds the SMBH in MWG-type galaxies.[86] The lack of such merger events in the past 10–11 billion years helps explain why the MWG's SMBH has such an exceptionally low mass.

Figure 7.7: Two Huge Bubbles of X-Ray and Gamma-Ray Emission Balloon Out from the Center of the Milky Way Galaxy
Credit: NASA Goddard Space Flight Center

The exceptionally low mass of our galaxy's SMBH and the tiny size of its surrounding cloud of asteroids and comets help explain why life has been able to survive and thrive on a body within the MWG throughout the past 3.8 billion years. However, even with an SMBH weighing in at only 4.15 million solar masses and surrounded by a relatively tiny asteroid-comet cloud, inevitably some episodes of x-ray and gamma-ray emission are likely to occur. Indeed, astronomers discovered two enormous bubbles, nearly the size of the MWG, comprised of diffuse, uniform, low-level gamma rays[87] and soft x-rays[88] (see figure 7.7). A follow-up discovery revealed two chimneys of x-ray emission connecting the bubbles to the MWG's nucleus. These findings affirm that our galaxy's SMBH is responsible for the bubbles.[89]

Given that these bubbles are large and diffuse, the events that generated them would have occurred several million years ago, long before humans arrived in the MWG. The fact that the radiation levels in the bubbles are so low indicates that any nonhuman life, though impacted by the events, would not have been driven to extinction. The activity level just outside the event horizon of the MWG's SMBH has been exceptionally low throughout the past 12,000 years, the same era during which human civilization has been launched and sustained.

Aging Well: Spurs and Feathers

Astronomers would say our galaxy has aged well, thanks in part to its mass and to the small fraction of its mass attributable to stars. For any star within a galaxy to contain enough carbon, nitrogen, oxygen, phosphorus, iron, thorium, and uranium to make the existence of advanced life possible within its planetary system, at least two generations of stars must form, burn, and explode to enrich the gas clouds that form the next generation of stars.

Galaxies more massive than the MWG form stars early and aggressively, quickly exhausting their gas supply. Consequently, star formation ends before an adequate supply of the life-essential elements can be built up. Advanced life also needs elements as heavy as uranium and thorium. Only if uranium and thorium are extraordinarily abundant on a planet can both plate tectonics and a protective magnetosphere be sustained for a long time.

Galaxies less massive than the MWG form their stars so late and at such a slow rate that not enough of the heavier elements, such as iron, copper, zinc, thorium, and uranium, are manufactured. Only in a galaxy like the MWG does star formation begin soon enough and last long enough to produce all the elements essential for advanced life.

As giant, dense molecular clouds pass through a spiral galaxy's arms, they drag material from the arms into the voids as they leave.[90] As this material makes additional passes through the spiral structure, further substructures form. Thus, as spiral galaxies age, they develop so much substructure in the form of spurs (radiating approximately perpendicular from the spiral arms) and feathers (frayed pieces of the spurs) between the spiral arms that the probability for planetary systems to encounter potentially disruptive dense regions dramatically increases.[91] For this reason, a planetary system capable of supporting advanced life must form sufficiently late for previous generations of stars to have produced life-essential elements, but before extensive substructures have formed.

Astronomy researchers have found that the processes that produce spurs and feathers are intricately complex, affected by multiple galactic parameters.[92] To keep the spiral arm fraying within an acceptable range to accommodate advanced life's needs, the galaxy's magnetic field must be relatively weak and yet strong enough to prevent the collapse of the spiral structure. Its disks, both thin and thick, must be dense enough but not too dense. The quantity of gas in the spiral arms as well as the differential compression of gas flowing through them must be relatively low, and yet high enough to sustain the spiral structure.

Minimal spiral arm fraying requires a narrowly limited range of spiral arm pitch angles.[93] The MWG's spiral arm pitch angles are at that precise level. Fraying is minimal only at a spiral arm's particular distance from the galactic center. That's precisely where our solar system resides.

Symmetrical, Uniform Arms

The MWG's spiral arms display an unusual symmetry and uniformity. The spiral arms of all spiral galaxies are populated by star-forming nebulae and clusters of young stars. Some examples appear in the detailed map of the MWG (see figure 7.2). High-resolution images of the spiral galaxies that most closely match the features of the MWG (see figure 7.8) show the MWG's uniqueness in several ways. They show that its star-forming nebulae (small pink spots in figure 7.2) are evenly distributed along its spiral arms, and none is very large. Many spiral galaxies contain star-forming nebulae measuring 10–100 times larger than the largest such nebulae in the MWG. As with star-forming nebulae, star clusters are evenly dispersed, and no very large star clusters populate the MWG's spiral arms. The presence of very large star-forming nebulae and very large star clusters within the spiral arms would pose a problem for advanced life because they produce significant gravitational disturbances and emit deadly radiation.

Compared with the spiral arm structure seen in the spiral galaxies that come closest to matching the MWG in appearance, the MWG's spiral arms most clearly and closely mimic the symmetry of idealized spirals. Such an arrangement allows for the existence and relatively long-term survival of advanced life.

A Galaxy Like No Other

As all *Star Wars* fans know, each movie that belongs to the franchise begins with this opening crawl: "A long time ago in a galaxy far, far away." Astronomers have a big problem with this opening. They have looked at galaxies far, far away and not one possesses the MWG's characteristics favorable to complex life.

Admittedly, astronomers can measure detailed structures of spiral galaxies only as far as a few hundred million light-years away. This limitation would seem to raise questions about advanced-life-support viability of more distant galaxies. Of course, because of the finite and constant velocity of light,

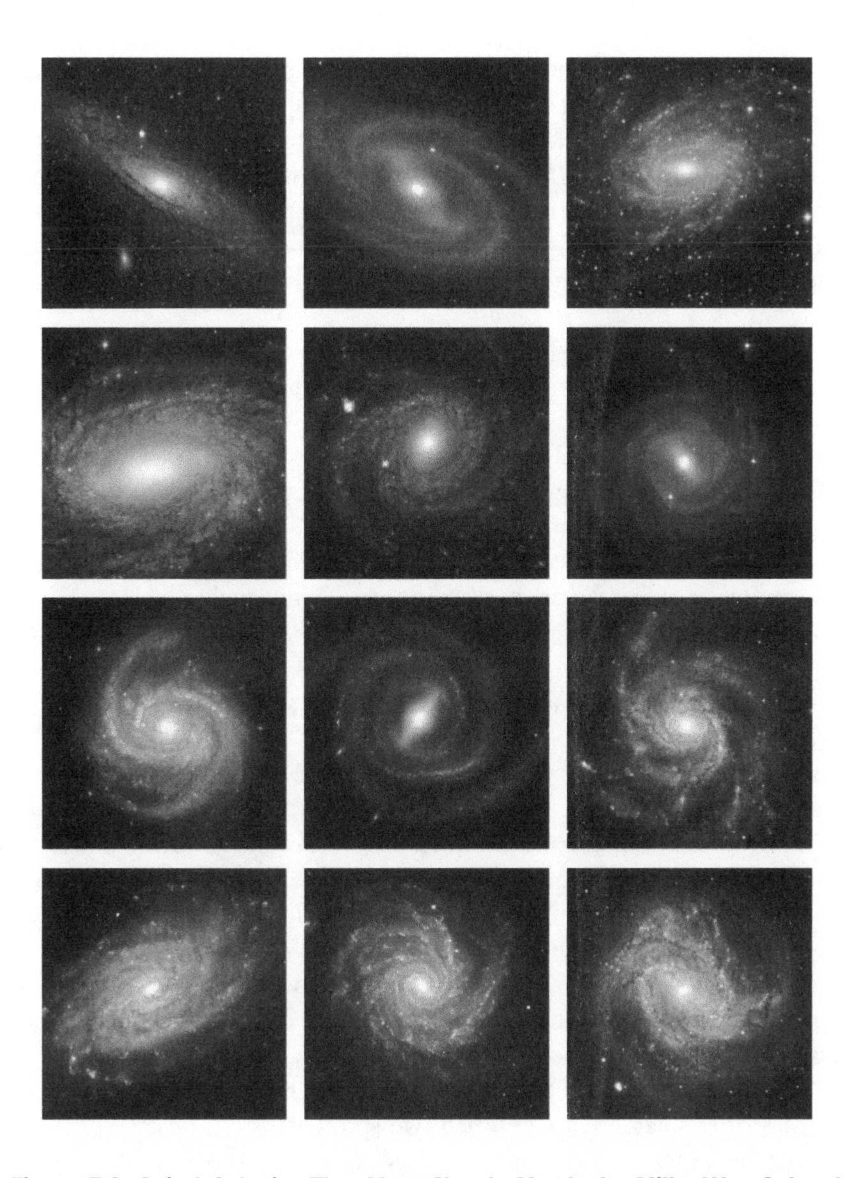

Figure 7.8: Spiral Galaxies That Most Closely Match the Milky Way Galaxy's Structure

First row, left to right: Andromeda Galaxy, NGC 4526, NGC 908; second row, left to right: NGC 6384, NGC 3344, NGC 4921; third row, left to right: M100, UGC 6903, Pinwheel Galaxy; fourth row, left to right: NGC 3370, NGC 1232, M83. *Credits: Adam Evans, Sloan Digital Sky Survey, ESO, NASA/ESA/Hubble, NASA/ESA/Hubble, NASA/ESA/Hubble Space Telescope; Shulman Foundation, NASA/ESA/ Hubble Space Telescope; ESA/NASA, NASA/ESA/Hubble Heritage (STScI/AURA), ESO, ESO, respectively* astronomers' view of galaxies more than a few hundred million light-years away shows them what those galaxies were like more than a few hundred million years ago. That far back in time, all galaxies lacked the necessary features that advanced life requires.[94] However, as galaxies developed through time, we can observe and analyze their future potential for advanced life support.

The MWG is unique in multiple respects, all of which have a bearing on its capacity to host an advanced life site. The long list of extraordinary features includes its

1. ratio of stellar mass to total mass
2. dark matter halo and gas disk
3. bar-bulge structure; its star distribution
4. astonishingly small, extremely quiescent supermassive black hole
5. inventory of elements
6. relative dimensions of its thin disk and thick disk
7. number of spiral arms and their precise pitch angle
8. symmetry of its spiral arms
9. few spurs and feathers between spiral arms
10. green hue from a balance of old, middle-aged, and young stars

And this list grows as research continues and new instruments become available.

Figure 7.8 captures the images of twelve spiral galaxies, those twelve that, among all the galaxies astronomers have been able to image in structural detail, come closest to matching the MWG's morphology. A comparison of these twelve images with the detailed image of the MWG (in figure 7.2) helps to illustrate at least some of the MWG's uniqueness, most clearly its arms' beautiful symmetry and freedom from spurs, feathers, large nebulae, large star clusters, and gravitational disturbances.

Zooming closer to our home, the next chapter focuses on the neighborhood of Earth's solar system, between two spiral arms of our galaxy. This region, like the larger sites examined thus far, manifests its own unique interior features that permit the existence of advanced life.

Chapter 8

The Local Arm

Chapter summary: *Only one tiny region within the Milky Way Galaxy (MWG) has the features advanced life crucially depends upon. This safe zone—free of dangerous stars, star clusters, gas clouds, stellar-mass black holes, and pulsars—is situated just inside the galactic corotation distance, where spiral arm crossings occur least frequently. The solar system resides right in the midst of this region, safely ensconced in the Local Bubble, where the Local Fluff maximally protects nearby life from both cosmic and the Sun's radiation. Astronomers can finally explain the puzzling enigma of how a star well-endowed with life-essential metals and its planetary system ended up in a metal-poor neighborhood.*

The grandeur of the MWG could never be captured in a single chapter, nor could its unique interior filled with life-favoring characteristics. However, one specific locale within the MWG, a relatively small spot tucked between two of its spiral arms, deserves special attention, given its ultrarare qualities. It hosts the only planetary system among all known planetary systems appropriately configured to house advanced life. One might be inclined to consider it the cosmic version of *Mister Rogers' Neighborhood*.

Thanks to the Very Long Baseline Array, a chain of ten 25-meter (82-foot) diameter radio telescopes distributed across the earth, from Hawaii to St. Croix, creating a baseline of 8,611 kilometers (5,351 miles), astronomers can make accurate trigonometric distance measurements to specific radio sources (called masers) in our solar system's nearby spiral arms. These measurements and others made by the European Very Long Baseline Interferometry Network and the Japanese Very Long Baseline Interferometry Exploration of Radio Astrometry

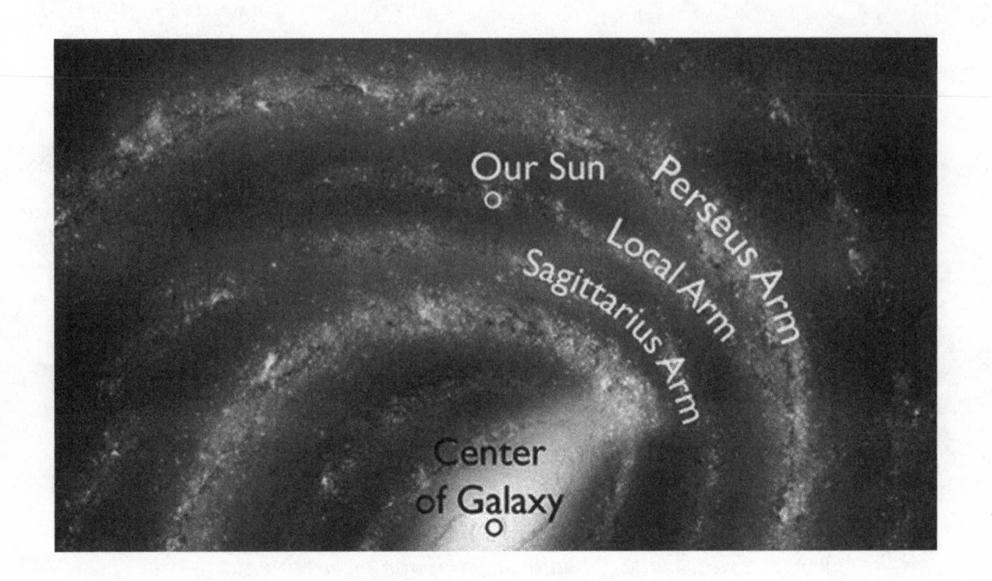

Figure 8.1: Milky Way Galaxy Spiral Arms Hosting the Sun
Credit: IPAC, Robert Hurt; NRAO/AUI/NSF, Bill Saxton

project provide researchers with a detailed map of the MWG's arms, particularly in the vicinity of our solar system.[1] Figure 8.1 shows a portion of that map.

Nearest Neighbors in the Galactic Arms

The map reveals that the Sun is located roughly halfway between the MWG's two major arms, the Sagittarius and Perseus. It resides in what astronomers refer to (rather blandly) as the Local Arm, an appendage that split off from the Perseus Arm about 75 degrees back from the Sun's current position.

That portion of the Sagittarius Arm nearest the Sun contains only small- to medium-sized star-forming nebulae and star clusters, no large ones. The portion of the slightly more distant Perseus Arm that comes closest to the Sun likewise contains smaller-sized star-forming nebulae and star clusters. The absence of large nebulae and clusters means the Sun and its planetary system are protected, at least for the time being, from any major gravitational disturbances or life-threatening radiation coming from either the Sagittarius or Perseus Arm.

Meanwhile, the Local Arm where the Sun resides carries still smaller star-forming nebulae and star clusters than either the Sagittarius Arm or the Perseus Arm, and especially in the region nearest the Sun. The closest nebula to the Sun with significant star formation shows up as a pink spot (in the online color version of figure 8.1) slightly above and to the left of the Sun. That pink spot shows the Orion Nebula, with a total mass about 2,000 times that of the Sun.

Because figure 8.1 is a two-dimensional map, the proximity of the Orion Nebula to the Sun is deceptive. The actual distance between Orion and the solar system is 1,345 ± 19 light-years.[2] On the distance scale of figure 8.1, the Orion Nebula is 4.5 times farther from the Sun than that pink spot makes it appear. The point, here, is that the Orion Nebula is sufficiently distant that it poses no risk to the habitability of the Sun's planets.

The nearest star clusters to the Sun are the Hyades, Coma, and Pleiades. They are 153, 282, and 444 light-years away, respectively.[3] The Hyades Cluster contains 710 confirmed member stars,[4] the largest no more than 3 times the mass of the Sun, and no known black holes or neutron stars. The nearness of the Hyades Cluster to the solar system presents no risk to any kind of life within the system.

The Coma Cluster contains 148 confirmed member stars.[5] These stars range between 0.06 and 2.3 solar masses. Their peak population equals 0.3 solar masses. The more distant Coma Cluster appears totally devoid of black holes and neutron stars, thus it poses no threat to the possibility of complex life within the solar system.

Astronomers have determined that at least 2,010 stars have a greater than 75% probability of belonging to the Pleiades Cluster.[6] Nine are B-type stars, all visible to the naked eye. They range in mass from 3.4–5.3 solar masses. If these stars were close to the solar system, they would cause trouble for advanced life, but at 444 light-years away, they are not a problem. They remain, however, a spectacular collection of jewels in the constellation of Taurus.

The Sun and its collection of planets reside in the safest region of the Local Arm, which resides within the safest region of the MWG's set of spiral arms—a reminder that location is *almost* everything, in space as in real estate.

A Scarcity of Stellar-Mass Black Holes

All galaxies host a population of stellar-mass black holes. Any star that retains more mass than 2.3 solar masses (the Tolman-Oppenheimer-Volkoff limit) at the end of its nuclear-burning cycle will suffer gravitational collapse and become a black hole.[7] Typically, stars that begin with greater mass than 15 solar masses end up with sufficient mass to become black holes.

Once a star becomes a black hole, it can continue to accrete mass from its surroundings. If a stellar-mass black hole accretes mass from its surroundings, the resultant radiation can pose a threat to advanced life within 1–2 thousand light-years. To date, the smallest black hole among confirmed and measured black holes equals 5 solar masses,[8] while eight candidates among microlensing black holes range between 2.4 and 5.0 solar masses.[9]

Beyond the dozens of black holes that exist near the galactic center,[10] the MWG's disk has an exceptionally low population of detectable black holes. To date, just 23 of known mass have been confirmed to exist.[11] Their population peaks at slightly less than 8 solar masses, with a sharp drop-off above 10 solar masses.[12] Only one, Cygnus X-1, measures more than 11 solar masses.[13]

None of these 23 black holes is closer to the Sun than 5,500 light-years.[14] A0620-00, a black hole of indeterminate mass with very weak associated emission, hovers 3,200 light-years away.[15] At such distances, black holes pose no danger to any life in the Sun's planetary system.

The possibility remains, however, that several black holes even quieter than A0620-00 reside in the Sun's vicinity. The discovery of one such black hole was announced in May 2020.[16] It was found lurking within a binary star system of two bright blue B-type stars located just 1,000 light-years away.

A team of astronomers led by Thomas Rivinius detected a 40-day wobble in the position of one of these two stars, a B3 III star. Further observations revealed that the B3 III shared a tight orbit with an unseen companion, with an orbital period of 40.333 ± 0.004 days. The mass of the B3 III star is 6.3 ± 0.7 solar masses. The mass of its unseen companion is 5.0 ± 0.4 solar masses.

The unseen companion's high mass and lack of radiation emission can only mean one thing: it is a black hole. Normally, a black hole of this mass would be stripping matter from its companion star, and that stripping process would cause deadly radiation to emit from just outside its event horizon. However, in this case the black hole is less massive than the companion star. So, any gas or dust headed toward the black hole is sucked up by its more massive companion. Therefore, the black hole and its vicinity is truly black, emitting no deadly (or even measurable) radiation.

The remaining black hole risk for the Sun's local neighborhood could come from the stellar-mass and intermediate-mass black holes residing in the galactic arms' globular clusters. By comparison with other large galaxies, however, the MWG hosts a remarkably low population of globular clusters. Only 157 have been discovered to date. The closest two to the Sun are M4 and NGC

6397 at distances of 7,200 and 7,500 light-years, respectively.[17] Only six reside closer to the Sun than 13,000 light-years.

No intermediate-mass black hole has yet been detected in the six globular clusters.[18] Theoretically, hundreds of stellar-mass black holes are expected to form in a typical globular cluster.[19] However, even in the youngest globular clusters, most of these black holes would have been ejected to locales where available matter for accretion is lacking and, thus, would pose no risk of deadly radiation emission. Those black holes that remain would have such a sharp reduction in accretion that any radiation they still produce would be weak.

Observational evidence seems to sustain this theoretical deduction. To date, despite diligent searches, only two stellar-mass black holes have been positively identified in any of the MWG's globular clusters.[20] These two, both at low radiation levels, reside 10,500 light-years away in M22, which means they pose no risk to potential advanced life in the Sun's vicinity. Astronomers found one likely black hole candidate in NGC 6397.[21] Again, the radiation from its environs is too weak to be of any concern.

A Paucity of Pulsars

All galaxies also host a large population of pulsars, highly magnetized neutron stars that emit narrow beams of intense electromagnetic radiation. Pulsars resemble lighthouses in that, as they rotate, their beam of radiation rotates with them. Astronomers see the beam only when it is pointed directly at their telescopes. The observed times between radiation pulses range from 1.4 milliseconds (from PSR J1748-2446ad) to 23.5 seconds (from PSR J0250+5854).

The ultrahigh radiation intensity in a pulsar beam would present a problem for any nearby advanced life. Astronomers have found only 11 pulsars within 1,000 light-years of the Sun.[22] Of these, the nearest is slightly more than 500 light-years away, far enough to be of no danger.

Corotation Distance

Newton's laws of motion determine the rate at which stars revolve around the galactic center. The greater a star's distance from the center, the longer it takes to make a revolution around it.

Density waves determine the rotation rate of the spiral arm structure. The farther a star from the galaxy's corotation radius (the distance from the galactic center where stars revolve at the same rate as the spiral structure rotates), the more frequently that star crosses a spiral arm. Spiral arm crossings are hazardous to life. Spiral arms host young supergiant stars, giant molecular clouds, and star-forming nebulae that shower their vicinity with deadly radiation. These stars, clouds, and nebulae also gravitationally disturb any nearby planetary system's asteroid-comet belts, unleashing an enhanced bombardment on those planets. Only stars near the corotation radius avoid frequent spiral arm crossings.

The corotation radius is different, of course, for each spiral galaxy, depending on the galaxy's total mass, stellar mass, gas mass, bulge mass, magnetic field, and stellar disk dimensions. For the MWG, the corotation radius is far enough from the galactic center that planetary systems near the corotation radius will not be exposed to deadly radiation coming from the galactic nucleus. However, any planetary system forming much farther out from the corotation radius would be unable to accrete life-essential quantities of heavy elements. (The density of matter in the galactic disk decreases with distance from the galactic center, and the ratio of heavy-to-light elements also varies according to distance from the galactic center, as figure 7.3 shows.)

Yet, the safest place for life would not be exactly at the corotation distance. A planetary system in that precise place would experience the chaos of destructive mean motion resonances.[23] The safest orbital distance would be just inside the corotation radius. As figure 8.2 shows, the Sun orbits the center of the MWG at 98% of the corotation radius.[24]

Just inside the corotation radius, galaxy arm fraying is minimized. A move in either direction away from the corotation radius would result in increased formation of an arm's spurs and feathers (see chapter 7). And in this location near the corotation radius, the density of stars is at a minimum.[25] For the possibility of advanced life, no better location for our star, the Sun, can be imagined (see figure 8.4).

Local Stellar Population

The total stellar mass found within 30 light-years of the Sun (including the Sun) is 115 solar masses.[26] Compared with other stellar regions at the same distance from the galactic center, this stellar-mass value in the Sun's neighborhood proves exceptionally low.

What's more, the stellar population in this region includes no O- or B-type stars, the highest mass stars. The most massive star within 30 light-years is Vega, an A-type star measuring 2.135 solar masses, and it resides 25 light-years away. The next most massive star in the region, Sirius, at 2.063 solar masses, is 8.6 light-years away. These large stars tend to pour out a high abundance of ultraviolet radiation, but neither is close enough to pose a problem for advanced

Figure 8.2: Corotation Radius of the Milky Way Galaxy
Credit: NASA/JPL-Caltech (R. Hurt)

life. Neither has the potential to become a supernova.

To date, astronomers have discovered 332 stars within 30 light-years of the Sun.[27] This number is considered complete. Of these 333 stars (including the Sun), 79% (263) are M-type stars, the smallest stars in the universe. M-type stars measure in the mass range of 0.08–0.56 solar masses and in the luminosity range of 0.00015–0.13 solar luminosities. The Sun indeed exists in a stellar neighborhood optimally suited to host life.

The Local Bubble

The Sun also happens to reside in the midst of a rare and temporary feature referred to as the Local Bubble (see figure 8.3), a magnetized cavity, or void, of exceptionally low-density gas extending 160–640 light-years in all directions from the Sun.[28] Research indicates that beginning between 10–15 million years ago, some 14–20 supernova eruptions within a comoving group (surviving members comprise the Scorpius-Centaurus star association) passed by the Sun's vicinity and excavated the region now called the Local Bubble.[29] These supernovae likely caused several megafaunal species to go extinct at the times

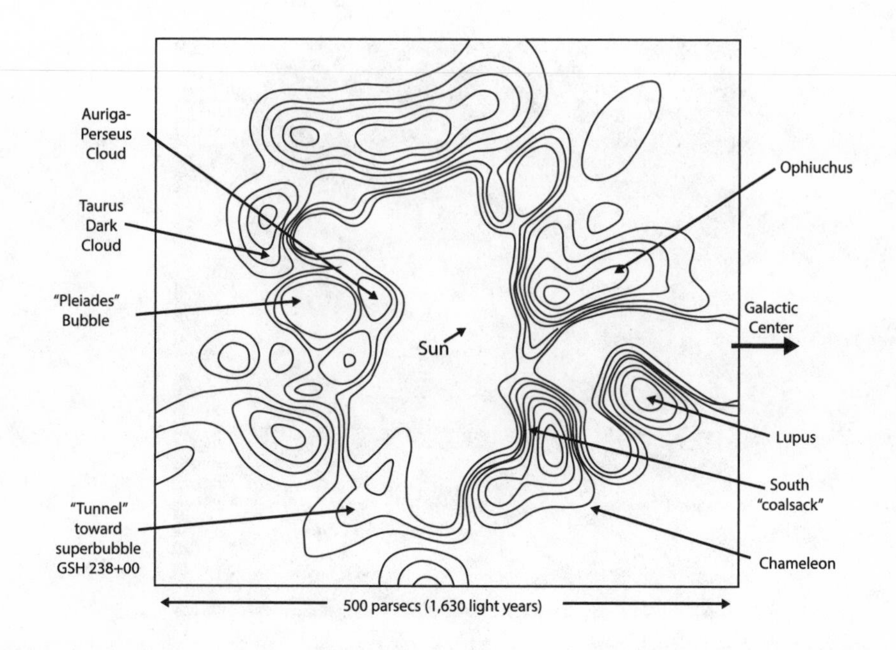

Figure 8.3: The Local Bubble
Credit: Helmut A. Abt, "The Age of the Local Interstellar Bubble," Astronomical Journal *141, no.5 (May 1, 2011): id. 165, doi:10.1088/0004-6256/141/5/165.*

of their eruptions.[30] Winds from the supernova eruptions blew dust outward, forming the bubble's shell of cold, dusty, relatively high-density gas.[31]

Favorable conditions result from the Sun's location near the center of a largely vacuous, relatively dust-free magnetized region encased in a dense wall of molecular clouds and comprised of cold neutral gas and dust.[32] It means extraordinary protection for potential advanced life on a planet that forms around it. This protection has been enhanced by the recent million-year time window of the bubble's quiescence.[33] Further, by impacting the directionality of cosmic rays and producing cosmic ray diffusion,[34] the Local Bubble has mitigated, at least to some degree, the potential damage to advanced life caused by cosmic radiation.

Local Fluff

Local Fluff refers to several small diffuse interstellar clouds near the Sun comprised of warm, low-density interstellar gas inside the much larger Local Bubble of even warmer but less-dense gas.[35] These clouds formed as a result of distortions in the magnetic field along the boundary of the Local Bubble.

The last one or two supernova eruptions at the end of the Local Bubble's formation (roughly 3 million years ago) generated maverick magnetic flux tubes that funneled tiny amounts of matter into the Local Bubble's interior. This matter became the Local Fluff.

The Sun and its planetary system moved into the Local Fluff cloud complex sometime within the past 200,000 years.[36] The clouds' magnetic fields compress the solar heliosphere and play a significant role in determining the extent and conditions of the Sun's astrosphere.[37] At the Earth's distance from the Sun, the Local Fluff helps minimize the effects of deadly components in both cosmic and solar radiation.

The G-Dwarf Problem, Solved

How is it that some stars in the Sun's vicinity are metal-rich while others are metal-poor? Astronomers refer to this disparity as the G-dwarf problem. G-dwarf stars are hydrogen-burning stars with mass measuring between 0.7–1.0 the mass of the Sun. On the assumption that G-dwarf stars formed near their current locations, far fewer than the expected number within 100 light-years of the Sun are metal-poor (possessing a much lower than average abundance of elements heavier than helium),[38] while far more than expected are metal-rich.

The Sun is part of the G-dwarf problem. For a G-dwarf star in its location in the MWG and its age (typically the older the star the lower its metallicity), the Sun is far richer in metals than astrophysics says it should be.

Figure 7.3 shows the abundance of metals in the MWG's thin disk relative to distance from the galactic center. The variation results from the MWG's accretion of matter from gas streams and small dwarf galaxies, and distribution of this accreted gas and dust along its spiral arms.

This distributed gas and dust are the materials from which stars form. Thus, figure 7.3 shows star metal abundance relative to star distance from the galactic center—with one notable exception. Astronomers have observed an exception among stars in the Sun's vicinity that are several billion years old and more massive than 0.7 solar masses.

Many astronomers thought the G-dwarf problem resulted from an incomplete sample of accurate element abundance measurements for stars in the Sun's vicinity. However, extensive observations of a sample of 5,561 stars within 130 light-years of the Sun revealed that "the G dwarf problem is even larger than earlier results indicate."[39] A follow-up analysis of 16,682 nearby F- and G-dwarf stars "confirm the lack of metal-poor G dwarfs."[40]

These larger samples and more detailed analyses show large departures from the age-metallicity correlation (the older the star, the lower the metallicity) for G-dwarf stars in the solar neighborhood.[41] Strangely, the departures are most dramatic for older G-dwarf stars like the Sun.[42] Such departures suggest that stars more massive than 0.7 solar masses born in more metal-rich regions of the MWG must have migrated into the current solar neighborhood.

Astronomers see three possible drivers of such substantial migration in the MWG:

1. scattering attributable to a galactic orbital resonance[43]
2. scattering by a giant molecular cloud[44]
3. overlapping resonance of the central bulge-bar and the spiral arms[45]

Likely, all three drivers played a part.

According to astronomers Yue Wang and Gang Zhao, the observed metallicities of G-dwarfs in the solar neighborhood are well explained if most of the G-dwarfs formed in the local region while the others formed in the inner disk of the MWG and then migrated outward to where they currently reside.[46] The astronomers further deduced that the greater the G-dwarf age, the more likely its migration from the MWG's inner disk. Therefore, even without taking note of its high metallicity, the Sun's age of 4.57 billion years increases the probability that it migrated to its current location from the inner galactic disk.

This stellar migration explains why a star of the just-right mass, just-right age, and just-right metallicity to meet life's requirements also resides in the just-right location to host a planet on which advanced life can possibly exist and thrive. After the Sun formed 4.57 billion years ago in the most metal-rich part of the MWG, it exited its deadly-for-life birthplace and moved into the safest-for-life location in the MWG (see figure 8.4).

No Recent Nearby Supernovae

In spiral galaxies most similar to the MWG, astronomers observe the occurrence of supernovae at the rate of three per century.[47] These colossal explosions at the end of a massive star's burning cycle have the potential to outshine an entire galaxy. During the time the Sun has resided just inside the MWG's corotation distance, which is most of its history, supernovae within 5,000 light-years'

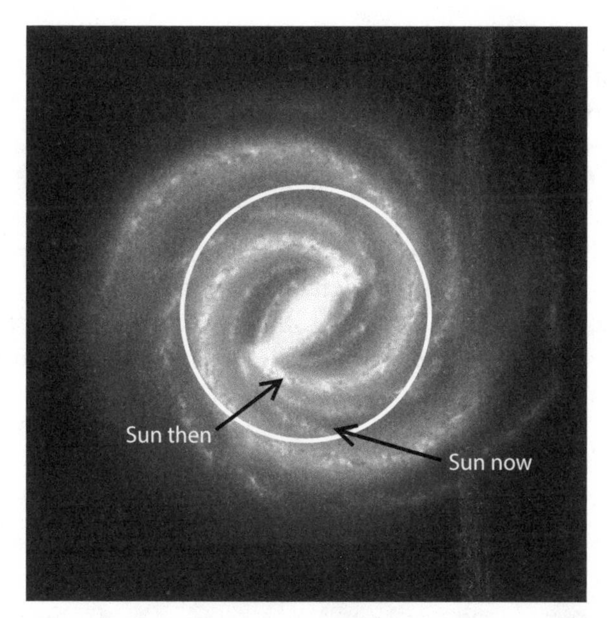

Figure 8.4: Sun's Journey from Danger to Safety
The annulus marks the Milky Way Galaxy's corotation distance. *Image credit: NASA/JPL-Caltech (R. Hurt); Diagram credit: Hugh Ross*

distance have occurred about once every 300 years, and closer than 1,000 light-years, about once every 10,000 years. Astronomers determined these rates from observation of the locations, sizes, and expansion rates of supernovae remnants. By measuring the diameter of a supernova remnant and the rate at which that diameter expands, astronomers can calculate the date of the supernova occurrence.

Confirmation of the supernova rate in the Sun's vicinity has come from radioisotope evidence from geologic records. A study by Richard Firestone established that in the past 300,000 years, a minimum of 23 supernovae have occurred closer than 980 light-years from the Sun.[48] Each of these have showered the Sun's neighborhood with life-damaging radiation.

During the past 10,000 years, however, the nearest supernova was the AD 1006 event 5,080 light-years away. The next closest, the AD 1054 supernova, produced the Crab Nebula, located 6,500 light-years away. During the past 416 years, no unobscured supernovae have occurred within 10,000 light-years of Earth. (A supernova occurring behind a dense dust cloud could possibly escape detection, but the dust would also block any deadly radiation from reaching the vicinity of the Sun.)

A supernova eruption within 1,000 light-years would degrade any planet's stratospheric ozone layer to a level where the health of any advanced life and production of food crops on it would be seriously diminished. Supernovae beyond 5,000 light-years would have no measurable impact either on advanced life or crops. In terms of safety from supernovae and all other potential dangers to life, especially advanced life, the Sun resides in an astonishingly ideal neighborhood.

The Sun, itself, not just its location and timing, differs in profound ways from other stars, ways that favor its ability to host a planetary system in which advanced life can exist. The next chapter unveils the most significant of these features astronomers have yet discovered.

Chapter 9

Interior Features of the Sun

Chapter summary: *The Sun appears to have no "twin." Among the hundreds of billions of stars in our galaxy, none possess all the specific features required for advanced life to exist within its planetary system. Thanks to its mass, age, unique interior structure, and elemental composition, the Sun maintains its luminosity with five times greater stability than any other known star. Currently, its flaring activity level and emission of dangerous radiation fall below that of any other known star like it. These optimal features, along with the Sun's optimal orbital position about the galactic center, hold major significance for the possibility of life.*

Astronomers pursue any number of "holy grails," depending upon the focus of their research and passion. Many would consider finding an Earthlike planet the ultimate discovery. Others, however, recognize that for any planet to potentially host life, a host star virtually identical to the Sun would be required. So, some astronomers make it their focus to find and study a star they could refer to as a "solar twin." To date, this search has not led to a discovery of a duplicate. Rather, the pursuit has increased awareness of our Sun's unique features—specific characteristics that match the needs of advanced life—and how those features prevent the annihilation of advanced life. The Sun is, after all, an ongoing nuclear explosion.

To understand and appreciate how the Sun works would seem to require the impossible—a look inside. However, thanks to technological breakthroughs of the past few decades, researchers now have tools to probe the Sun's interior, indirectly, of course, but revealingly. These tools include neutrino observatories, spectroscopes, and solar seismographs.

Solar Neutrinos

The nuclear furnace in the Sun's core emits enormous quantities of photons (elementary light particles) and neutrinos (subatomic particles with no electrical charge, extremely small mass, and little interaction with ordinary matter). By studying these particles coming from the Sun, astronomers can gain detailed insights into the operation and status of the Sun's nuclear furnace. In fact, each of the Sun's nuclear fusion reactions has its own signature of photon and neutrino outputs.

Every minute, roughly 16 trillion solar neutrinos pass through the thumbnail of every person on Earth. Neutrinos so weakly interact with protons, neutrons, electrons, and photons that virtually all of them pass through us and our Earth without perturbing or being perturbed in any way. Nevertheless, technological advance has enabled us to detect their presence. The most sensitive neutrino detector, the Borexino Experiment, is located under Gran Sasso Mountain at the Laboratori Nazionali del Gran Sasso, 100 miles northeast of Rome, Italy.

Even though neutrino interactions with matter are extremely rare and weak, the 300 tonnes (331 tons) of scintillator liquid in the Borexino detector (see figure 9.1) and the vast number of solar neutrinos emitted by the Sun make possible the detection of nearly 100 neutrino "events" (signals of their presence) per day at the Borexino observatory. To distinguish between neutrino events and cosmic ray signals and radioactive background activity, this detector is shielded by a 4,600-foot layer of sedimentary rock above, some 2,400 tons of water around it, and a thick outer thermal blanket.

With all this protection in place, the Borexino Experiment can detect neutrinos down to an energy level as low as 100 kiloelectron volts. This detection limit is more than adequate, as the energy range for even the least energetic of the nuclear fusion chains is 190–16,000 kiloelectron volts.[1]

Measurements of solar neutrinos over a ten-year period of observations confirm that at least 99% of the Sun's energy output is produced via proton-proton chain nuclear fusion that converts hydrogen (protons) into helium.[2] Thanks to the predominance of this fusion process, the Sun radiates with exceptional stability.

Because neutrinos interact so weakly with protons, neutrons, electrons, and photons, they can travel from the Sun's nuclear core to its surface in just 2.4 seconds. From there, they reach the Borexino Experiment in just 8 minutes, 21 seconds. Meanwhile, because photons strongly interact with protons, neutrons, and electrons, they take at least 100,000 years to travel from the Sun's

Figure 9.1: The Borexino Neutrino Detector
The man on the staircase lends perspective to the detector's size. *Credit: Borexino Collaboration*

nuclear furnace to its surface, but then just 8 minutes, 19 seconds to reach Earth's surface.

This difference in travel times allows astronomers to determine the stability of the Sun's nuclear furnace over the past 100,000 years. A comparison of the Sun's neutrino and photon fluxes shows that the Sun has been extraordinarily stable—no discernible solar variability—throughout this entire period.[3] Thanks to the remarkable stability of solar energy output, Earth's climate and surface temperature changes have been minimized over the past 100,000+ years.

Helioseismology Revelations

Helioseismologists study the Sun's interior structure and dynamics by making detailed observations of the Sun's oscillations, events roughly analogous to earthquakes. The Sun's oscillations are primarily caused by sound waves that are driven and damped by convection that occurs in a thick layer just below the Sun's surface (see figure 9.2) Just as terrestrial seismology provides geophysicists with insights about Earth's interior structure and dynamics, so, too, helioseismology offers astronomers a window into the Sun's interior features. However, because the Sun lacks a solid surface, it cannot support shear waves (transverse waves that change the shape without changing the volume of a layer). So, solar astronomers cannot gain quite as clear a window into the Sun's interior as geophysicists do into Earth's interior.

Astronomers have known for several decades that all hydrogen-burning stars of the Sun's approximate mass possess a core in which the nuclear fusion of hydrogen into helium occurs. This core is surrounded by a thick radiative layer, overlaid by a thick convective layer, wrapped in a very thin radiative surface layer. Though astronomers long lacked accurate measures of the thicknesses of each of the Sun's interior layers, helioseismology spectacularly delivered.

Measurements tell us the Sun has a radius of 696,342 ± 65 kilometers.[4] Figure 9.2 shows the Sun's interior layers.

Its core extends out to about 174,000 kilometers from the center and contains half of the Sun's total mass. The inner boundary of the thick radiative layer, where radiation transports the Sun's energy, begins at 174,000 kilometers and extends out to 495,000 kilometers from the center. The thick convective layer, where convection is the dominant mechanism for transporting energy, extends from 495,000 kilometers to just a few kilometers from the Sun's surface.[5] The Sun, a spinning, gaseous body, lacks a clearly defined surface.

One of helioseismology's great achievements has been to determine rates with which the Sun's interior layers rotate. As figure 9.3 illustrates, the Sun rotates at a fixed rate from its core, out through its radiative layer, and up to the base of the convection zone. However, within its convection zone the rotation rate differs by as much as six or seven days, according to degree of distance (latitude) from the solar equator. The farther from the equator, the slower the rotation.[6]

Solar Tachocline

Helioseismic observations have also revealed that the Sun has a tachocline,[7] an ultrathin layer between its convection zone and radiative zone. A very large shear can be seen from the rapid change in rotation rate that occurs there.[8] The Sun's tachocline in many ways explains the operation and stability of the solar dynamo and the Sun's general magnetic field. Helioseismology shows that the

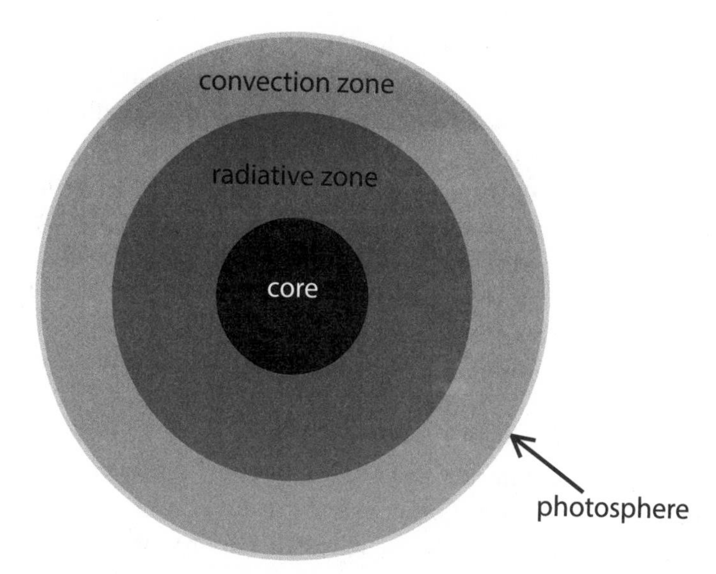

Figure 9.2: Sun's Interior Layers
Diagram credit: Hugh Ross

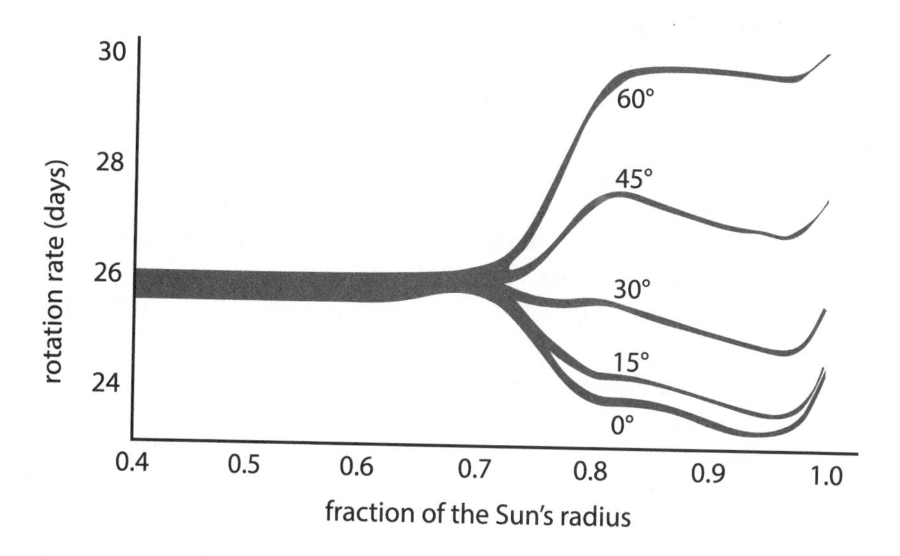

Figure 9.3: Sun's Interior Differential Rotation from 0–60° Latitude
In the Sun's convection zone, rotation is most rapid at the equator and least rapid at the poles. The Sun's equatorial rotation rate is 24.47 days. *Data credit: NSO/NSF; Diagram credit: Hugh Ross*

Sun's tachocline is a region of fine balances among gas and magnetic pressure gradients and gravitational and magnetic curvature stresses.[9]

The tachocline ensures that the convection zone circulation penetrates only weakly and shallowly into the radiative zone.[10] It prevents any significant quantity of lithium from penetrating the Sun's nuclear fusion zone.[11] This barrier explains, in part, two things: the relatively high lithium abundance observed at the Sun's surface, and the Sun's (current) exceptionally stable luminosity. The properties of the Sun's tachocline and of the convection zone above it keep the Sun's flaring activity at an extremely low level, an important feature for the possibility of life, particularly of advanced life on any planet in its orbit.

An Elemental Abundance Anomaly

Before the development of helioseismology, astronomers studied the internal structure of the Sun and other stars by external means. They constructed and tested theoretical models based on how the known fusion reactions in the Sun's core nuclear furnace would affect its structure as it aged.

Helioseismology gave astronomers a *new* means to observe the Sun's interior structure. The match between the theoretical models and the observational measurements made by helioseismologists persuaded astronomers that they had developed a fairly accurate picture of the Sun's interior. This picture appeared consistent with spectroscopic measurements of elements in the Sun's surface, as well as with three-dimensional hydrodynamic models of the Sun's atmosphere and laboratory measurements of spectral line wavelengths and strengths.

However, a set of spectroscopic studies (measurements of the Sun's spectral line strengths) completed in 2009[12] disagreed with all previous findings. They yielded a lower solar "metallicity" (abundance of elements heavier than helium) than indicated by the older spectroscopic studies. The difference was especially noticeable for carbon, nitrogen, and oxygen. This disparity became known as "the solar abundance problem."[13] Astronomers understood that this difference could impact the Sun's luminosity and luminosity stability.

Astronomers immediately set about proposing possible solutions.[14] Only two of the five they came up with could make a great enough difference to resolve the problem: adjusting the radiative opacity (reduction of outgoing flux along the line of sight) of their models and/or adjusting their spectroscopic analysis.

In 2010, astronomer Francesco Villante thought he had solved the problem by the first of these means, adjusting radiative opacity.[15] But, in 2015, a team of physicists overturned that solution when they published the first-ever measurement of opacity under the conditions existing at the bottom of the solar convection zone. Their study of the element iron showed that while the previously published radiative opacity was in fact low, it was low only by a few percent, not Villante's 15–20 percent.[16] In 2017, Villante and a team of astronomers concluded that although more accurate opacity determinations might bring resolution to the original high-metallicity solar model, it would not do so for the 2009 low-metallicity solar model.[17]

In 2018, two nuclear physicists predicted that forthcoming calculations relevant to solar atomic spectroscopy would revive the high-metallicity model.[18] Soon thereafter, the Borexino Collaboration published precise neutrino spectroscopic measurements of the entire proton-proton fusion chain operating in the Sun's nuclear furnace.[19] These results were consistent with measurements made by two other neutrino detectors, the Super-Kamiokande-IV in Japan[20] and the Sudbury Neutrino Observatory in Canada.[21] The 2018 Borexino results included measured fluxes of solar beryllium-7 and boron-8 neutrinos. These findings fulfilled the predictions of the high-metallicity models at a 96.6% confidence level.

A detection of the solar neutrino flux arising from the carbon-nitrogen-oxygen (CNO) nuclear fusion cycle would provide a clear and direct reading of the metal abundance in the Sun's core, independent of any assumed opacity figures.[22] On June 23 at the Neutrino 2020 Conference, Gioacchino Ranucci announced on behalf of the Borexino Collaboration that such a detection had, in fact, been made.[23] Although possible statistical and systematic errors in their measurement were not quite small enough to rule out the low-metallicity models for the Sun completely, their finding clearly favored the high-metallicity model over the low-metallicity model.

Current information about the elemental abundance profile of the Sun's interior is sufficient for astronomers to confirm that it plays a major role in accounting for the Sun's extraordinary stability—a significant feature for the potential existence of advanced life in any possible planetary system.

Lithium Abundance

More important than a star's overall metallicity level is its relative abundance of certain elements heavier than helium. For several decades, astronomers have known that, compared with stars most like the Sun in mass, age, and effective temperature, the Sun is deficient in lithium. It also has an underabundance of refractory elements (those with high boiling points), and a slightly greater abundance of volatile elements (those with low boiling points). Examples of refractory elements include aluminum, silicon, titanium, and iron. Examples of volatiles include nitrogen and oxygen. Also carbon is considered a volatile element since compounds derived from it—for example, carbon dioxide, carbon monoxide, and methane—have low boiling points.

Twenty years of observations and analysis by astronomers has uncovered an astonishing link between the Sun's unique relative abundances of lithium, refractory elements, and volatile elements, and the unique array of rocky planets that formed around it. See "Solar Elemental Abundance—Rocky Planet Configuration Link" in the appendix for details on how this astonishing link was uncovered.

Magnetic Fields

Most stars, including the Sun, possess an overall magnetic field punctuated by much stronger localized magnetic fields. These localized magnetic fields are associated with star spots (sunspots), and star spots are associated with flaring activity—sources of intense and potentially dangerous-to-life radiation.

For Sunlike stars, the magnetic field is produced by a dynamo generated at the base of the convection zone, specifically in the shear layer between the radiative core and convective envelope.[24] (The tachocline is at the bottom of this shear layer.) Given that such stars are comprised entirely of charged particles (plasma) interacting at high temperatures and, within the convection zone, amid varying rotation rates (see figure 9.2), significant turbulence is associated with the dynamo. This turbulence allows the internal magnetic field to penetrate to the star's surface, at times, in localized regions of intense magnetic activity. This magnetic activity is manifested as dark spots, bright faculae, flares, and coronal mass ejections.

Dark spots appear, grow, shrink, and vanish over timescales ranging from a few days to a few months. Faculae (strongly magnetic bright spots often associated with dark spots) form and dissipate on timescales of several minutes. For flares and coronal mass ejections, the timescales are minutes to tens of minutes. These events, combined with a star's rotation rate, play a significant role in the variability of a star's luminosity.

Precise brightness measurements of our weakly magnetic star (only 1–2 gauss) have been made by more than a dozen dedicated instruments on board spacecraft since 1978.[25] These measurements reveal a median solar brightness variability of only 0.07%.[26]

Accurate measurements of the positions and sizes of sunspots extend back

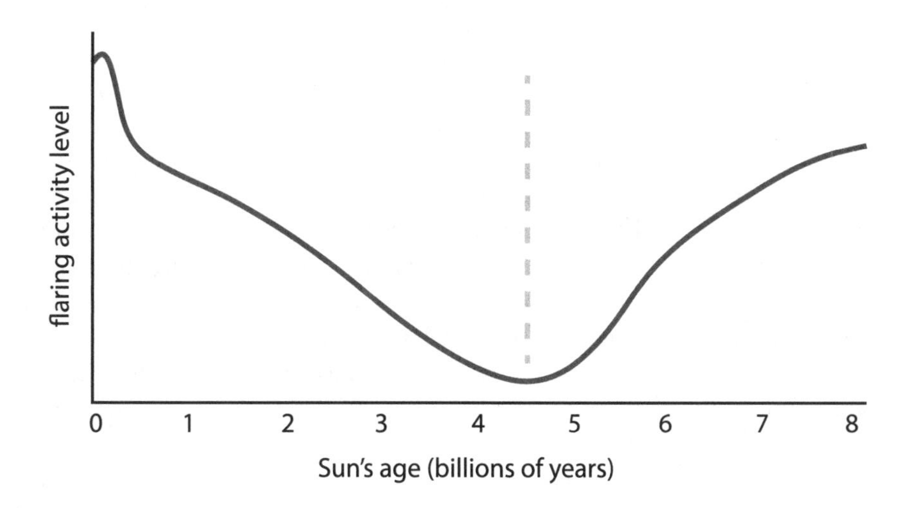

Figure 9.4: Sun's Flaring Activity and X-Ray Radiation Levels throughout Its History
The y-axis is logarithmic. The Sun's flaring activity level would have been more than 100,000 times greater shortly after its formation than it is now. The Sun's intensities of particle radiation and gamma-ray, x-ray, and ultraviolet emission strongly correlate with its flaring activity level. The dotted line indicates the present time. *Diagram credit: Hugh Ross*

to 1874. Astronomers have used this data to reconstruct the Sun's brightness variations throughout the century before 1978.[27] Records of the number of sunspots allow astronomers to infer solar brightness variations back to 1610.[28] These older records reveal a solar brightness variability consistent with the spacecraft measurements.

Measurements of the concentrations of carbon-14 and beryllium-10 in tree rings and ice cores yield a measure of solar brightness variability throughout the past 9,000 years.[29] The inferred luminosity variability is about 0.1%.

Unique Quiescence

It has been said that stars are like human beings—unstable when young and, again, when old, and maximally stable in middle age. Such is the case with stellar flaring activity.

All nuclear-burning stars produce flares, explosions due to the release of intense magnetic energy near star spots. Decades of observations of stellar flaring activity reveal that for stars of similar age to the Sun, those more massive and less massive than the Sun exhibit greater flaring activity. However, the most important factor in flaring activity is a star's age. For stars of equivalent mass to the Sun, one younger than 100 million years old can produce a hundred thousand times the flaring activity of a star the Sun's age, 4.6 billion years old.[30] A solar-mass star a few billion years older than the Sun can produce thousands of times the flaring activity.

Solar-mass stars exhibit minimal flaring activity during a narrow time window in their nuclear-burning history. That sliver of time is when the star reaches almost exactly the midpoint in its nuclear-burning cycle (see figure 9.4).

More than a decade ago, astronomers began a quest to ascertain whether the Sun is unique among all stars of similar mass, age, and effective temperature in manifesting such an extremely low level of flaring activity and luminosity variation. When the Kepler Space Telescope launched in 2009 to detect planets via the transit method, it was equipped with a sensitive photometer that monitored the brightness of 530,506 stars.[31] (Any planets orbiting these stars would be detectable by periodic dimming as they passed in front of the stars.)

Astronomers quickly realized, though, that data from Kepler could be used to achieve two additional missions: (1) to discern the enhanced brightening of stars caused by major stellar flares, and (2) to analyze stellar brightening variability caused by star spots and by the stars' rotation. The brightness changes due to flares and spots are easily distinguished given that flares vary over minutes while spots vary over days to months.

In 2012, a team of Japanese astronomers led by Hiroyuki Maehara used Kepler data to analyze the brightness variability of 83,000 G-dwarf stars (the Sun is a G-dwarf star) over a period of 120 days.[32] They detected 365 superflares with observed energies ranging from 3 x 10^{33} ergs to 3 x 10^{36} ergs.[33] For comparison, the most energetic solar flare ever detected was the Carrington Event of 1859, a flare that ignited fires by the arcing it induced in telegraph wires both in the United States and Europe.[34] Its total energy release according to one estimate was 1 x 10^{32} ergs,[35] and to another, 5 x 10^{32} ergs.[36]

Maehara's team then developed a subsample of 14,000 stars in the Sun's effective temperature range of 5,000–6,000 kelvin (Sun = 5,772 kelvin) and with a similar rotation rate. In this subsample they detected 14 flares with energies exceeding 4 x 10^{34} ergs. This number indicates that flares at least 80 times more energetic than the Carrington Event occur once every 350 years per star.

In follow-up studies—500-day observing runs—published in 2013 and 2015, Maehara's team detected 1,547 superflares (energies greater than 10^{34} ergs) on 279 G-dwarf stars[37] and 187 superflares on the 23 stars most similar to the Sun.[38] They calculated that for this latter group of stars, superflares occur once every 800–5,000 years per star.[39]

They further noted that a flare's energy release correlates closely with the proportion of the stellar surface covered by the star spot responsible for a given flare.[40] This finding, they concluded, explains why the Sun has produced no superflares during the past several thousand years. Its sunspots have been small throughout this era.

In 2019, a team of astronomers led by Yuta Notsu complemented the Kepler data with data from the Gaia spacecraft, launched in 2013. They also included observations performed on the Apache Point 3.5-meter telescope. They limited their analysis to Sunlike stars with rotation periods of about 25 days.[41] (Stars exhibit rotation rates ranging from 0.2 to 70 days.[42] The Sun's rotation period at the equator is 24.47 days.[43]) They determined that superflares (energies greater than 5×10^{34} ergs) on these stars occur once every 2,000–3,000 years per star.

In 2020, a team of astronomers led by Timo Reinhold combined the latest data from the Gaia spacecraft with Kepler data to produce a sample of 369 Kepler-observed stars from 4- to 5-billion years old with effective temperatures between 5,500 and 6,000 kelvin, surface gravity and metallicity values close to the Sun's, and rotation periods between 20 and 30 days.[44]

By limiting their sample to stars with ages and surface gravity values similar to the Sun's, Reinhold's team eliminated evolved (inactive) stars.[45] Their study of 369 stars represents the largest sampling, to date, of stars closely matching the Sun's characteristics. They determined that the average variability in brightness for the 369 stars equals 0.36%. This variability contrasts with the Sun's median variability of 0.07%. That is, the brightness variability of stars most like the Sun in effective temperature, rotation period, metallicity, surface gravity, and age measured 5 times greater than the Sun's variability over the 4-year period during which Reinhold's team conducted their analysis.

Figure 9.5 shows, to scale, the Sun's brightness variations compared to one of these solar-like stars, KIC 7849521. Its brightness variations represent the average variability of the 369 stars in the sample Reinhold's team studied.

The same day that Reinhold's team published the results of their variability study, a team of astronomers led by Jinghua Zhang published theirs—a comparison of the Sun's variability with data on 254 stars assembled by Kepler and

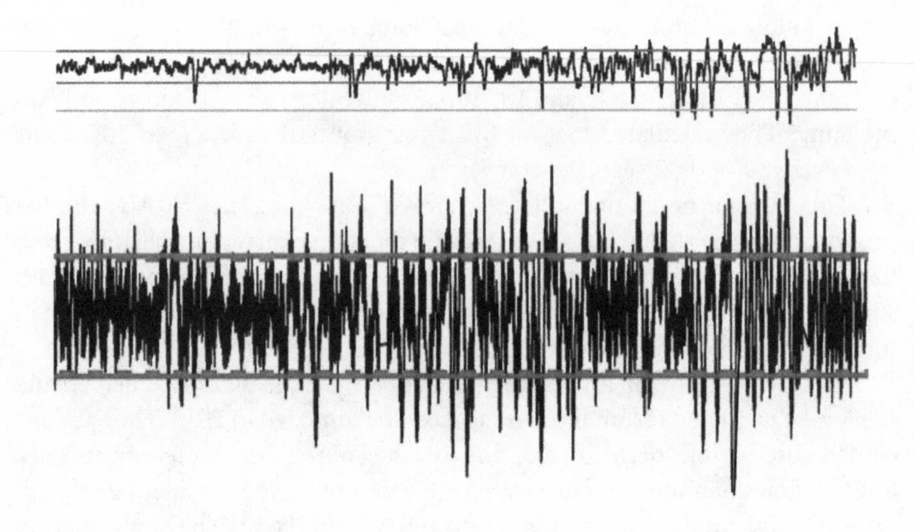

Figure 9.5: Brightness Variations for the Sun (top) and KIC 7849521 from March 2009 to April 2013
Figure adapted from Figure 2, Timo Reinhold et al., "The Sun Is Less Active Than Other Solar-Like Stars," *Science* 368 (May 1, 2020): 519, doi:10.1126/science.aay3821.

the Large Sky Area Multi-Object Fiber Spectroscopic Telescope (LAMOST).[46] The LAMOST provided measures of the chromospheric activity of solar-like stars while Kepler data was used to determine the photospheric variability of solar-like stars. Zhang's team concluded that the Sun is much less active than solar-like stars (stars with similar rotation periods) both in terms of photospheric variability and chromospheric activity.

Reinhold's and Zhang's teams also analyzed a large number of stars with unknown rotation periods that otherwise came close to matching the Sun's characteristics. They hypothesized that if these stars' sunspots were as few and small as the Sun's, their rotation periods would be undetectable and, therefore, a population of solar-like stars as photospherically stable as the Sun could possibly exist. The Sun, however, is both photospherically *and* chromospherically stable. This combination dramatically lowers the likelihood of finding a match and may explain why such a match has yet to be discovered.

Astronomers have developed two different scenarios to explain the Sun's exceptional stability. One suggests that the solar dynamo is currently in transition to a lower activity level due to a change in the differential rotation rates deep in its convective layer. This explanation builds upon astronomers' identification, long ago, of a relationship between stellar rotation rate and the duration of its star spot cycle.[47]

Over the past 410 years, the Sun has exhibited a sunspot cycle (lower-to-higher activity level) with a period of 11.06 years, on average.[48] In this respect, the Sun is, again, an outlier. A star with an 11-year sunspot cycle would typically rotate much more slowly than the Sun.[49] This observation implies that the Sun's rotation rate and magnetic field may be in a transition phase now that the Sun is halfway through its nuclear-burning period.[50]

The second explanation proposed for the Sun's exceptional stability is that the Sun may be alternating between epochs of high and low activity on time scales of 9,000 years. In other words, a cycle much longer than the 11-year average sunspot cycle may also be in operation. Whatever the case, we know that the past 9,000 years or more has been a period of truly remarkable solar stability, both in luminosity and in flaring activity. What's more, it has been a period devoid of superflares.

This alignment of specific solar time windows seems uncanny. The Sun exhibits a period of maximal luminosity stability and minimal flaring activity (in terms of rate and intensity) and is free of superflares. These events occur just as the Sun reaches the safest position (in terms of potential gravitational disturbances and radiation exposure) in its quarter-billion-year orbit around the MWG's center.[51] All of these coincide with an era of exceptional quiescence for the MWG's supermassive black hole, and an era free of nearby supernovae and gamma-ray bursts. Such an alignment defies all reasonable probability estimates. Somehow, multiple *independent* time windows involving both the Sun's neighborhood and favorable-for-life internal features perfectly aligned.[52]

The next two chapters examine the interior characteristics of the Sun's unique array of orbiting bodies—its rocky planets, gas giants, comets, and asteroids. As with the Sun itself, this planetary system is full of surprises. Its unique qualities make not only the existence of life and advanced forms of life possible, but also abundant life and technologically advanced civilization.

Chapter 10

Our Planetary System

Chapter summary: *Astronomers have discovered and made measurements of more than 3,500 planetary systems. What they have seen indicates that our solar system differs substantially from what's now recognized as the "norm" for planetary systems, both in its population and orbital features. Just as the Sun has no "twin," neither do any of the planets held in its orbit. The solar system is the only multiplanet system yet discovered with a population and configuration that would allow for the possible existence of advanced life and, what's more, provide for the ongoing development and sustenance of a large, technologically and culturally sophisticated civilization within it.*

From the moment the first exoplanets (planets beyond the solar system) were discovered orbiting nuclear-burning stars in the mid-1990s,[1] the world's astronomers became intent on finding at least one, if not many, sufficiently like Earth that could be a candidate to host life. After the first several hundred discoveries, however, they began to realize that for an Earthlike planet to possibly host and sustain life, that planet would need to be part of a planetary system with a population and configuration similar to our solar system. Thus, the quest began to find not only an Earth twin, but also a solar system twin. Ardent pursuit of this quest has led to a growing recognition that our solar system is one of a kind, with features uniquely suitable for the enduring existence and sustenance of advanced life.

Exoplanet Discovery and Measurement

Among the various methods astronomers have developed for finding and measuring the properties of exoplanets,[2] the two most frequently used are the transit method and the radial velocity method. Some 97% of discoveries and measurements have come through application of these methods.

The transit method, as its name suggests, reveals the presence of an exoplanet by the subtle dimming that occurs when it passes in front of its host star (with respect to the observer). The periodicity of this slight dimming of the star allows astronomers to determine both the planet's orbit and the planet's diameter. However, this method enables measurement of a planet's diameter and orbit only. It does not provide for measurement of the planet's mass.

Follow-up measurements to detect the host star's radial velocity help astronomers determine an exoplanet's mass. The radial velocity method measures the movement of the star along Earth's line of sight. When astronomers observe a star moving slightly away from and toward Earth in a cyclical pattern, they then know that the gravitational attraction of a body orbiting the star is responsible for the observed movements. Measurements of the magnitude and periodicity of the movements reveal the planet's orbit and indicate a lower limit for its mass. (Because the radial velocity method by itself gives no information on the tilt of the planet's orbital plane relative to the observer, it reveals only the mass lower limit.) When a planet has been detected by *both* the transit *and* radial velocity methods, astronomers can determine not just a lower limit on the planet's mass, but its actual mass.

The radial velocity method favors the detection of high-mass exoplanets and of low-mass exoplanets orbiting low-mass stars. In their study of the 4,835 confirmed exoplanets (to date), astronomers have produced reasonably accurate measurements of (1) each planet's mass, (2) each planet's radius (and, therefore, density), and (3) the primary orbital features (period, semi-major axis, eccentricity) for 741 of these planets.[3] For a total of 1,069 exoplanets, astronomers have measured the planets' masses, radii, and at least one of their orbital features. For a total of 2,210 exoplanets, astronomers either have measurements of the planets' radii and at least two of their orbital features and estimates of the planets' masses or measurements of the planets' masses, radii, and one of their orbital features.

Quest for an Earth Twin

Of all the confirmed exoplanets to date, 286 have radii within 20% of Earth's or masses within 20% of Earth's. All these planets, however, orbit their host stars more closely than Earth orbits the Sun.[4] Of these 286 planets, 264 orbit their host stars by less than 0.1 astronomical units (AU), where 1 astronomical unit is Earth's orbital distance from the Sun (149,597,871 kilometers or 92,955,807 miles). Only 2 orbit their host stars by more than 0.2 AU: Kepler-394c at 0.236 AU and Kepler-186f at 0.432 AU. Technically, Kepler-186f is not an Earthlike planet since its estimated mass is 44% larger than Earth's.[5]

The proximity of all 286 planets to their host stars poses huge habitability problems. The tidal forces that a star exerts on one of its planets increases by the fourth power of the inverse of the distance between the star and the planet. Therefore, a planet need only be slightly closer to its host star than Earth is to the Sun before tidal forces result in the planet's rotation period becoming equal or nearly equal to its period of revolution. For such a planet, one hemisphere will face the star for all or most of the planet's orbital journey around it, and the other hemisphere will face away. Consequently, the temperature differences between the hemisphere facing the host star and the hemisphere facing away will be extreme. While liquid water conceivably could exist in the twilight zone on such a planet's surface (transition zone at the edge of stellar illumination), atmospheric transport would move water to the coldest parts of the planet where it would freeze.[6]

These close orbits also imply that for the planets to possibly possess liquid water, their host stars must be low luminosity stars. Low luminosity stars are characterized by extreme flaring and x-ray activity. Astronomers used the MUSCLES (Measurements of the Ultraviolet Spectral Characteristics of Low-Mass Exoplanetary Systems) Treasury Survey to establish that, even for the least active low luminosity stars, the flux of ultraviolet and x-rays is more than sufficient to erode away the atmospheres and hydrospheres of planets orbiting these stars that reside inside the liquid water zone.[7]

Three-dimensional magnetohydrodynamic models of the impact of the stellar winds of low luminosity stars show that, for planets orbiting these stars in the liquid water zone, the stellar wind pressure on the planets is 100–100,000 times greater than the solar wind pressure on Earth.[8] This greater stellar wind pressure will compress any possibly existing magnetospheres around the planets to a degree that erosion of the planetary atmospheres cannot be prevented. That is, the greater stellar wind pressure will speed up the erosion of planetary atmospheres and hydrospheres generated by the stellar flux of ultraviolet and x-rays.

Close orbits pose yet another problem. Any planet with an atmosphere thicker than 1% of Earth's (a requirement for life) that is closer to its host star than 0.9 AU will very likely possess an atmospheric electric field strong enough to completely and quickly dry out the planet.[9] Venus, for example, with an atmospheric electric field of 10 volts, suffered this fate early in its history.[10]

For a planet to be truly habitable, it must orbit its host star not only within the liquid water zone but simultaneously within twelve other known planetary habitable zones.[11] One of those other habitable zones is the ultraviolet zone.[12] To remain in this ultraviolet safety zone, a planet must orbit its star no more than 4% nearer to or farther from Earth's orbital distance, and the star it orbits would require Sunlike stability in luminosity and flaring stability. Of the planets with an Earthlike diameter (measured within 30% of Earth's) or mass (measured within 30% of Earth's), not one orbits in the appropriate distance range.[13]

Therefore, for several independent reasons none of the 286 planets are viable candidates for life. Table 10.1 lists the five best "analogues" to Earth discovered to date. It also includes Venus, for the sake of comparison. As the table shows, Venus far outstrips known exoplanets in matching four significant-for-life characteristics of Earth, and yet no astronomer would consider Venus, Earth's sister planet, a possible candidate to support either long-term or advanced life.

For reasons mentioned in the previous chapter and in the appendix, it is unlikely that future exoplanet surveys will discover Earth analogue planets that match Earth's features better than does Venus. The exquisite fine-tuning

Table 10.1: Best Earth Analogue Planets Discovered to Date
Planet masses and diameters relative to Earth's

planet	mass	diameter	orbit (AU)	orbit eccentricity
OGLE-2016-BLG1195Lb	1.43		1.16	
Kepler-186f	1.44	1.17	0.432	0.04
Kepler-84c		1.132	0.236	
Kepler-102f	0.64	0.886	0.165	
Kepler-1649c	1.2	1.06	0.0649	
Venus	0.815	0.95	0.723	0.0068

needed for a star like the Sun to transfer a huge quantity of both refractory elements and angular momentum to its system of rocky planets implies not even a remote possibility that any other star in our galaxy will possess such a high total mass of dense rocky planets orbiting at such great distances.

Quest for a Solar System Planet Twin: Rocky Planets

Astronomers define rocky planets (also known as terrestrial or telluric planets) as planets up to 110% Earth's mass, composed primarily of silicate rocks and/or metals. Rocky planets, unlike their gaseous counterparts, possess a solid surface, and only a small fraction (less than 5%) of their total volume is comprised of volatiles (gases and liquids).

Astronomers' detailed knowledge of extrasolar planets is, of course, limited. What they know of the internal structure of planets comes from studying the rocky planets in the solar system. Such planets have a central metallic core (of variable size) composed primarily of iron, surrounded by a thick silicate mantle, encased within a thin silicate crust, and sometimes covered by a thin atmospheric and/or hydrospheric layer.

When it comes to extrasolar rocky planets, astronomers have found that their densities are directly proportional to the effective temperature of their host star and inversely proportional to their mass and their distance from their host stars. These relationships are expected, based on the laws of physics. The closer a planet is to its host star and the hotter the host star, the greater the incident heat and radiation the planet receives from that star. The greater the heat and radiation, the more the planet's volatile elements and compounds and light refractory elements will be blasted away. The smaller a planet's mass, the weaker its gravitational strength. The weaker the planet's gravitational attraction, the lower its escape velocity, which means the planet will retain only the higher atomic weight elements and molecular weight compounds, while elements such as hydrogen and helium and compounds such as methane and ammonia escape to space.

Except for Earth, the solar system's rocky planets follow this expected pattern of proportionalities. The densities for Mercury, Venus, and Mars are 5.427, 5.243, and 3.934 grams per cubic centimeter, respectively. They show the expected density decline with respect to distance from the Sun. Earth's density, at 5.514, is anomalously high due to an extraordinary event early in its history.

Another solar system rocky planet, Theia, orbiting in roughly the same plane, collided with the proto-Earth. This collision caused the primordial Earth to lose nearly all its atmosphere and hydrosphere and to gain an infusion of heavy elements from Theia's core.[14] This event also led to the formation of the Moon.

Ongoing research shows that Earth is not the only solar system planet with an unusually high density. Relative to densities of known rocky planets in exoplanetary systems, all the solar system's rocky planets are anomalously dense. The 17 known rocky planets outside the solar system for which densities have been *measured* orbit their host stars at 0.006–0.0746 AU (0.9–11.2 million kilometers). By contrast, Mercury orbits at 0.387 AU (58 million kilometers) from the Sun, and Mars at 1.524 AU (228 million kilometers). Despite proximity to their host star, the measured densities of the 17 average 3.774 grams per cubic centimeter.[15] This measurement strongly suggests that the densities of solar system rocky planets are even more anomalously high than the numbers might seem to indicate.

The discovery that these 17 rocky planets exist no farther from their host stars than a fifth of Mercury's distance from the Sun raises an interesting question. Is the solar system unique in possessing distantly orbiting rocky planets?

Currently, in the context of direct observations of exoplanetary systems, this question remains difficult to answer (for a more definitive answer from stellar physics, see the appendix: Solar Elemental Abundance—Rocky Planet Configuration Link). The farther a planet from its host star, the more difficult for astronomers to measure its mass and radius. The transit method, by which roughly three-fourths of confirmed exoplanets have been discovered to date,[16] favors the detection of planets that orbit close to their host stars. For planets orbiting their stars at Earth's distance from the Sun—one astronomical unit (AU)—the probability of detection by the transit method drops to only 0.47%. Thus, even though no rocky exoplanets have yet been detected orbiting at distances greater than Mercury's distance from the Sun (0.387 AUs), the transit method cannot rule out the possibility of their existence.

To further constrain the possible existence of exoplanets akin to Venus and Earth, two astronomers developed the largest planet catalog to date. They independently analyzed 200,000 stars observed by the Kepler spacecraft, supplemented by their analysis of the second data release from the Gaia spacecraft. They found a complete absence of planets with orbital periods between 200 and 400 days (orbital periods for Venus and Earth are 225 and 365 days, respectively) and diameters less than 1.41 Earth's diameter for F-, G-, and K-type stars (stars in the mass range of 0.5–1.4 solar masses).[17] Only F-, G-, and K-type stars possess the long-term luminosity stability (see chapter 9) that advanced life requires of its host star.

NASA has chosen to assume that planets with diameters up to 125% of Earth's diameter (regardless of mass) orbiting up to 2.0 AUs from their host star may be rocky planets. Based on this generous estimate, the NASA Exoplanet Catalog management team reports that 166 rocky exoplanets have been discovered.[18] Of these 166 planets, only 2 orbit their stars at a distance greater than Mercury's distance from the Sun. Kepler-186f orbits its star at 0.432 AU. KIC 5522786b orbits its star at a distance ranging from 1.64 to 1.98 AUs (for comparison, Mars orbits the Sun at 1.38 to 1.67 AUs).

Unlike most of the other 165 planets included in NASA's list of rocky exoplanets, the mass of KIC 5522786b, not just the diameter, has been determined. This lone planet orbiting its star equals 208% Earth's mass. Given such a high mass, this planet fails to fit any category astronomers have established and defined for rocky planets. Instead, it is a member of the "super-Earth" category. KIC 5522786b's host star is an A-type star at 1.79 solar masses and a luminosity 11 times that of the Sun.[19] Given KIC 5522786b's eccentric orbit and its host star's luminosity, astronomers know it lacks both an atmosphere and a hydrosphere. It is not, therefore, habitable.

As for Kepler-186f, the Gaia Data Release 2 showed that the initial measurement of Kepler-186f's diameter at 11% higher than Earth's diameter was incorrect. Its actual diameter is 131% Earth's diameter, also placing Kepler-186f outside of the rocky planet category and into the super-Earth category.[20]

As more and more exoplanets were discovered and studied, NASA began to group them according to defined categories. Each rocky exoplanet in the NASA Exoplanet Catalog is listed in one of four categories, based on its distance from its host star and implied relative surface temperature: hot, warm, cool, or distant. Hot exoplanets (rockies, for short) orbit their host stars at distances less than 0.1 AU. Warm rockies orbit their host stars between 0.1 and 0.387 AUs. Cool rockies orbit their host stars between 0.387 and 1.524 AUs (average orbital distances of Mercury and Mars, respectively). Distant rockies orbit their host stars at greater than 1.524 AUs.

Figure 10.1 shows the relative population of rocky planet types in exoplanetary systems alongside the rocky planet types in the solar system. (NASA no longer includes Kepler-186f and KIC 5522786b in its list of rocky planets.[21]) It shows how starkly the solar system differs from all known exoplanetary systems. Only the solar system is known to possess cool rockies.[22]

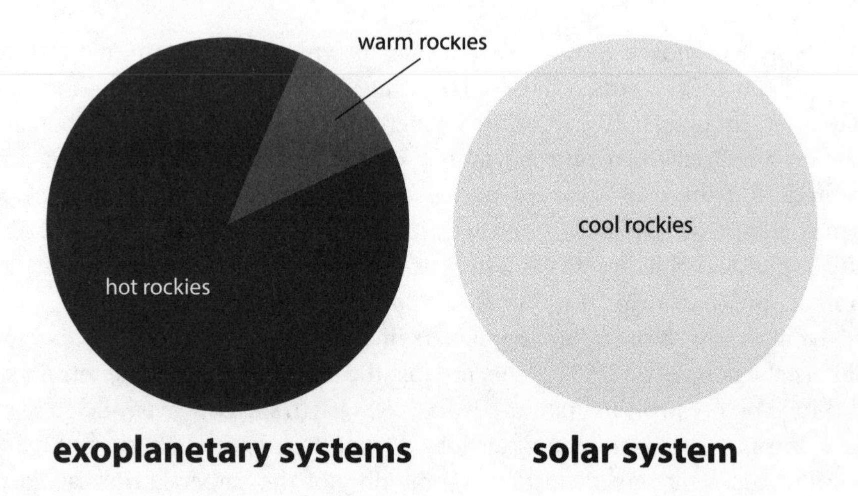

Figure 10.1: Relative Population of Known Rocky Planets (NASA Exoplanet Archive)
These graphs show the stark difference between exoplanetary systems and our solar system, a difference that holds significance for habitability. The data is based on the NASA Exoplanet Archive, which is continually growing/being added to. *Diagram credit: Hugh Ross*

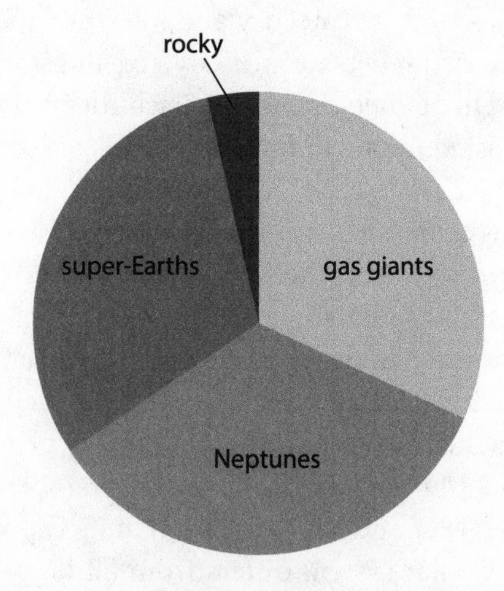

Figure 10.2: Relative Populations of Known Exoplanets (NASA Exoplanet Catalog)
Data based on 4,509 exoplanets listed in the NASA Exoplanet Catalog, which is continually growing. *Diagram credit: Hugh Ross*

Missing: Super-Earths and Warm Neptunes

The NASA Exoplanet Archive also lists three types of exoplanets in addition to rocky planets: gas giants, Neptunes (or Neptune-like), and super-Earths. NASA's Exoplanet Exploration Program defines gas giant planets as those either just as massive or more massive than Saturn; Neptunes are planets less massive than Saturn but more massive than Neptune; super-Earth planets are more massive than Earth but less massive than Neptune. These are the percentages of planet types: gas giants 31.7%, Neptune-like 34.0%, super-Earth 30.7%, and rocky 3.7%.[23] Figure 10.2 shows the relative populations of the 4,509 classifiable exoplanets listed to date in the NASA catalog.

Ongoing research reveals that the fraction of exoplanets in the rocky categories is lower than figure 10.2 indicates. A follow-up study on the seven "rocky" planets in the TRAPPIST-1 system, for example, revealed that five of the seven planets in that system have "envelopes of volatiles in the form of thick atmospheres, oceans, or ice" of sufficient magnitude to disqualify them as rockies.[24] Similar follow-up studies on planets in other exoplanetary systems may yield similar reclassifications.

Definitions used in the astronomical literature for super-Earths and Neptunes may differ slightly from one journal to another. Planetary astronomers define super-Earths as planets more massive than 1.1 times Earth's mass but less massive than 10 times Earth's mass. They categorize Neptunes as planets more than 10 times Earth's mass but less massive than Saturn. The definitions used for gas giants and rocky planets, however, are the same as the NASA definitions.

Planetary astronomers identify three specific classes of Neptunes: warm, cool, and cold. Neptunes that orbit their host stars closer than Earth orbits the Sun are called warm; those that orbit their host stars at distances between that of Earth and of Jupiter fit the cool classification; cold Neptunes orbit at distances greater than Jupiter's orbital distance. Super-Earths can be similarly classified as warm, cool, and cold. However, the cold class of super-Earths has only one potential member, to date. Its density measures a minuscule 0.003 grams per cubic centimeter, and it orbits a newborn star with planets still forming.[25] Most likely it is just a cloud of dust and debris, not yet a true planet.[18] Three of the six known cold Neptunes are hyper-cold Neptunes. They orbit their host stars at 105, 117, and 160 AU respectively, compared to just 30 AU for the Sun's Neptune. Figure 10.3 shows the relative populations of these exoplanet types, as listed in the Exoplanet TEAM catalog,[26] compared with the population of the solar system's planets (gas giants excluded).

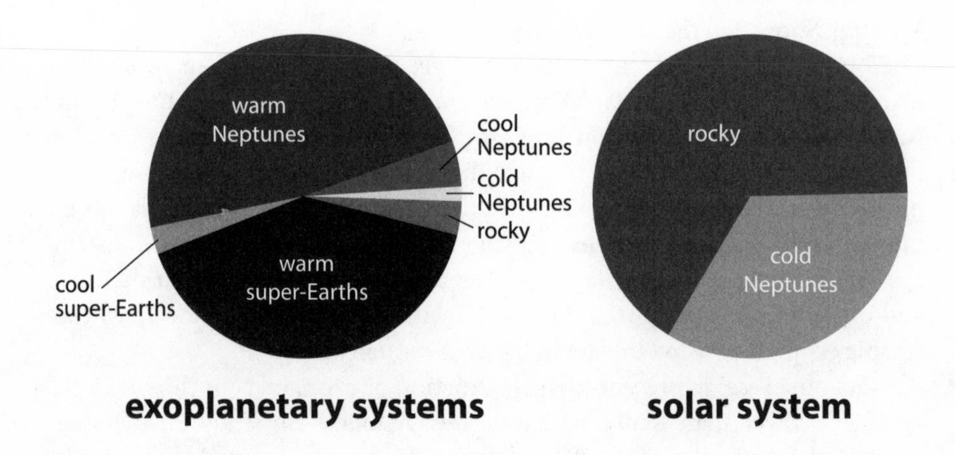

Figure 10.3: Relative Populations of Known Exoplanets (Exoplanet TEAM Catalog)
In this illustration, gas giant planets have been excluded. The pie chart on the left may change slightly with future improved detection instrumentation. The pie chart on the right is for the solar system's present four rocky planets and two cold Neptune planets.
Diagram credit: Hugh Ross

Instrumental limitations in both spacecraft and ground-based telescopes tend to skew the count of various exoplanet types. When these limitations are considered, it becomes even clearer that smaller planets (rockies and super-Earths) far outnumber larger planets (Neptunes and gas giants) and that Neptunes outnumber gas giants.[27]

In 1995–96, when the first exoplanets orbiting nuclear-burning stars were discovered,[28] most astronomers expected to find multiple exoplanetary systems like the solar system in population and other characteristics. A quarter of a century later and more than 3,500 exoplanetary systems detected, early expectations have been overturned. Super-Earths, warm Neptunes, and cool Neptunes comprise 95.8% of all known exoplanets with measured masses less massive than Saturn in these exoplanetary systems.[29] The solar system hosts *no* super-Earths and *no* warm *or* cool Neptunes.

The solar system's unique composition also contributes to its suitability as a home for advanced life. The presence of one or more super-Earths (97% of known super-Earths orbit their stars more closely than Mars orbits the Sun), warm Neptunes, or cool Neptunes would undoubtedly generate orbital chaos among a planetary system's cool rocky planets. While this orbital chaos would not necessarily rule out the possible brief existence of microbial life, it would make conditions for advanced life tenuous, at best, and completely shatter the possibility of any advanced civilization.

Super-Earths and Gas Giants

Our solar system's lack of super-Earths and warm Neptunes highlights its uniqueness even more clearly and profoundly, especially since our solar system includes not just one, but two cold gas giants, Jupiter and Saturn. Astronomers have discovered two correlations between gas giant planets and super-Earth planets that reveal how exceptional the solar system is and why the quest to find a cool rocky planet, let alone an Earth twin, is doomed to fail in virtually all exoplanetary systems.[30] One of these is an inverse (or anti) correlation, the second, a direct correlation.

Anticorrelation: Warm gas giants (planets more massive than Saturn orbiting their host stars more closely than 1 AU) frequently occur in exoplanetary systems. When present, however, rocky planets, warm or cool, are missing.

Detailed computer models show that a warm gas giant planet will gravitationally disturb—to a catastrophic degree—the orbit of any planet less massive than 21 times Earth's mass (much larger, even, than super-Earths) orbiting more closely than 1 AU.[31] This finding explains why known exoplanetary systems with one or more warm gas giants appear to be devoid of both warm and cool rocky planets.[32]

Of the 566 exoplanetary systems containing one or more warm gas giants, seven were initially thought to contain at least one super-Earth.[33] However, additional observations reveal that the seven may not be super-Earths after all. For example, the "super-Earth" in the Kepler 87 system has been found to have an extremely low density—only 0.152 grams/cubic centimeter—placing it in the "super-puff planet" category.[34] Super-puffs are "planets" with very thick, hyperinflated atmospheres of gas and dust and little or nothing else.[35]

Correlation: Exoplanetary systems with cold gas giants (planets more massive than Saturn and more distant from their host stars than 1 AU) "almost certainly have super-Earths."[36] The efficiency of detecting one or more cold gas giants, aka cold Jupiters, in a planetary system "is nearly 100% in a system with a super-Earth already detected."[37] Studies show that most, or possibly all, super-Earths possess very thick atmospheres super-rich in hydrogen gas.[38] Such atmospheric envelopes imply that super-Earths, like cold Jupiters, form early within their host stars' protoplanetary disks of debris, dust, and gas.

Because gas giants form outside the disks' ice line (the distance from a star beyond which volatiles such as carbon dioxide and water remain frozen) and super-Earths form inside that line, the two types of planets do not compete for protoplanetary material. However, any super-Earth inside the ice line would prove gravitationally disturbing to any cool rocky planets inside that line, thereby ruining their candidacy for advanced-life habitability. The solar system, by contrast with the norm, includes two cold gas giants and no super-Earths.

Unusual Gas Giant Planets

The Exoplanet TEAM's catalog lists 936 planets with measured masses greater than Saturn's.[39] These planets fall into four categories based on orbital distances from their host stars: warm, cool, cold, and distant. Warm gas giants orbit their hosts stars within 1.0 AU. Cool gas giants orbit their host stars between 1.0 and 5.2044 AUs (the orbits of Earth and Jupiter, respectively). Cold gas giants orbit their host stars between 5.2044 and 30.11 AUs (the orbits of Jupiter and Neptune, respectively). Distant gas giants orbit their stars at distances greater than 30.07 AUs.

Figure 10.4 compares the population of gas giants in known exoplanetary systems with the population of gas giants in the solar system. It shows the predominance of warm giants and cool gas giants in exoplanetary systems. The cold giants make up just 4% of the gas giant population while the warm and cool giants together comprise 75%. The solar system, by contrast, has only cold giants.

The apparent rarity of cold gas giants in exoplanetary systems can no longer be explained as an artifact of observational efficiency bias. Current technology has significantly improved astronomers' capability to detect gas giants, even those at great distances from their host stars. This technology now allows astronomers to fully account for observational biases. What they now reliably conclude is that fewer than 1% of all stars possess one or more gas giants beyond 3 AUs,[40] and their rate of occurrence decreases sharply with distance from the star. In the case of Sunlike stars, fewer than one in ten host any gas giants at all.[41] The presence of even one warm or cool giant planet in our solar system would have generated so much orbital chaos for Mercury, Venus, Earth, and Mars as to make life's existence, beyond briefly existing microbes, impossible on any of these planets.

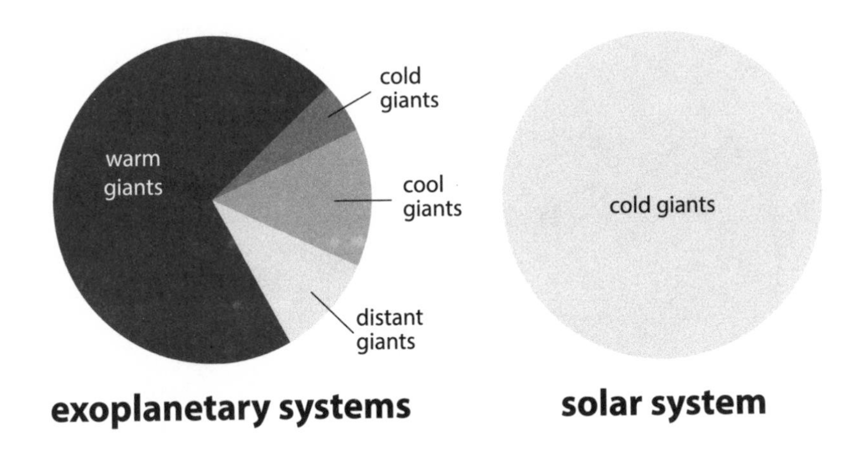

Figure 10.4: Relative Populations of Known Gas Giant Exoplanets (Exoplanet TEAM Catalog) Compared to the Solar System's
The pie chart on the left may change slightly with future improved detection instrumentation. *Diagram credit: Hugh Ross*

Gas Giant Orbital Eccentricities

The solar system's uniqueness becomes further accentuated by our cold giants' departure from the typical orbital pattern. In 2018, Wei Zhu and Yanqin Wu noted that "typical cold Jupiters (defined by them as gas giants with orbits greater than 1 AU) have significant orbital eccentricities."[42] (The eccentricity of an orbit is defined by this basic geometric equation: eccentricity equals the distance from one focus of an ellipse to the center, divided by half the maximum orbital diameter [see figure 10.5]. This equation shows that an ellipse with an eccentricity of 0 is a perfect circle, and an ellipse with an eccentricity of 1 is a line.)

At that time, 83% of cold exoplanetary Jupiters detected had measured orbital eccentricities equal to or greater than 0.09. Zhu and Wu demonstrated that cold Jupiters with eccentricities larger than 0.15 would catastrophically disturb the orbits of smaller planets orbiting more closely to the same host stars, possibly ejecting smaller planets from the system or causing them to fall into their host star. Where cold Jupiter orbital eccentricities are between 0.09 and 0.15, the resultant orbital catastrophes may not be so extreme, but they would at least render these other planets uninhabitable.

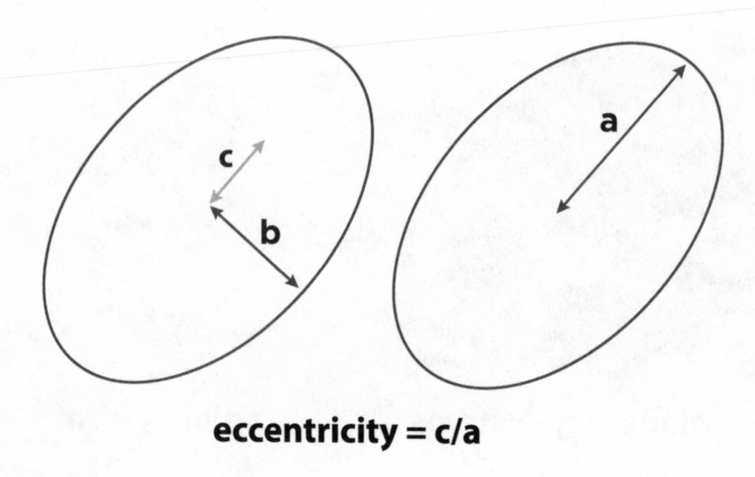

Figure 10.5: Orbital Eccentricity
Left: b represents the semi-minor axis and c represents half the distance between the two foci. Right: a is the semi-major axis. *Diagram credit: Hugh Ross*

Three years later, an analysis of the Exoplanet TEAM's catalog affirmed the two astronomers' conclusions. Of the cold exoplanetary Jupiters with measured orbits, 80% have orbital eccentricities equal to or greater than 0.10.[43] The average orbital eccentricity for these cold Jupiters is 0.30. This finding implies that orbital chaos for smaller planets orbiting closer to the host stars would be even greater than what Zhu and Wu predicted.

By contrast, the orbital eccentricities of the solar system's cold gas giant planets, Jupiter and Saturn, measure 0.0489 and 0.0565, respectively. Furthermore, Jupiter and Saturn are relatively low-mass gas giants. Their average mass equals 0.65 times Jupiter's mass. The average mass of known exoplanetary gas giants at orbital distances greater than 5.0 AU equals 12.31 times Jupiter's mass.[44] Jupiter and Saturn are also relatively distant from the Sun compared to the average distance of known cold gas giants in exoplanetary systems. Thus, the solar system's gas giant planets exert only minor gravitational influence on the orbits of Venus, Earth, and Mars.

The gravitational influence of Jupiter and Saturn on Earth, specifically, is small enough for Earth's orbit to remain for hundreds of millions of years within the multiple, specific orbital zones required for advanced life's existence.[45] On the other hand, they are large enough to generate Milankovitch cycles (variations in orbital eccentricity, rotation axis tilt, and precession) of just-right magnitude to produce exactly the kind of ice age cycle needed to supply the needs of a large population of technologically advanced creatures.[46]

Gas Giant Orbital Separation

For life to be possible in a planetary system, any habitable rocky planet would require cold gas giant companions. These cold gas giants would be needed to gravitationally shield the habitable planet from too many asteroid and comet impacts. For shielding to be adequately protective without disturbing the rocky planet's orbit, it must come from more than one cold gas giant.

More specifically, the cold gas giant planets must be arrayed on widely spaced orbits. If not, the habitable planet's rotation axis tilt would vary by such a significant degree as to induce extreme climate fluctuations and climate instabilities.[47] However, wide orbital separations for pairs of cold and cool gas giant planets are rare.

Only nine such pairs have been discovered outside the solar system: beta Pictoris b and c; HR 8799 d and e; PDS 70 b and c; GJ 676 A, b, and c; NN Ser (AB) c and d; upsilon Andromedae c and d; NY Virginis (AB) b and c; HIP 75548 b and c; and HIP 73990 b and c.[48] For all but two of these pairs, PDS 70 b and c and HR 8799 d and e, the planets are so massive as to render a stable orbit for a life-habitable rocky planet in the same system impossible. For both PDS 70 b and c and HR 8799 d and e, the gas giants orbit too distantly to provide adequate gravitational shielding for a life-habitable planet in the same system.

Additional Jupiter-Saturn Uniqueness

Astronomers long anticipated finding exoplanets just like some of the Sun's planets. After fifteen years of finding exoplanetary systems and exoplanets radically different from the solar system and its eight planets, the discovery of a planet nearly identical to Jupiter in mass, orbital distance, and orbital shape generated considerable excitement.[49]

The announced Jupiter twin, upsilon Andromedae e, has a measured mass nearly equal to Jupiter's, just 6% greater or somewhat larger if the orbital plane of upsilon Andromedae e is tilted with respect to the line of sight. It orbits its host star at a distance only 1% greater than Jupiter's distance from the Sun, and its orbital shape is nearly circular, like Jupiter's. Upsilon Andromedae e comes closer, by far, than any other known exoplanet to matching the characteristics of any solar system planet.

Upsilon Andromedae e differs radically from Jupiter, however, in two

Table 10.2: Best Jupiter Analogue Planets Discovered to Date[53]
Planet masses are relative to Jupiter's. Only one known planet in the system unless otherwise noted.

planet	mass	orbit (AU)	orbital eccentricity
Jupiter	1.00	5.20	0.0489
OGLE-2012-BLG0026Lc	0.68	4.63	inner large Neptune
OGLE-2018-BLG1269Lb	0.69	4.61	
UKIRT-2017-BLG001b	1.28	4.18	
HD 13931b	1.88	5.15	0.02
OGLE-2003-BLG235Lb	2.6	5.1	
51 Eridani b	2.6	11.1	0.49
HD 154345b	1.3	4.3	0.26

important features. First, the upsilon Andromedae system contains three additional planets even more massive than upsilon Andromedae e. These three (b, c, and d) weigh in at 1.7, 13.98, and 10.25 Jupiter masses, respectively.[50] Jupiter, on the other hand, is more massive than all the rest of the solar system planets combined. It makes up 68% of the total mass of its system's planets. Upsilon Andromedae e accounts for less than 4% of the total planetary mass in its system.

Second, while Jupiter has the smallest orbital distance of all gas giant and Neptune-type planets in the solar system, upsilon Andromedae e has the largest in its system. Andromedae b, c, and d at 1, 16, and 49% Jupiter's orbital distance, respectively, all orbit their host star more closely than does e.[51] The great mass of planets c and d, as well as their proximity to the host star, rules out any possibility this planetary system includes a body with life-support capacity.

Whether or not upsilon Andromedae e is the closest twin to a solar system

Table 10.3: Best Saturn Analogue Planets Discovered to Date[53]
Planet masses are relative to Saturn's. Only one known planet in the system unless otherwise noted.

planet	mass	orbit (AU)	orbital eccentricity	
Saturn	0.299	9.58	0.0565	
OGLE-2011-BLG0173Lb	0.19	10		inner large Neptune
OGLE-2008-BLG092Lab	0.18	15		
OGLE-2006-BLG109Lc	0.271	4.5	0.15	inner Jupiter
OGLE-2012-BLG0838b	0.25	4.2		

planet has likely become moot. When certain instruments on the Lick Telescope that played the predominant role in the "discovery" of upsilon Andromedae e were changed,[52] upsilon Andromedae e became undetectable. The observational database for its exoplanetary system still allows for the possibility of a fourth planet, but that possible fourth planet is not the upsilon Andromedae e planet once listed in exoplanet catalogs.

The database of known gas giant planets is now sufficiently large and diverse that one would expect it to include a reasonably close analogue to Jupiter or Saturn. Tables 10.2 and 10.3 list the closest analogues discovered to date. Not one comes close to matching the mass and orbital features of Jupiter or Saturn.

Update Test

The time between the completion of the first draft of this chapter and its final update was more than a year. During that time the database of discovered and measured exoplanets grew from just over 4,100 to 4,835 at the time of this final update.[55] It grew in another important way. Follow-up measurements on already discovered and confirmed exoplanets yielded more accurate and comprehensive determinations of their characteristics.

With a database now 18% larger and much more detailed, I was anticipating alterations to at least a few of this chapter's conclusions. Some minor rewordings were needed but no conclusion alterations. It was an encouraging test. The update of this chapter is at least initial evidence that the current extrasolar planet database indeed is large enough and broad enough to draw reasonably secure conclusions about the design implications for our solar system.

Our solar system and its eight planets differ from all known planetary systems and planets not only in the physical features described in this chapter. Still more uniqueness can be seen in the migration history of the Sun's planets and in the resultant orbital architecture of the entire system. The following chapter provides a story of exquisite planetary choreography, all for the benefit of life in all its wondrous diversity and complexity.

Chapter 11

Planetary Migration and Orbital Configuration

Chapter summary: *One reason our solar system planets possess the features that make advanced life on Earth possible is that they formed and migrated in surprising ways. Their unique origin and history explain, in part, how Earth acquired and has retained the atmosphere and hydrosphere advanced life requires. Research findings now provide abundant evidence that every one of the Sun's eight planets provides for the needs of advanced life on Earth in some crucial way.*

Planets, like individuals in our highly mobile society, rarely end up where they begin. In fact, during the early stages of planetary system formation, most planets migrate a considerable distance from their place of origin. Migration within a planetary system typically reduces the system's population of planets and, in the process, significantly alters the system's architecture—the positions and orbits of its members. In this respect the solar system is no exception. Its initial population was slightly reduced and its forming planets moved. Its uniqueness becomes evident in the details of its planetary formation history, migration history and, most importantly, in the outcome of its history.

Ice Line and Planet Migration

As research made it possible to study exoplanets and the systems in which they exist, the differences between them and the solar system prompted deeper investigation into what shapes these systems: what determines their planetary population, arrangement, and orbital features? Differences show up in all these features, especially in the population and arrangement of gas giants and Neptune-type planets. No system yet studied resembles the solar system in this regard.

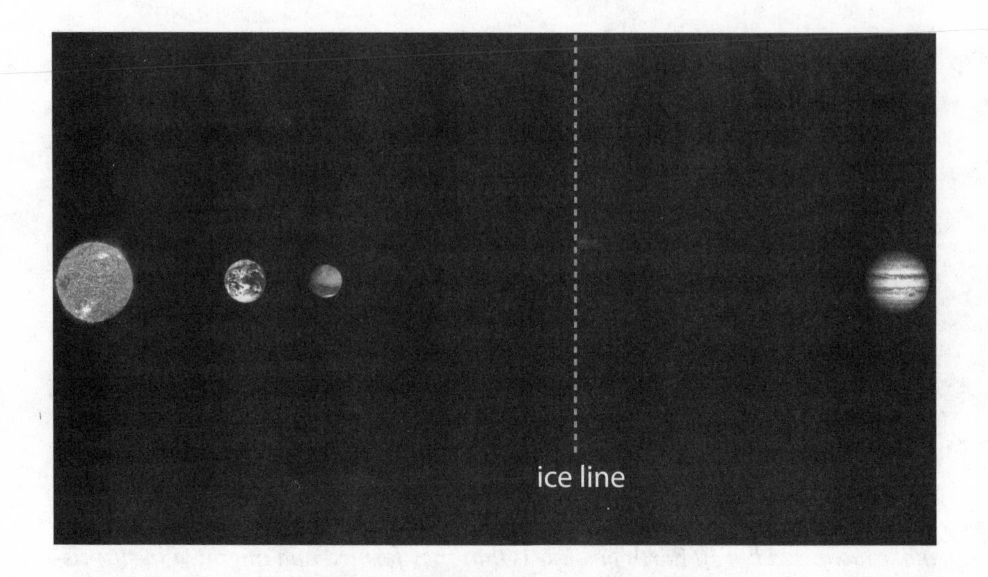

Figure 11.1: Position of the Solar System's Ice Line
Distances but not object sizes are to scale. The ice line lies 3.1 times more distant from the Sun than Earth and 2.0 times more distant from the Sun than Mars. *Diagram credit: Hugh Ross*

Long before the discovery of any exoplanets, astronomers had determined that gas giant and Neptune-type planets form only beyond their host star's ice line (the distance where volatiles such as water, carbon dioxide, carbon monoxide, and ammonia freeze into ice grains), also known as the snow line. At this distance from the host star, radiant temperature falls below 150 kelvin (150 degrees Celsius above absolute zero), and only at such a distance and temperature can a forming planet accrete the enormous quantities of volatiles that epitomize gas giants and Neptune-type planets. Figure 11.1 shows the solar system's ice line.

While gas giant and Neptune-type planets can form only at or beyond the ice line, most do not remain there. Some 72% of the more than 2,600 gas giants and Neptunes (defined as greater than 10 Earth masses or greater than 200% Earth's diameter) observed to date are orbiting their host stars deep inside the ice line.[1] This observation raises an obvious question: how did they arrive there?

Detailed computer modeling of the interactions between newly forming gas giants and Neptunes and their protoplanetary disk (the rotating circumstellar disk of dense gas and dust surrounding a newly formed star) has provided some insight. It shows that the transfer of angular momentum from the "embryonic" gas giants and Neptunes to the rotating disk causes them to migrate inward toward the host star.[2] These planets migrate relatively rapidly at first, and later more slowly across the ice line, and then move slowly closer to their host star. The journey stops either when a large gap opens up in the protoplanetary disk or when thermodynamic effects in the inner part of the protoplanetary disk brings it to a halt.[3]

Planet migration can also result from an angular momentum exchange between newly coalescing planets and planetesimals (solid bodies from one kilometer to just under 100 kilometers in diameter that form from dust grains in the protoplanetary disk[4]) still remaining in the protoplanetary disk.[5] Where this exchange occurs, the planet migration can be either inward or outward. If the planetary system resides in a star cluster, dynamical interactions between two or more stars can scatter the stars' planets, typically ejecting the more distantly orbiting planets and forcing the remaining planets into closer orbits about their host star.[6]

In some newly forming planetary systems, the gas and dust in their protoplanetary disk are exhausted quickly. In these cases, little or no planet migration occurs.[7] In rare instances, where two or more forming gas giant planets exist within a common gap in the protoplanetary disk, mean motion resonances can propel two or more gas giants outward ten times or more beyond the distances at which they initially formed.[8] Mean motion resonances are orbital periods related to one another by a ratio of small integers; for example, one planet making exactly two orbits for every single orbit of another planet in the same system.

These patterns of gas giant migration (or lack thereof) apply to all known planetary systems except one, the solar system. Jupiter and Saturn, which formed beyond the ice line, never migrated interior to the snow line, nor did they migrate outward from their birth locations, and yet, they did migrate. They underwent a unique "grand tack" migration that placed them and Uranus and Neptune in a unique orbital configuration, one that reordered the system's rocky planets and worked to make advanced life possible on one of the rocky planets.

Grand Tack Migration

All standard planetary formation models, when applied to the solar system, were once stymied by two irregularities: the "Mars Problem" and the "Main Belt Problem."[9] Most solar system formation models could explain the mass and orbit of each of the solar system's two gas giants, Jupiter and Saturn, and even the masses and orbits of Mercury, Venus, and Earth. However, they also predicted that (1) Mars should be 1.1–1.5 times more massive than Earth, (2) the Main Belt of asteroids should be much larger in total mass and should include a few bodies as massive or nearly as massive as Mars (Mars is 0.11 Earth masses), and (3) the Main Belt should extend from just outside Earth's orbit to Jupiter's orbit.

Any one of these predicted outcomes would have been catastrophic for advanced life and civilization. The combination of all three would have been catastrophic for all but a low population and low diversity of microbial life.

For over a decade, a team of astronomers in Nice, France, toiled to solve the Mars Problem. Their efforts culminated in a comprehensive and detailed "grand tack" model. According to their model, the solar system began with two gas giant planets and three ice planets. (An ice planet is a planet 10–90 times Earth's mass that orbits its host star beyond the ice line.)

The solar system originally included three ice planets: Uranus, Neptune, and an unnamed planet about 10 times more massive than Earth. One of the gas giants, Jupiter, either ejected the smallest ice planet into interstellar space, or the combined "tacking" movements of Jupiter, Saturn, Uranus, and Neptune sent it into the farthest reaches of the solar system.[10] The Nice team used the sailing term "tacking" to refer to the directional changes made by the solar system's gas giants, first inward toward the Sun and then outward.

This initial inward migration results, as described above, from an exchange of angular momentum between the gas giant planets and the gas, dust, rocks, and planetesimals still remaining in the disk from the earlier period of planet formation. This migration pattern represents the norm for gas giants. The Nice team went on to show that if a planetary system's most massive gas giant happens to form closer to its host star than the second most massive gas giant, that planetary system's gas giants and Neptune-type planets will initially migrate inward and then change direction and begin to migrate in an outward direction. However, this specific grand tack motion would occur only if each of the multiple features of the solar system fell within highly precise ranges—features such as the mass and the orbit of each gas giant planet and the mass and the orbital range of each of the primordial asteroid and comet belts.[11]

The change in migration direction of the gas giants occurred because Saturn moved inward at a faster rate than Jupiter. Due to the difference in their migration velocities, Jupiter and Saturn became temporarily locked into a 3:2 mean motion resonance. Jupiter would make exactly three trips around the Sun for every two of Saturn's. This resonance meant that the gravitational tugs of Jupiter and Saturn frequently aligned in such a way as to disturb the orbits of the other ice planets and the primordial asteroid and comet belts.

The resonance caused the smallest of the three ice planets to be forcefully ejected from its place of origin. It also caused both the gas giants themselves and the other ice planets to change their migration trajectory. It reduced the size of the Main Belt down to a mere 0.1% of its primordial size,[12] and it reduced the sizes of the solar system's other belts of asteroids and comets by nearly the same degree. At the same time, it impacted the formation of the inner rocky planets.

The Nice model initially explained how the Main Belt became so reduced, how the inner (most dangerous to life) part of the Main Belt was eradicated, how the remaining asteroids became radially mixed, and how the orbital inclinations of Main Belt constituents ended up with such extreme and chaotic values. However, it did not explain how the orbital eccentricities of Main Belt constituents likewise developed such extreme and chaotic values. Chapter 12 goes into greater detail about solar system asteroid-comet belts, including the Main Belt.

In a paper published in *Icarus*, the Nice team extended their model, running it forward an additional 4.1 billion years.[13] This extension fully explained the eccentricities in the orbits of the Main Belt asteroids. As a bonus, it also explained the distribution of the Main Belt asteroids' semi-major axes. (The semi-major axis is half the diameter of a body's orbit at the orbit's widest point.)

A separate team of astronomers reanalyzed the grand tack model by fully accounting for the effects of viscous heating in the pre-planetary disk as the Sun was still forming.[14] They also incorporated a more realistic mass-radius relationship for the growing terrestrial planets (Mercury, Venus, Earth, and Mars). Their reanalysis accurately reproduced both the orbits and the masses of Mercury, Venus, Earth, and Mars. However, to get Earth orbiting the Sun at its current distance, this team had to adjust the point at which Jupiter reversed direction, moving it from the 1.5 astronomical units (AUs) to 2.0 AUs from the Sun (see figure 11.2).

Another follow-up analysis by a different team of astronomers showed that

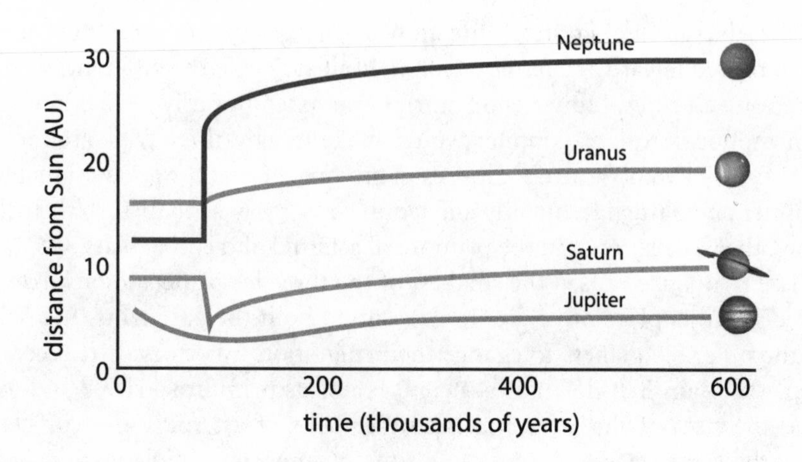

Figure 11.2: Updated Grand Tack Determination for Jupiter, Saturn, Uranus, and Neptune
1 astronomical unit (AU) = distance from Earth to the Sun. A third Neptune-like planet, about 10 times Earth's mass, gets ejected by a close encounter with Jupiter and/or Saturn. *Diagram credit: Hugh Ross*

to achieve the current orbits of the eight solar system planets, the masses and initial orbit features of Jupiter and Saturn required fine-tuning, as did the timing of their formation.[15] Still another independent team showed that the distribution of mass in the inner portion of the protoplanetary disk also must fall within a specific, narrow range.[16]

To date, astronomers are considering two possible zero points for the beginning of the major grand tack migrations: (1) soon after the dissipation of gas from the protoplanetary disk, less than 100 million years after the solar system began to form, and (2) about 600 million years after the formation of the Moon, about 695 million years after the solar system began to take shape.[17]

The latter of these two possible dates would explain the Late Heavy Bombardment of the inner solar system bodies, an era during which Earth and the Moon were pounded by large asteroids and comets.[18] However, an analysis of the Oort Cloud asteroids (the most distant of the solar system asteroid and comet belts) strongly favors a grand tack migration involving not only Jupiter and Saturn, but Uranus and Neptune as well, and the earlier of the two possible dates.[19] An analysis of the orbits of objects in the Kuiper Belt of asteroids and comets (the belt just beyond Neptune, 30–50 AUs from the Sun) also favors the earlier date.[20]

The inward migration of Jupiter from its original place more than 5 AUs from the Sun to just 2 AUs and then back outward again helps explain the mass of each of the inner planets—Mercury, Venus, Earth, and Mars—and much more.[21] For example, it explains the absence of planets interior to Mercury. The grand tack caused a collisional cascade of remaining planetesimals so intense as to drive previously existing short-period planets right into the Sun. This occurrence likely plays a significant role in explaining the Sun's unique elemental abundance ratios. The migration also implies that Mercury, Venus, Earth, and Mars "formed from gas-starved, mass-depleted debris that remained after the primary period of dynamical evolution."[22] Thus, it helps to explain not only the Sun's unique abundances and ratios of elements heavier than helium, but also those of the solar system's rocky planets. It also explains why the Sun's large rocky planets, Venus and Earth, possess atmospheres and hydrospheres tens to hundreds of times smaller than those of their closest exoplanet equivalents.[23] (See sidebar, "Earth's Unique Water Abundance.")

The grand tack migrations of Jupiter, Saturn, Uranus, and Neptune explain many of the differences between the solar system and all known exoplanetary systems.[29] Of the 3,468 exoplanetary systems orbiting nuclear-burning stars known to date, 99.7% either possess (1) super-Earths, (2) planets with orbital periods less than 80 days, (3) Neptunes with orbital distances less than 2.0 AUs, or (4) gas giant planets either more than 4 times Jupiter's mass or with orbital eccentricities greater than or equal to 0.10 or with orbital distances less than 3 AUs.[30] The solar system stands apart in that it has none of these planets. Furthermore, out of the known planetary systems, the solar system is the only one with known planets less massive than 1.4 Earth masses that orbit between 0.35 and 2.0 AUs.[31]

Jupiter and Saturn's migrations also help explain why the orbital eccentricities of solar system planets beyond 0.95 AUs are so low while those of gas giants in exoplanetary systems are so high. The norm for exoplanetary systems is for two or more planets to migrate on divergent trajectories with increasing orbital separation.[32] Such migration dramatically increases the planets' orbital eccentricities.[33] For many exoplanetary systems, the orbital eccentricities and inclinations of its planets are further pumped up by close flybys from other stars.[34]

Convergent orbital migration, as was the case with Jupiter and Saturn, represents the exception. As one team of planetary astronomers commented,

Earth's Unique Water Abundance

Earth orbits the Sun at a little less than one-third the distance to the solar system's ice line. All models for Earth's formation, including all grand tack models, confirm that Earth formed at or very near its present orbital distance from the Sun.[24] The planetary building blocks available at this distance would've been bone dry, by all accounts. So, where did Earth gets its water? The best explanation is that it came from beyond the snow line.

The initial migration of Jupiter and Saturn inward toward the ice line scattered a significant fraction of carbonaceous chondrite asteroids and meteors from the outer asteroid belts into the Main Belt and into the region where Mercury, Venus, Earth, and Mars were forming.[25] An abundance of evidence suggests that the parent bodies of carbonaceous chondrite meteorites originated from beyond Jupiter's current orbit.[26] The measured deuterium-to-hydrogen ratio in hydrated minerals in carbonaceous chondrite meteorites is unique among solar system meteorites, and it matches the span of ratios in the Earth's ocean and interior.[27] This alignment affirms that carbonaceous chondrite meteorites are the source of all, or nearly all, of Earth's water.

Jupiter's inward migration reversed when Jupiter reached 2.0 AUs from the Sun. Saturn's migration direction also reversed. This change of direction, the grand tack, limited the amount of water delivered to Earth in a beneficial way.

In 80% of exoplanetary systems, Jupiter and Neptune-like planets migrate inward and don't turn around. So, they move much closer to their host stars than Jupiter and Saturn did to the Sun. This greater inward migration explains the presence of super water-rich small exoplanets astronomers have discovered. In other exoplanetary systems, where no significant migration of large planets occurs, astronomers find bone-dry small planets.

Why then do Earth's atmosphere and hydrosphere prove much smaller than Jupiter and Saturn's inward migrations warrant? The collision of primordial Earth with the smaller planet in its orbital pathway (Theia), an event that gave rise to the formation of the Moon, reduced Earth's primordial atmosphere and hydrosphere to their current volume—a volume that happens to be just-right for the needs of advanced life.[28]

"[O]ther planetary systems with giant planets are not expected to have experienced a Grand Tack-like evolutionary path."[35] This unique migration event explains virtually *all* the orbital and mass distribution characteristics of the Sun's planets, as well as of its asteroid and comet belts, and in minute detail.

Unique Planetary System Architecture

The precise positioning of Jupiter, Saturn, Uranus, and Neptune in their orbits beyond the ice line provide Earth with the best possible gravitational shield. Their masses, orbital distances, and close-to-zero orbital eccentricities assure that, in nearly all instances, asteroids and comets on a trajectory to collide with Earth instead are deflected away or absorbed by one of the four. Comet Shoemaker-Levy's collision with Jupiter in 1994[36] serves as one example of the Jupiter-Saturn-Uranus-Neptune gravitational shielding.

This shielding of Earth from asteroid and comets is not total, however—a fact that's beneficial for advanced life. For the shielding to be total, Jupiter, Saturn, Uranus, and Neptune must either be closer to Earth, more massive than they are, or both. In that case, the gravitational influences of Jupiter, Saturn, Uranus, and Neptune would generate a level of chaos in Earth's orbit that would make global civilization impossible. It also would rule out many benefits Earth receives from occasional encounters with asteroids and comets. Even the specific configuration of the shield proves beneficial.

The shield is optimized by the position of Jupiter, the most massive planet in the shield being the closest, followed by Saturn, the second most massive planet, at nearly double Jupiter's distance from the Sun. The optimization is further enhanced by Jupiter and Saturn being followed by Uranus and Neptune, considerably less massive, considerably more distant, and considerably more separated from one another, but optimally located relative to the Centaur, Scattered, and Kuiper belts of asteroids and comets (see chapter 12). Neptune's extremely low orbital eccentricity of only 0.009456 also proves beneficial.

With two gas giant and two Neptune-type planets orbiting between 5 and 31 AUs, it would seem inevitable that two or more of these planets would be at risk of encountering mean motion resonances. Jupiter makes 7.083 orbits for every single orbit of Uranus. Uranus makes 1.961 orbits for every single orbit of Neptune. Jupiter makes 4.967 orbits for every two orbits of Saturn. They certainly come close to whole integer resonances, but they never quite get there. If they did, strong gravitational disturbances would regularly ripple throughout the inner solar system.

Even tiny differences in the orbits of Jupiter, Saturn, Uranus, and Neptune could move them into nearly perfect 7:1, 2:1, and 5:2 resonances, respectively, with catastrophic effect.[37] The disturbances would produce much larger variations, for example, in the eccentricity of Earth's orbit. Greater eccentricity would bring greater seasonal temperature extremes. It would also generate more extreme temperature differences in the ice age cycles. As a result, Earth would freeze completely or lose all surface and atmospheric water.[38]

No significant mean motion resonances exist among the other solar system planets, either. Among Mercury, Venus, Earth, and Mars, the closest are the nearly 3:1 between Mars and Venus and the nearly 5:3 resonance between Earth and Venus. Nor are there any significant mean motion resonances between any of the large solar system planets and the solar system's rocky planets. The only solar system planet at risk of orbital instability is Mercury, but not until several billion years from now. Its small mass, just 0.055 Earth masses, and its high orbital eccentricity, 0.2056, make it particularly susceptible to gravitational disturbances from Jupiter and Saturn.

Numerical simulations of the future orbital architecture of the solar system reveal a small probability that gravitational disturbance exerted by Jupiter and Saturn will bump Mercury's orbital eccentricity high enough to result in a collision between Mercury and the Sun, or Mercury and Venus, within the next five billion years.[39] These same simulations show that Earth's Moon plays a significant role in keeping this probability as low as 1%.

A team of Canadian astronomers demonstrated that the orbits of Venus, Earth, and Mars must be precisely fixed to prevent mean motion resonances that could otherwise prove damaging for life on Earth.[40] They showed that the orbital features of the Earth-Moon system are able to suppress a resonance in Venus's orbit, a resonance generated by the orbits and masses of Jupiter, Saturn, Uranus, and Neptune. The precise configuration of the Earth-Moon system and the increasing distance separating Earth and the Moon prevent the destabilization of Venus' orbit and, thus, avert destructive orbital chaos throughout the inner solar system.

In 2014, another team of astronomers demonstrated that relatively small changes in Jupiter's orbital distance would be enough to destabilize the entire solar system.[41] They also established correlations between Jupiter's orbital distance and the frequency of Earth's Milankovitch cycles (periodic variations in the rotation axis tilt, orbital precession, rotational precession, and orbital eccentricity). For example, moving Jupiter slightly closer to the Sun would shorten the periodicity of variations in the inclination and eccentricity of Earth's orbit. Moving Jupiter slightly more distant from the Sun would lengthen the periodicity. In either case, the periodicity of Earth's ice age cycle would be altered, with significant negative consequences for the possibility of advanced life and civilization.[42]

A year later, this same team showed that Venus's orbit must also be fine-tuned.[43] If Venus's orbit were less than 0.49 or more than 0.92 AUs, Venus's gravity would so strongly interact with that of either Mercury or Earth as to bring about the disintegration of the Sun's array of planets. If Mars's orbital distance of 1.524 AUs were increased slightly to 1.587 AUs, inner solar system orbital chaos would result. If Venus were to orbit near the location of mean motion resonance with either Mercury or Earth, the orbital chaos generated within the inner solar system would be sufficient to rule out advanced life on Earth.

Research reveals that the migration history, mass, and orbital features of every planet in our solar system and of the Earth-Moon system contribute to the possible existence of advanced life on one planet: Earth. For advanced life to thrive on Earth, the orbital architecture of the solar system's eight planets and Earth's Moon must be exactly as it is.

This chapter and the previous one by no means exhaust the known characteristics of the solar system that make advanced life possible within it. The chapters reveal, however, the most important of these features. Furthermore, rather than confirming the expectations and predictions made by astronomers in the 1990s, the findings indicate that the more we learn about the solar system in comparison and contrast with exoplanetary systems, the more evidence we uncover for the utterly unique architecture of the entire system.

This uniqueness applies not just to the planets, but also to the Sun's system of asteroid and comet belts. The solar system's belts of smaller bodies also manifest fine-tuned features. The next chapter describes the more significant of these known features.

Chapter 12

Small Solar System Bodies

Chapter summary: *Another feature of the solar system that distinguishes it from all known exoplanetary systems is its asteroid-comet belts. Exoplanetary systems either lack asteroid-comet belts altogether or have belts hundreds of times larger than those in the solar system. Each of the Sun's five asteroid-comet belts manifests a just-right total mass, population and distribution of asteroids and comets, and orbital configuration that allows for the possibility of advanced life on Earth. Each serves to enhance Earth's capacity for civilization.*

The solar system's eight planets and 200+ moons are accompanied by five major asteroid-comet belts. Asteroids are rocky or metallic bodies ranging in size from 1 meter to 2,500 meters in diameter and masses less than 25% the Moon's. With bodies of the same size and mass range as asteroids, comets are an amalgamation of rocks, dust, and frozen volatiles (frozen water, carbon dioxide, carbon monoxide, methane, and ammonia). Frozen volatiles typically make up about 85% of a comet's mass.

An asteroid-comet belt is a torus-shaped or spheroidal zone surrounding a star, a revolving conglomeration of at least a thousand asteroids and/or comets. An individual belt may include as many as trillions. One common feature all asteroid-comet belts share is that they change over time.

Evolution of Asteroid-Comet Belts

The way stars and planets form within a given star system determines the characteristics of the system's asteroid and comet belts. Theoretical models show that the intense radiation emitted by stars more than three times the Sun's mass interferes with the formation of asteroid and comet belts. This calculation is affirmed by surveys of debris disks around stars.[1]

Astronomers can detect comet and asteroid belts around stars other than the Sun from observing the dust generated by collisions among comets and asteroids.[2] Stars other than the Sun and less massive than three times the Sun fall into two distinct categories: (1) stars surrounded by asteroid-comet belts with vastly larger populations, at least hundreds of times larger, than the Sun's belts, and (2) stars that have no detectable asteroid-comet belts.[3] The Sun is an outlier in that it hosts a handful of small asteroid-comet belts.

Observations as well as models of planet and asteroid-comet belt formation point to the significant role of gas giants and Neptune-type planets. Stars with no gas giant planets are surrounded by large clouds of dust and debris indicative of the presence of enormous belts of asteroids and comets.[4] Exoplanetary systems with gas giants or Neptunes orbiting their host star inside the ice line (see chapter 11) lack the dust and debris that would indicate the presence of asteroids and comets.[5]

Because these gas giants and Neptunes form outside their host stars' ice line and, in most cases, migrate inward across the ice line,[6] they gravitationally scatter the belts of asteroids and comets that formed inward of the gas giants' and Neptunes' locations, eradicating them from their systems. Outward migration likewise eradicates the outward belts. In those few instances where no migration occurs, both the inward and outward belts remain largely intact.

What makes the solar system's asteroid and comet belts unique is the peculiar migration history of the solar system's big planets and the relatively small mass of these planets by comparison with the gas giants in exoplanetary systems. Jupiter and Saturn, as the previous chapter describes, migrated inward, stopped just inside the ice line, reversed direction, and settled into stable, nearly circular orbits not far from their original locations. Meanwhile, Uranus and Neptune migrated inward only slightly, reversed direction, and migrated outward to 19 and 30 astronomical units (AUs) from the Sun (see figure 11.2).

Jupiter and Saturn's relatively low masses and relatively limited inward migration radically reduced the solar system's innermost asteroid belt (the belt between Mars and Jupiter) without eliminating it. The outward migration of Uranus and Neptune radically reduced, but did not eliminate, the solar system's outward asteroid and comet belts. The remarkable "grand tack" left the solar system with five small but intact belts of asteroids and comets in just-right places at just-right times.[7]

Features of the Belts

The solar system's asteroid and comet belts are significant because of their potential to bombard Earth with crucial resources—water, minerals, metals, and more—and to do so safely, without devastating the planet or its potential for advanced life. The level of bombardment, as well as the material delivered by asteroids and comets, must fall within extremely precise ranges to bring benefit, rather than disaster, for life's sake. Each belt's position, configuration, and composition play a part.

Astronomers refer to the innermost asteroid-comet belt, which orbits between Mars and Jupiter, as the Main Belt. Most of its constituents (more than 99%) are asteroids, but a few comets reside there, too. Most Main Belt objects orbit between 300 and 500 million kilometers (190 and 300 million miles) from the Sun.

The Main Belt's total mass prior to the migration of Jupiter and Saturn (with the scattering effect) was approximately equal to Earth's mass.[8] Its current mass is $4.008 \pm 0.010 \times 10^{-4}$ of Earth's mass.[9] Roughly 75% of Main Belt asteroids are carbonaceous, and these asteroids dominate the belt's outer part. Approximately 15% of its asteroids are silicate-rich. The remaining 10% are metal-rich, comprised almost entirely of iron, cobalt, nickel, and elements heavier than nickel.

The asteroids and comets orbiting between Jupiter and Neptune are referred to as the Centaurs. For the most part, the Centaurs are immigrants from the more distant (thus colder) Kuiper Belt. As Neptune continues to slowly erode the Kuiper Belt by gravitational scattering, it sends some Kuiper Belt objects inward to become Centaurs and others outward to populate the Scattered Belt.[10] Orbiting close to Jupiter, Saturn, Uranus, and Neptune, the Centaurs experience strong gravitational perturbations. As a result, their orbits display a wide range of eccentricities and inclinations.[11] The Centaurs, roughly half of which are asteroids and half comets, have a total mass approximately 10^{-4} (0.0001) Earth masses.[12]

The Scattered Belt extends from Neptune's orbit, at about 4.5 billion kilometers (2.8 billion miles) from the Sun, out to 33 billion kilometers (20 billion miles) from the Sun. Scattered Belt objects are characterized by large orbital eccentricities. Their total mass, about 0.05 Earth masses,[13] is more than 100 times greater than the Main Belt mass and about 500 times greater than the mass of Centaurs.

The disk-shaped Kuiper Belt[14] resides just outside Neptune's orbit, between 4.5 and 7.5 billion kilometers (2.8 and 4.7 billion miles) from the Sun.

Before Neptune's outward migration, the Kuiper Belt orbited between about 2.5 and 5.0 billion kilometers (1.6 and 3.1 billion miles) from the Sun.[15] Its primordial mass equaled about 30 Earth masses.[16] Its current mass equals 0.061 ± 0.001 Earth masses.[17] The outward migration of Uranus and especially that of Neptune reduced the Kuiper Belt's total mass to just 0.2% of its original, rendering it far less dangerous to Earth.

The Kuiper Belt's reduced mass and reshaped structure resulted from a complex outward migration by Neptune. The last close encounter between Uranus and Neptune catapulted Neptune out to 27 AUs from the Sun into a low inclination orbit with high eccentricity, approximately 0.3.[18] Subsequently, over a million years or so, Neptune migrated farther out to 30 AUs, and in this process, its orbital eccentricity dropped down to its present 0.009456.

Neptune's complex migration history, known as the "jumping Neptune," altered the Kuiper Belt's properties in these ways, all of which have a bearing on the possibility for advanced life and civilization on Earth.[19] There are six additional ways Neptune's migration shaped the Kuiper Belt for the benefit of Earth's advanced life. The jumping Neptune

1. formed the "kernel," the concentration of Kuiper Belt objects at 44 AUs with orbital eccentricities of about 0.05 and inclinations of less than 5°, which plays a major role in stabilizing the Kuiper Belt and regulating the rate at which its objects (primarily comets) impact Earth;
2. set the outer edge of the Kuiper Belt at a 1:2 mean motion resonance with Neptune (the distance where Kuiper Belt objects orbit the Sun once for every two Neptune orbits), an adjustment that plays a secondary role in stabilizing the Kuiper Belt and regulating the rate of Earth impactors;
3. aligned the Kuiper Belt plane with the solar system plane, thus lowering orbital chaos not only in the Kuiper Belt, but in other solar system belts as well;
4. established the Kuiper Belt halo, a ring of high-orbital-inclination objects that contribute to Earth's impactor rate;
5. played the major role in the formation and subsequent evolution of the Scattered Belt; and
6. altered the size distribution of Kuiper Belt objects, influencing what kinds, sizes, and frequency of objects impact Earth.

Many of the comets that reach the inner solar system are Kuiper Belt comets whose orbits were perturbed by one or more of Neptune, Uranus, Saturn, and Jupiter.

The fifth belt, the Oort Cloud, stretches from about 7.5 billion to 15 trillion kilometers (4.7 billion to 9 trillion miles or 0.0008 to 1.5 light-years) away from the Sun. Tidal influences exerted by the Milky Way Galaxy (MWG) in the outermost reaches of the Oort Cloud define its outer boundary.[20] That's the point at which objects can possibly remain gravitationally bound to the Sun. It may seem too distant to influence the inner solar system in any way, but its objects can and do reach Earth.

The Oort Cloud is by far the most massive of the solar system's asteroid-comet "belts." The outer Oort Cloud is more like a sphere than disk. Astronomer Paul Weissman calculated that the current total mass of the Oort Cloud is approximately 1.9 Earth masses.[21] Fortunately for life on Earth, the inner Oort Cloud is the least populated of the three Oort Cloud components. The outer cloud is the most populated.

The primordial Oort Cloud, however, was likely at least a hundred times more massive. As the Sun, with its 4.57-billion-year-old planetary system, has orbited the MWG galactic center about 18–20 times, it has encountered many giant molecular clouds—dense clouds of gas and dust several hundred thousand times the mass of the Sun. These encounters eroded the Oort Cloud down to its current size.[22] The vast majority of Oort Cloud objects are comets. Only about 1–2% are asteroids.[23]

Since the Sun is more massive than 90% of the MWG's stars, its gravitational strength has stolen some comets from adjacent stars, pulling them into the Oort Cloud. Apparently, these accreted comets account for only a tiny percentage of the Oort Cloud population and, therefore, do little to alter the chemistry of cometary material delivered from the Oort Cloud to the inner solar system. The isotope ratios for Oort Cloud comets observed by astronomers are the same as they are for Jupiter-family comets.[24] This similarity is strong evidence that virtually all the solar system's asteroids and comets originated from the same source.

Delivery of Resources for Life

One feature of these five asteroid-comet belts is the consistent size distribution of objects within them. The smaller the object, the exponentially larger its population in each belt. For this reason, nearly all belt objects that strike Earth are small, rather than large. For the sake of life on Earth, the distribution of impactors in terms of size and number is just-right. Life needs what these objects deliver, but delivery can be dangerous—depending on the sizes and numbers of packages.

About 25 million interplanetary bodies heavier than 0.1 grams enter Earth's atmosphere every day. The total mass of this delivery adds up to an estimated average of 15–70 million kilograms per year (equivalent to 150–700 of the largest aircraft carriers per year). However, nearly all are either pieces of broken comets that vaporize upon entering Earth's atmosphere or meteoroids (lumps of rock and dust that orbit the Sun) so small that they burn up in Earth's atmosphere before reaching the surface. Nevertheless, life needs what material does make it through.

Earth loses water to interplanetary space as the Sun's ultraviolet rays strike water molecules in the upper atmosphere. Although the current water loss rate is relatively low, only about 500,000 kilograms per year, the Sun's ultraviolet radiation was more intense in past eras, and at many times Earth's ozone shield was much less protective than it is today. Averaged over the 3.8-billion-year history of life on Earth, water loss likely approached 10 million kilograms per year.

Earth's deep water cycle also depletes Earth's surface water supply. Surface water flows to the mantle through subduction of Earth's tectonic plates and then most, but not all, returns to the surface through volcanic activity. Through time, the delivery of water via meteoroids has counterbalanced the total combined water loss from ultraviolet radiation, ozone shield erosion events, and the deep water cycle.

Measurements of 13 enstatite chondrite (EC) meteorites affirm that Earth likely received most of its water from EC comets and meteorites.[25] The rate of meteoroid water delivery throughout the past 3.8 billion years has been neither too low nor too high to pose any significant threat to Earth's life. This rate is optimal thanks to the just-right abundance, location, and orbital characteristics of the solar system's asteroid-comet belts.

Analysis of nitrogen isotope ratios in Earth's atmosphere, mantle, Archean sedimentary rocks, and crustal hydrothermal systems reveals that Kuiper Belt comets delivered 5–10% of Earth's atmospheric nitrogen during the Archean eon, 4.0–2.5 billion years ago.[26] This extra nitrogen made both the long-term survival of primitive life and the later survival of advanced life possible.

Nitrogen, though not a greenhouse gas, enhances the greenhouse heat-trapping capability of atmospheric carbon dioxide and methane. If Earth's atmosphere had been enriched by comets with more nitrogen, Earth's atmosphere would've been warmer, and Earth would've lost more surface water to outer space.

Unlike microbial life, advanced life cannot tolerate major temperature changes. If the atmospheric nitrogen content were greater, Earth's surface temperature would be too hot for advanced life. If the quantity were any lower, Earth's surface temperature would be too cold for advanced life.

The molecular-nitrogen-to-molecular-oxygen ratio determines whether lungs can function efficiently and continually for years and decades. Because molecular nitrogen in the atmosphere is biologically inert, it buffers oxygen's deleterious mechanical and chemical effects on the functioning of the lungs. If the nitrogen-to-oxygen ratio in Earth's atmosphere were slightly lower or higher than it is, birds and mammals would be unable to sustain high activity levels for years on end.

The quantity of nitrogen in Earth's atmosphere also determines the degree to which nitrogen fixation occurs (the process by which microorganisms harvest molecular nitrogen from the atmosphere and chemically convert it for use by plants). Less atmospheric nitrogen or more atmospheric nitrogen would change nitrogen fixation levels so as to reduce the diversity of plant species.

Delivery of Resources for Civilization

Carbonaceous and metallic meteoroids and asteroids large enough to survive entry through Earth's atmosphere have made important contributions to Earth's mineral supply. Depending on the meteoroid composition, the minimum mass to survive passage and make a delivery to Earth's surface is 5–20 grams.[27] Some metallic asteroids and meteoroids are comprised entirely of iron, nickel, cobalt, and trace amounts of elements heavier than nickel. The concentrations of nickel and cobalt in these asteroids make them a better grade of stainless steel than some of Earth's best manufactured stainless steel.

The nickel content in these asteroids and meteoroids (5–26%) makes them malleable enough to be cold-forged into a variety of tools. Humans collected iron-nickel meteorites and hammered them into knives, axes, spears, and daggers at least as early as 6000 BC, if not earlier. The Inuit, for example, made trips to northwest Greenland to collect small pieces from the massive Cape York meteorite (over 60 tons),[28] itself a piece of the 1.5-kilometer diameter Hiawatha Impactor that struck about 12,800 years ago.

Large asteroid and comet strikes over the past two billion years have provided Earth's richest metal ore deposits. An asteroid or comet 10–15 kilometers in diameter struck 1.849 billion years ago just north of what is now Lake Huron in Canada to form the Sudbury Basin.[29] The impactor, rich in nickel, cobalt, and platinum group metals, struck with such force that it also brought nickel- and copper-rich magma from Earth's mantle to the surface, filling its impact crater. This large crater, 150–260 kilometers in diameter, ranked as the world's leading source of nickel until the 1970s. For many decades, it accounted for 95% of the world's nickel market.[30] It still accounts for a third. People of the Plano culture used the native copper in the area to manufacture tools, weapons, and jewelry at least as far back as 10,000 years ago.[31] Due to the high mineral content of its soil, the Sudbury Basin is the best agricultural land in northern Ontario.

Earth's crust contains no naturally occurring highly siderophile (iron-loving) elements, such as gold, platinum, iridium, osmium, rhenium, palladium, rhodium, and ruthenium, and little of such moderately siderophile elements as cobalt, nickel, silver, and tungsten. However, these elements exist in great abundance in Earth's core and lower mantle. Only asteroids or comets larger than 10 kilometers in diameter striking Earth at high velocity could have brought these lower-mantle materials to the surface. Such impacts were much more frequent prior to 3 billion years ago. Thus, it comes as no surprise that the only pristine continental crust older than 2.5 billion years—the Kaapvaal Craton in South Africa and the Pilbara Craton in Western Australia—hold rich endowments of both highly and moderately siderophile elements.

The Kaapvaal Craton is the site of the world's largest remaining impact crater, the Vredefort Crater. Geologists calculate that the Vredefort Crater was more than 300 kilometers across when it formed 2.023 billion years ago.[32] If not for the Vredefort impactor, the gold and platinum group deposits beneath the Kaapvaal Craton's surface would never have been brought close enough to Earth's surface to be discovered, or the deposits would have eroded away long before they could be discovered.

The Vredefort Crater overlaps the Witwatersrand Basin, site of the largest gold and platinum group deposits on Earth. Even after the extraction of over 47,000 tons of gold, the Witwatersrand Basin still contains about half as much gold as the rest of Earth's surface combined.[33]

An asteroid 5–8 kilometers in diameter created the 100-kilometer diameter Popigai Crater in northern Siberia 33.7 million years ago. The asteroid struck with such force that it instantaneously transformed graphite in the nearby ground into an abundance of diamonds, the world's largest known diamond deposit. The diamonds in this deposit range in size from 0.5–10.0 millimeters in diameter (0.001–4.0 carats).

A team of geologists has demonstrated that virtually all Earth's impact craters larger than 2 kilometers in diameter have provided economically valuable mineral deposits.[34] These mineral deposits include not only highly siderophile and moderately siderophile elements, but also hydrocarbon fuel deposits.

The history and features of the solar system's asteroid-comet belts, along with the gravitational influence of the Moon's mass and early orbital proximity, ensured that Earth would receive sufficient impact events, especially before animals appeared, to salt Earth's crust with rich ore deposits. These ores played a crucial role in the early launch of metallurgy and, more recently, in the development of global, high-technology civilization. On the other hand, major impact events during the human era have been so infrequent as to pose no risk to humanity's survival nor to global civilization.

During the last 2.58 million years, Earth has been struck three times by asteroids or comets larger than 1 kilometer in diameter.[35] One struck Earth 2,580,000 years ago below the southern tip of South America; another struck 800,000 years ago in the South China Sea and Laos; and another, 12,800 years ago in northwest Greenland.

The first of the three played the major role in launching Earth's ice age cycle.[36] The second helped change the ice age cycle's periodicity from 41,000 years to approximately 100,000 years.[37] The third was largely responsible for the beginning of an unprecedented era of extreme climate stability that has persisted throughout the past 9,500 years.[38] These three impactors of the right size and composition struck Earth at just-right times, in just-right locations to facilitate the launch of global civilization and make the Earth habitable for billions of people.

Compensation for the Sun's Increasing Brightness

The impactors from the solar system's five asteroid-comet belts also generated extinction events that helped compensate for the Sun's increasing brightness and helped permit the sustenance of abundant, diverse life throughout the past 3.8 billion years. Major impactors (5-kilometer-diameter or larger) strike Earth about once every 30–35 million years, on average. These impactors shake up Earth's tectonic plates, throw up huge quantities of debris, dust, and aerosols, and ignite supervolcanic eruptions that wipe out 25–95% of Earth's species.

After each mass extinction event, though, a mass speciation event has occurred. Those speciation events each played an important role in making possible future advanced life. I document exactly how in depth in *Improbable Planet*.[39]

The solar system's asteroid-comet belts clearly played a crucial role in making this long-term habitability possible on one planet within the system. So did that one planet's unusual formation history, in which the Moon—unlike any other moon—was a significant participant.

Chapter 13

The Lunar Interior

Chapter summary: *Earth's Moon is unlike any other moon in the solar system and beyond. Its unique formation resulted in its huge mass, far greater than that of any other known moon, relative to the mass of its host planet. This extraordinary mass and the manner in which it is distributed inside the Moon stabilized Earth's rotation axis tilt and slowed down Earth's rotation rate, a stability and a rate advanced life requires. The early proximity of the Moon to Earth and its temporary molten iron core enabled a "coupling" event that protected the early Earth from a solar wind that could have sputtered away Earth's hydrosphere and atmosphere. Thanks to the Moon's interior structure and the current size of its ever-widening orbit, animal ecosystems on Earth are optimized and Earth-bound inhabitants can observe perfect solar eclipses—time markers that have enabled humanity to make discoveries of great significance for their civilization.*

The fact that a rocky body as small as the Moon plays a significant role in the architecture of the solar system and in Earth's habitability may seem surprising, but in one aspect, the Moon must be considered enormous. Of the 205 known moons (aka satellites) orbiting the eight solar system planets,[1] Earth's Moon is by far the most massive in relation to the planet it orbits—some 50+ times more massive, by comparison.

The Moon's mass relative to Earth's mass is a mere 0.01230,[2] but to put this number in perspective, some comparisons with other moons can be helpful. Moon-to-Earth mass ratio exceeds that of Titan-to-Saturn by 52 times, Triton-to-Neptune by 59 times, and Ganymede-to-Jupiter by 158 times. In this respect, it is a true heavyweight.

The Moon as an Orbital Stabilizer

The Moon's anomalously high mass relative to its host planet results from its unique manner of formation. Other satellites coalesce alongside their planets in the protoplanetary disk or, in some cases, are captured by their host planet's gravity. By contrast the Moon emerged from a collision-merger event between proto-Earth and Theia, a planet slightly more massive than Mars.[3] This formation event sent the Moon spiraling away from Earth in an ever-widening orbit.

For most of its history the Moon has been moving away from Earth. This movement is a consequence of tidal forces the Moon exercises on Earth. The Moon's proximity to Earth and its high mass relative to Earth means the Moon exerts a substantially stronger gravitational attraction on Earth's side nearest the Moon compared to the side farthest away.

The difference between the Moon's gravitational forces on the near and far sides of Earth generates tidal friction. The tidal friction has a heating effect, resulting in a loss of angular momentum and the gradual movement of the Moon away from Earth. Presently, the Moon moves away from Earth at a rate of 3.82 ± 0.07 centimeters per year.[4]

The combination of the Moon's high mass, its mass relative to Earth's mass, and its more distant orbit from Earth explains the Moon's current role in stabilizing the orbital architecture of the inner solar system.[5] Right now, this stabilization is the best it has ever been in the 4.47-billion-year history of the Earth-Moon system.

The Moon as a Brake

The difference in the Moon's stronger gravitational pull on the near side of Earth than on the far side acts as a brake on Earth's rotation rate. Consequently, for the past few billion years, Earth's rotation rate has slowed from its initial few hours per day to its present 24 hours.

Two research teams have shown that the Moon-forming event generated Earth's rapid rotation immediately after the collision.[6] The large angular momentum produced by this rapid rotation was transferred to the Moon via the mutual tidal interaction between Earth and the Moon.[7] This angular momentum transfer continually slowed Earth's rotation rate while causing the Moon to gradually move away from Earth.[8]

If the Moon were more massive, or if it were receding from Earth at a slower rate, Earth's present rotation rate would be longer than 24 hours. On the other hand, if the Moon were less massive or receding from Earth at a faster pace, Earth's rotation rate today would be shorter than 24 hours.

A 24-hour per day rotation rate is optimal for advanced life for at least two reasons. A faster rotation rate would generate greater equator-to-pole temperature differences on Earth and produce greater climate zone extremes and greater climatic fluctuations.[9] Even a 23-hour rotation rate would yield climate variations of such magnitude as to seriously limit the growth of human population and the development of global civilization. An eventual 25-hour rotation rate will mean much greater day to night temperature extremes, with catastrophic consequences for the health of humans, domesticated and wild animals, and food crops. However, another rotation-slowing problem carries even greater significance for the possibility of human civilization.

The Moon as an Axial Tilt Stabilizer

The gravitational influences of Jupiter, Saturn, Uranus, and Neptune on Mars generate enormous axial tilt variations. Mars's rotation axis tilt chaotically varies by as much as 60°.[10] If it were not for the Moon, Earth would have met the same fate. Such large-scale changes in Earth's atmospheric circulation and climate would have rendered global human civilization impossible.[11]

Thanks to the Moon's great mass relative to Earth's mass and to tidal interactions generated by the Moon's proximity to Earth, the tilt of Earth's rotation axis has remained phenomenally steady for the past 5 million years. The tilt varies from 22° 2' 33" to 24° 30' 16" degrees with a periodicity of 41,040 years.[12]

Even this tiny ± 1.2° variation in Earth's rotation axis tilt causes Earth's surface ice coverage to oscillate between 10 and 23% on timescales of tens of thousands of years. It also typically generates severe climate instabilities. A rotation axis tilt variation as small as ± 2.4° would induce climate instabilities and surface ice fluctuations far too severe for the survival of billions of humans.

If the Moon's mass were just 2% greater, even greater axial tilt variations would be induced. Earth's rotation axis tilt would be too unstable for either a large human population or global civilization.[13] On the other hand, if the Moon were a mere 2% less massive, the tidal forces between the Moon and Earth would have been insufficient to slow Earth's rotation rate to the optimal 24 hours.

At least two more requirements must be met for Earth's rotation axis tilt to remain sufficiently stable for the existence and survival of a large human population. First, the Moon's angular momentum must manifest the same high degree of fine-tuned precision as the Moon's mass.[14] Second, as described in chapter 10, the gas giant planets in the solar system must orbit at widely spaced distances from one another and from the Earth-Moon system.[15]

As it turns out, Earth's current 24-hour/day rotation rate and uniquely steady rotation axis tilt perfectly coincide with the era when the Sun's flaring activity and luminosity variability hit their lowest point (see chapter 9). All four features prove not simply favorable for, but crucially important to, the well-being of advanced life and the possibility of civilization.

The Moon as a Gravitational Funnel

Given its sizable mass and the relationship between mass and gravity, the Moon has accreted an unexpectedly low abundance of heavy elements. Measurements show a major mismatch, for example, in the quantity of highly siderophile (iron-loving) elements (gold, platinum, palladium, iridium, rhenium, rhodium, ruthenium, and osmium) in the Moon's crust and mantle compared to their quantities in Earth's crust and mantle.[16] Since highly siderophile elements (HSEs) bind tightly to iron, nickel, and cobalt, they are an excellent measure of a body's total heavy element abundance.

Computer simulations of asteroid impacts on the Moon and Earth show that Earth retains impactor mass for all but the most glancing blows by the most massive asteroids, whereas the Moon gains mass only from low-mass asteroids that strike nearly head-on.[17] The data suggest that Earth's proximity to the Moon enhances its gravitational pull on asteroids, while Earth's much greater mass (a factor of 81 times greater) enables it to seize asteroids that otherwise would strike the Moon. Since the two bodies formed, the difference between Earth's gains in mass (from asteroids) and the Moon's gains exceeds 1,000 to 1.

Astronomers have determined that many asteroids in the Main Belt (between Mars and Jupiter) are metallic asteroids, as were those from the no-longer-existent E-belt (between the current inner boundary of the Main Belt and Mars). Due to the Moon's precise mass and position, relative to Earth, the Moon enhanced Earth's endowment of HSEs with elements crucial to sustaining global high-technology civilization.

The Moon as a Light

Many of the benefits the Moon brings to life on Earth depend on the Moon's mass and distance from Earth. However, other life-favorable features depend on the Moon's exceptionally low density. At only 3.344 grams per cubic centimeter (g/cc) the Moon has the lowest density of any astronomical body larger than 1,000 kilometers diameter interior to the Sun's ice line. The average density for such bodies, other than the Moon, is 5.029 g/cc.

How the Moon's density happens to be so low is an enigma that lunar researchers solved only recently. The solution involves several wonders that reinforce how amazingly beneficial the Moon is for advanced life on Earth (see sidebar, "Marvel of the Moon's Low Density").

The Moon's high mass and low density mean that the Moon has a large diameter. The Moon's diameter and current distance from Earth prove beneficial for life in more than one way. For example, the Moon provides the just-right level of brightness terrestrial mammals need.[18] If the Moon's diameter were larger, or if it were orbiting more closely to Earth, it would be so bright that terrestrial mammals would have difficulty sleeping at night, and large predators would have difficulty gathering enough food at night for their survival. If the Moon's diameter were smaller, or if the Moon were orbiting more distantly from Earth, the night sky would be so dimly lit that terrestrial herbivores would face greater difficulty foraging at night. As a result, they would suffer too great a loss either from predation or from excessive energy spent avoiding predators. As it is, the Moon's diameter and current distance from Earth provide the optimal nighttime illumination for support of a diverse and healthy ecosystem of terrestrial mammals.

The Moon as an Eclipser

The Moon's large diameter also provides a different kind of light. It allows for all the scientific insights made possible by exceptional solar eclipses. Currently, the Moon's diameter and distance from Earth are such that, from the perspective of observers on Earth, the angle subtended by the Moon in the sky is nearly identical to the angle subtended by the Sun. This similarity permits the observation of perfect and nearly perfect solar eclipses, observations responsible for monumental advances in science.

A perfect solar eclipse occurs when the Sun's and the Moon's angular diameters in Earth's sky are so nearly identical that the disk of the Sun's photosphere is blocked, though for less than 3 minutes. On those occasions, astronomers can observe the solar corona as it radiates outward as far as 10 degrees from the Sun's visible disk. Such eclipses also permit detailed observation of the Sun's atmosphere, chromosphere, and flares. Much of what astronomers have discerned about stellar coronae, chromospheres, atmospheres, and flaring has come through observational data from multiple perfect solar eclipses.

The timing of perfect solar eclipses visible from various locations on Earth provides humans with a sophisticated clock. Records of perfect solar eclipse observations have allowed historians to produce a calendar of events during

Marvel of the Moon's Low Density

Evidence that the Moon possesses an iron core and that its mantle and crust have a high iron content made the Moon's low density something of an enigma.[19] Astronomers were aware, however, that for a body of the Moon's mass and distance from the Sun, the Moon's iron core is much smaller than what the physics of accretion—formation by buildup of planetesimals, rocks, dust, and gas—would predict.

A laser reflector placed by Apollo astronauts and seismic experiments had revealed that the Moon's core accounts for about one-fifth the Moon's total diameter.[20] Analysis of data from 15 years of lunar laser ranging established that the Moon's core diameter is 762 ± 24 kilometers.[21] On this basis, we know that the Moon's core comprises only 1.59–1.77% of the Moon's total mass.[22]

The difference between the Moon's gigantic size and its unexpectedly tiny iron core indicated that it had formed differently from other moons. Extensive analysis and modeling have shown that the Moon formed from the debris cloud produced when planet Theia (mass of 11–15% Earth's current mass)[23] impacted the primordial Earth at an oblique angle.

A team of astronomers showed that a compositional similarity between the Moon and Earth's mantle is a natural outcome of a giant impact event.[24] Another research team analyzed lunar surface samples and the deep mantle and demonstrated that the compositional similarities and differences between the Moon and Earth are well explained by a giant impact of lunar origin.[25]

The Moon's porous crust also contributes to its low density. Data from the Gravity Recovery and Interior Laboratory spacecraft reveal that the bulk density of the lunar highlands crust is only 2.550 g/cc.[26] This measurement, combined with remote sensing and sample data, reveals an average lunar crustal porosity of 12% down to depths of several kilometers and perhaps extending throughout the entire 30- to 43-kilometer-thick lunar crust into the uppermost mantle.[27]

The Moon's density has remained low due in part to Earth's proximity. Earth has drawn nearly all high-density impactors away from the Moon.

humanity's early history. It has also allowed astronomers to measure the slowing of Earth's rotation rate because of tidal interactions among the Earth, Moon, and Sun. Solar eclipse timing measurements enabled astronomers to determine that Earth's rotation rate is slowing by two milliseconds per day per century.

Nearly perfect solar eclipses provided the first confirmation of Albert Einstein's theory of general relativity. When Einstein published this theory in 1916[28] it represented a radical departure from the (then) reigning model of the universe. Before Einstein's theory of general relativity, astronomers and physicists were convinced the universe was eternal and static throughout. Einstein's theory asserted that the universe was finite with respect to age—it had a beginning and, by implication, a cosmic Beginner. The universe, according to general relativity, is not static. It is either expanding or contracting. (Later observations by Vesto Slipher and Edwin Hubble affirmed that it is expanding.)

One implication of general relativity made clear in Einstein's paper was that when light passes by a massive body, it is bent by that body's gravity. Einstein showed that the Sun's gravitational field would bend starlight by a maximum of 1.751 arcseconds.[29]

A nearly perfect solar eclipse occurs when the disk of the Moon, at a closer point in its orbit of Earth, blocks out not only the Sun's entire photosphere disk but also a substantial portion of the solar corona. These total solar eclipses last between 3 and 7.5 minutes. They darken the sky to such a degree that stars near the Sun's disk are easily visible.

Britain's famed mathematical physicist, Sir Arthur Eddington, organized an expedition to observe the 6.85-minutes-long total solar eclipse in Brazil on May 29, 1919. Eddington's team made measurements showing that the Sun's gravitational field bent starlight by 1.8 ± 0.2 arcseconds.[30] This confirmation of general relativity launched several subdisciplines of physics and astronomy that remain active areas of research to this day.

The Moon's recession from Earth, at the rate of 3.82 centimeters per year, means that the window for observing perfect and nearly perfect solar eclipses is only about 300 million years wide. Humanity "happens" to be living on Earth at the midpoint of this 300-million-year window. The one place and time in the solar system that can accommodate advanced life is also the only place and time where perfect and nearly perfect solar eclipses occur.

The Young Moon as a Magnetic Shield

The Apollo astronauts' Moon landings between 1969 and 1972 continue to provide researchers with valuable data and, in some instances, great surprises. Some of these surprises have come thanks to the portable magnetometer the Apollo crews placed on different regions of the lunar surface. Others have come through detailed geological analyses of the hundreds of pounds of lunar rocks they carefully transported back to laboratories on Earth. The most astounding discovery to date has come from a recent mega-analysis of all the accumulated data. This comprehensive assessment has opened a new window to lunar events that prepared Earth to host life.

For decades, textbooks have reported that the Moon has no magnetic field and never had one of any consequence. The Apollo findings changed this story. Painstaking analysis of rocks recovered from the lunar surface tell us that the Moon does have a magnetic field, even if a faint one (~1,000 times weaker than Earth's magnetic field). Researchers describe it as a "magnetic memory" echoing from the Moon's earliest history. Further, this analysis reveals that the Moon possessed a much stronger magnetic field during the earliest several hundred million years of its existence. This early magnetic field holds great significance for the possibility of life on Earth—a significance only recently recognized by astrophysicists.

The magnetic field strength for both the Moon and Earth varies from place to place on each body's surface. Today, the magnetic field strength at Earth's surface ranges from a minimum of 23 microtesla (0.23 gauss) in the vicinity of Paraguay to a maximum 65 microtesla (0.65 gauss) in the region between Tasmania and Antarctica.

The recent mega-analysis showed planetary astronomers that between 4.25 and 3.50 billion years ago, the Moon's maximum magnetic field strength resembled Earth's, ranging from 20 to 100 microtesla (0.2–1.0 gauss).[31] While Earth's magnetic field strength has remained strong since then, the Moon's magnetic field dropped precipitously within the following 0.30 billion years, to about 5 microtesla (0.05 gauss).

According to this data, during the era when the Earth and Moon were much closer together, the Moon's magnetic field strength was similar to Earth's. While the current separation distance is 384,000 kilometers (239,000 miles), some 4.0 billion years ago, the two bodies were separated by a mere 114,700 kilometers (71,300 miles or 18 Earth radii), and 3.9 billion years ago, by just 133,800 kilometers (83,100 miles or 21 Earth radii).[32]

A liquid iron core by itself will not generate a magnetic field. The liquid iron in the Moon's core must be circulated to produce a dynamo. The only plausible source of such circulation would be powerful convection currents in the Moon's liquid iron core. This core was generated by the Moon-forming event, the collision-merger between Theia and the proto-Earth. The residual heat from that collision would have kept the Moon's iron core in a liquid state until 4.0–3.5 billion years ago. The Moon's proximity to Earth, specifically to Earth's gravity, in its earliest era provided the convection currents. The pull of Earth's gravity on the Moon's near side would have been much stronger than on its far side, causing the Moon to wobble substantially. (A much smaller wobble persists to this day.) This wobbling stirred up the liquid iron in the lunar core and thereby produced the convection currents that generated the Moon's early strong magnetic field.

Previous to 3.5 billion years ago, the Moon similarly exerted a substantially stronger gravitational influence on Earth's near side than on Earth's far side (as described above). The difference, likewise, helped generate convection currents in Earth's liquid iron core. Today, given the Moon's greater distance from Earth, the lunar contribution to convection in Earth's liquid iron core is several hundred times weaker. Thankfully, the lunar input to convection currents in Earth's core, input once essential to maintaining Earth's early magnetic field, has been replaced through time. The transformation of Earth's core from an entirely liquid state to a solid inner core and a liquid outer core generated new convection currents. (Chapter 14 describes these changes to Earth's core.)

If not for their proximity to one another, neither Earth nor the Moon would have possessed a strong magnetic field before 4.0 billion years ago. Additionally, the timing of their proximity made a magnetic linkage possible—with profound implications for Earth's life. It brought about a coupling of the two bodies' magnetospheres. The magnetosphere, created by an active interior dynamo, is the region of space surrounding an astronomical body in which charged particles are influenced by its magnetic field.

In the aftermath of the collision between Theia and proto-Earth, as the Moon and Earth were taking shape, the young but maturing Sun was blasting its surroundings with intense particle radiation carried along by a powerful solar wind. During its infancy and youth, while its flaring activity was highest, it produced intense gamma-ray, x-ray, and ultraviolet radiation (see figure 9.4).

This blast of deadly radiation from our youthful Sun would have sputtered away Earth's atmosphere and surface water if not for the timely presence of an effective magnetic shield. The temporary coupling of the magnetospheres of Earth and the Moon provided a shield of sufficient strength. Without the

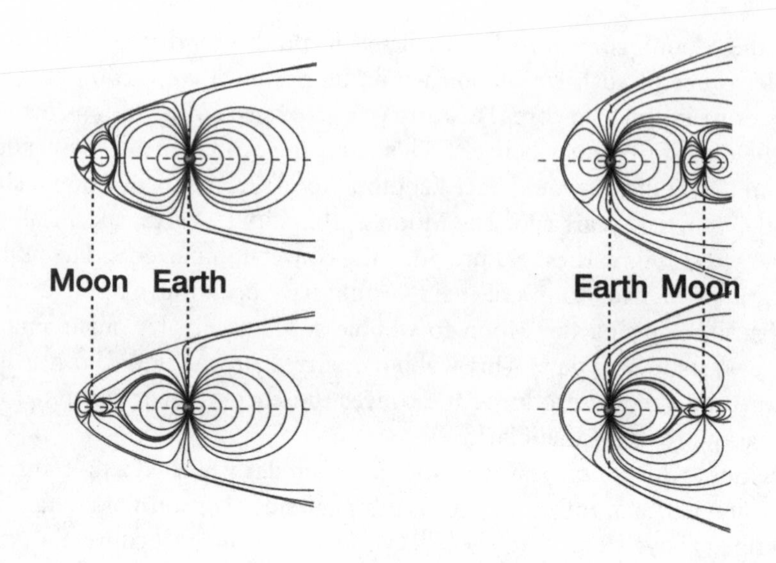

Figure 13.1: Coupled Magnetospheres for Earth-Moon System 4.0 Billion Years Ago

Top left: magnetic dipoles aligned with the Moon between Earth and the Sun; top right: magnetic dipoles aligned with Earth between the Sun and the Moon; bottom left: magnetic dipoles antialigned with the Moon between Earth and the Sun; bottom right: dipoles antialigned with Earth between the Sun and the Moon. *Credit: adapted from James Green et al., "When the Moon Had a Magnetosphere," Science Advances 6, no. 42 (Oct. 14, 2020): eabc0865, doi:10.1126/sciadv.abc0865.*

added boost from joining forces with the Moon's magnetosphere, Earth's magnetosphere would have been too weak to protect the young planet.

Four planetary astronomers led by NASA's James Green used the lunar magnetic field strength data, lunar distances from Earth at 4.4 to 3.0 billion years ago, and data on the solar wind intensities and radiation at that time to create diagrams showing the characteristics of the Earth-Moon coupled magnetosphere that existed 4.0 billion years ago.[33] Figure 13.1 shows that regardless of the orientation of their dipole magnets, whether aligned or not, and wherever Earth or the Moon were positioned relative to the Sun, the coupled magnetosphere of the Earth-Moon system proved capable of preventing either the loss or serious degradation of Earth's atmosphere or hydrosphere. Thus, it also proved strong enough and stable enough to protect the first microbes on early Earth's surface.

Green and his colleagues established that no later than 3.2 billion years ago, the Moon's magnetic field became too weak and the Moon too distant to provide any significant magnetospheric protection for Earth's atmosphere, hydrosphere, and life. In a follow-up study, a team of 14 astronomers, physicists, and geologists led by John Tarduno showed that the Moon lost its strong intrinsic magnetic field shortly after 4.0 billion years ago.[34] They demonstrated that earlier research indicating the Moon retained a strong magnetic field until as recently as 2.0 billion years ago had failed to take into account that lunar impactors can magnetize rocks at the impact sites. They analyzed six lunar samples and cited analysis on nine other lunar samples from non-impact sites in the date range 3.94–3.17 billion years ago. All fifteen had negligible measured magnetic fields.

Since 4.0 billion years ago, the level of protection necessary to retain the essentials for life diminished considerably. The Sun's wind, flaring activity, particle radiation, and intensities of gamma-ray, x-ray, and ultraviolet emission declined by a factor of about a hundred times to levels whereby the Earth's magnetosphere was sufficient by itself, as figure 9.4 shows.

Green and his colleagues concluded their study by saying that for any planet to host life more complex than a few microbial species for more than a brief time, it must be part of an astronomical configuration virtually identical to the Earth-Moon system with a virtually identical dynamical and magnetic history. It is important to add that such a planet-moon system must orbit a star virtually identical to the Sun, given that stars more massive or less massive than the Sun pose a significantly greater risk to any nearby planet's atmosphere and hydrosphere, and thus to life (see chapter 9).

The features of the Moon that contribute to the possibility of human civilization on Earth are so unique and specific that one lunar-formation modeler, Tim Elliott, wrote in a 2013 *Nature* article that he and his colleagues were experiencing "philosophical disquiet."[35] Now several more layers of fine-tuning evidence have been added.

As marvelous as the Moon's interior intricacies prove to be, they pale in comparison to Earth's. The next three chapters explore the interior features of our planet that make it a suitable home for advanced life, including long-term, high-technology, globally dispersed human civilization.

Chapter 14

Earth's Core Features

Chapter summary: *Earth's unique core is, at present, comprised of two parts, an inner solid core and outer liquid core. The structure, extraordinary composition, and heat exchange of these two core regions have allowed Earth, unlike any other known rocky planet, to sustain a powerful dynamo. This internal dynamo has generated and maintained Earth's strong, stable magnetic field for more than 4 billion years—an essential feature for the possible existence of advanced life on Earth.*

Given Earth's unique formation in the aftermath of a one-of-a-kind collision-merger event between two primordial planets, it comes as no surprise that Earth's core is unlike any other planetary core. Just as the interior structure of our supercluster of galaxies, our galaxy cluster, our galaxy, our local galactic neighborhood, our star, our system of planets, asteroids, and comets, and our Moon differ from the normal pattern in precise ways that favor the possibility of advanced life on Earth, so, too, does Earth's core.

Earth's core possesses all the necessary features to establish and sustain an internal dynamo (electrical generator). The operation of this dynamo in Earth's core has provided a strong and enduring magnetic field like no other. This magnetic field, in turn, provides essential protection to Earth's surface life from the deadly effects of solar and cosmic radiation. To do so, the dynamo requires a large, high-density core.

No planet of Earth's orbital distance from its host star has anywhere near such a high density. A major contributor to our planet's density is its core, with two crucial components, an inner solid portion and an outer liquid portion.

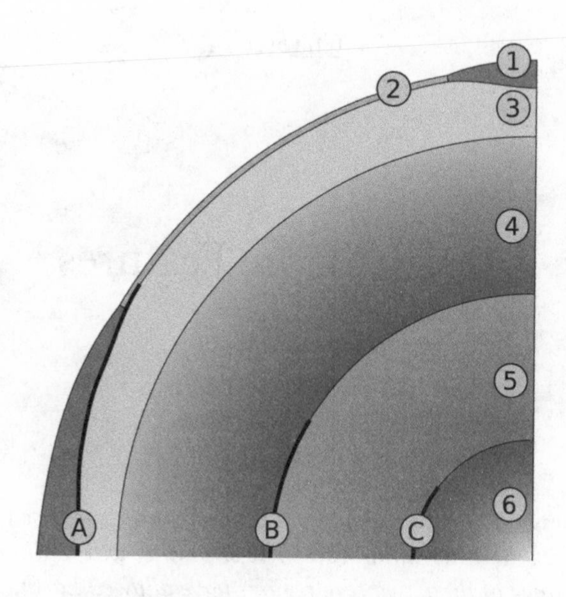

Figure 14.1: Earth's Interior Layers
(1) continental crust, (2) oceanic crust, (3) upper mantle, (4) lower mantle, (5) outer core, (6) inner core, (A) crust-mantle boundary, (B) core-mantle boundary, (C) inner core-outer core boundary. *Credit: Dake, Creative Commons Attribution*

The inner solid core, at present, has a radius of 1,221 kilometers (760 miles), or 19.2% of Earth's radius. The outer liquid core extends out to 3,480 kilometers (2,162 miles) from Earth's center, another 35.4% of Earth's radius. Together, the two portions of Earth's core comprise more than half (54.6%) of Earth's radius (see figure 14.1), and their influence on what happens above them plays a crucial role in our existence.

Inner Core Features

Researchers' deepest drill into Earth's interior has penetrated to a depth of only 12 kilometers,[1] some 5,138 kilometers short of the inner core boundary. However, this limitation does not prevent scientists from discovering what that core is like. The considerable knowledge we've been able to obtain has come primarily from seismic wave measurements.

Earthquake activity has subsided over the past 4 billion years, enough to make the infrastructure of Earth's life and global civilization possible. At the same time, it has remained strong enough to sustain the nutrient recycling and silicate-carbonate cycle on which life depends.[2] Earthquake activity, though it can be damaging, tragic, and even deadly, has given geophysicists a detailed look at the core's features.

Earth's inner core is composed almost entirely of an iron-nickel alloy. This alloy accounts for about 95% of the inner core, by weight, and nickel makes up about 5–6% of the alloy.[3] Light elements that likely make up the remaining 5% or so include silicon, sulfur, oxygen, carbon, and hydrogen.[4] Although none of these five elements can be the sole light element in the inner core,[5] some combination of them aligns with what astronomers have determined by assessing the density and pressure conditions of the outer core.[6]

Iron and nickel are both ferrous metals. Ferrous metals possess the property that they are easily magnetized and capable of storing a magnetic field for a long time. Earth's super endowment of iron and nickel plays a crucial role in the sustained operation of Earth's dynamo.

Inner Core Structure and Age

The solidity of the inner core is a relatively recent feature. Throughout most of Earth's history the entire core has been liquid. However, Earth's interior has been steadily cooling due to gradual heat dissipation from the collision and accretion events that formed Earth, as well as from the decay of its rich store of radioisotopes. When the temperature fell below the melting point of the iron-nickel alloy amid the high pressure at such great depth, the iron-nickel alloy began to crystallize (solidify), starting nearest Earth's center.

As the solid inner core continues to cool and to grow, its latent heat is released into the outer core. This latent heat transfer contributes to outer core convection.[7] Simultaneously, light elements gradually squeezed out of the inner core are exported into the outer core, where they rise in the liquid. Gravitational energy resulting from this rise creates another kind of outer core convection—compositional convection—that augments the already ongoing thermal convection.[8] These powerful convective motions in the liquid outer core (see figure 14.1) provide crucial support for the operation of Earth's dynamo and its generation of Earth's strong, enduring magnetic field.

The inner core's origin and subsequent growth have amplified convective currents in the liquid outer core over time. This increased convection has enhanced Earth's magnetic field, which proves crucial for Earth's animal life, especially considering that the Sun's flaring activity was much greater when animals first appeared on Earth.

To determine when this change occurred, researchers initially employed two independent methods. The first relies on the known composition and pressure of the inner core to create a thermodynamic model of Earth's interior cooling process. The second uses analysis of paleomagnetic measurements to determine when Earth first generated a strong dipolar magnetic field.

Surprisingly, these two approaches led to highly discrepant results. A team of physicists using the first approach concluded that the age of the inner core equals 1.0–1.3 billion years. Their age determination appeared consistent with an expanded Precambrian database of paleomagnetic intensity. It showed a substantial increase in Earth's average magnetic field strength and variability somewhere between 1.5 and 1.0 billion years ago.[11]

However, this time frame is at odds with other measurements of paleomagnetic intensity. Other measurements indicate that 565 million years ago, Earth's magnetic field strength was "more than ten times smaller than the strength of the present-day field."[12] Such measurements proved consistent with predictions from geodynamo simulations, studies that placed the onset of inner core growth at slightly less than 565 million years ago.[13]

With dates so discrepant—by more than a factor of two—it seemed impossible to identify how and to what degree features of Earth's core played a role in meeting the needs of advanced life. However, ongoing research has provided a viable resolution. What's more, the resolution sheds light on additional fine-tuned features of Earth's core that make our planet hospitable to advanced life. (See sidebar, "Inner Core Date Reconciliation.")

Outer Core

The composition of Earth's outer core resembles that of the inner core, except that the outer core, because it is under less pressure, remains in a liquid state. This outer core may be described as Earth's most dynamic region.

Ongoing cooling of the Earth's core leads to freezing conditions at the inner boundary of the outer core. Thus, the solid inner core gradually grows at the expense of the liquid outer core. Geophysicist John Jacobs calculated that it grows by about 1 millimeter per year.[29] This growth rate implies that Earth's liquid core will become completely solid approximately 2 billion years from now. When this happens, Earth's dynamo will cease operation and Earth's magnetic field will disappear.

As with the inner core, the structure of the outer core is complex. Seismic observations reveal that the deepest portion of the outer core (its bottom at 150–300 kilometers) is a slurry of solid particles of crystallized iron suspended

Inner Core Date Reconciliation

The iron alloys in Earth's interior will either be body-centered cubic iron (bcc iron, *alpha* iron) or hexagonal-close packing iron (hcp iron, *epsilon* iron).[14] At the intense pressure of Earth's central core region (365 billion pascals), the melting point of bcc iron is extrapolated to be close to 7,000 kelvin (K),[15] while the melting point of hcp iron is extrapolated to be about 6,000 K.[16] When each type of iron alloys (mixes) with small amounts of nickel or other light elements, its melting point lowers by 400–550 K.[17] This difference in melting points for bcc and hcp iron seems to account for differing date estimates for Earth's inner core origin, dates that initially differed by more than a half billion years.

A team of physicists led by Anatoly Belonoshko made a case that bcc iron comprises the largest fraction of iron alloy in Earth's inner core.[18] The team noted that seismic waves travel through hcp iron without energy dissipation. However, measurements show that seismic waves passing through the upper 350–400 kilometers of the inner core exhibit significant energy attenuation (reduction) and hemispherical heterogeneity in both velocity and attenuation.[19]

An inner core composed entirely of hcp iron would be a homogeneous, rigid, solid sphere, with a sharply fixed boundary between the inner and outer core. Seismic measurements reveal, instead, the presence of mushy zones, localized regions along the inner-outer core boundary some 4–8 kilometers thick.[20]

Some researchers proposed that liquid iron bubbles comprising up to ~10% of the inner core might account for the relevant seismic measurements.[21] However, such bubbles would have quickly been squeezed out of the inner core.[22] Other proposals include the possibility that hcp iron in the inner core could be anisotropic.[23] However, two independent research teams have demonstrated that hcp iron at the inner core's high temperatures must be isotropic.[24]

Given that solid phase bcc iron possesses a viscosity similar to that of a viscous liquid, another possible explanation for the data comes into view.[25] An inner core wherein the top 350–400 kilometers (64–70%) is composed predominantly of bcc iron and the bottom 820–870 kilometers (30–36%), of hcp iron, would fit all the seismic observations.[26] It also means the observed convection occurred in the upper part of the inner core.

The difference between the melting temperatures for bcc and hcp iron accounts for the discrepancy in inner core formation dates, especially given that bcc iron formed first, and hcp iron, later. Geophysicists Janneke de Jong, Lennart de Groot, and Arwen Deuss commented on this "remarkable correlation between the solidification time of the seismically observed layers and the occurrence of the magnetic regimes for two inner core ages: one with a nucleation at 1.4 Ga [1.4 billion years ago] and one at 0.6 Ga."[27] Newer paleomagnetic measurements and recalibration of previous measurements show that the first inner core nucleation (solidification) event must have occurred more recently than 1.3 billion years ago.

in a liquid alloy of iron and small percentages of nickel and lighter elements.[30] Seismic measurements also show that this lower layer, or "F-layer," is laterally heterogeneous.[31] The F-layer likely explains both the density jump (a bottom-to-top density increase) across the outer core and the heat flux across the core-mantle boundary.[32]

Measurements of seismic and geomagnetic variations suggest that another layer, in this case a thin, stably stratified layer, likely exists at the top of the outer core (see figure 14.1).[33] The structure, composition, and interaction of these various outer core layers impact Earth's interior heat flow, as well as the strength, functionality, and variability of both Earth's magnetic field and Earth's plate tectonic activity.

An especially important outer core feature is the temperature difference between the bottom and top. The temperature at the boundary between the inner and outer core is 5,120 ± 390 K.[34] The temperature at the boundary between the outer core and the mantle is 3,760 ± 290 K.[35] This extreme temperature difference contributes significantly to the powerful convection currents driving Earth's dynamo. The might of Earth's dynamo accounts for the strength and stability of Earth's magnetic field.

Magnetic Field

No known rocky body other than Earth has retained a magnetic field, much less a strong one, for billions of years. Very few rocky bodies possess any magnetic field at all. Mercury does have one, and it measures just 1% the strength of Earth's magnetic field, with part of that 1% coming from solar wind interactions.[36] Mars's magnetic field vanished between 4.1 and 4.0 billion years ago,[37] and Venus's dissipated sometime previous to 3 billion years ago.[38]

Analysis of lunar rocks reveals that when the Moon was less than 1 billion years old (prior to 3.5 billion years ago), its magnetic field strength ranged from 0.20–0.40 gauss.[39] Earth's gravity at that time exerted such powerful tidal forces on the Moon that the Moon wobbled. This wobbling stirred up the liquid iron that existed at that time in the lunar core, and the swirling iron briefly generated (at precisely the right moment for Earth's life) a lunar magnetic field (see chapter 13).

Jupiter, Saturn, Uranus, and Neptune do possess magnetic fields. Their strengths range from about half as strong as Earth's to about twenty times stronger than Earth's. However, these fields arise not from liquid iron cores, but rather from these planets' rapidly spinning metallic (frozen) hydrogen cores. Frozen hydrogen cores can exist only in massive planets that form under extremely low temperatures, far too low for any possible physical life.

The Galileo spacecraft magnetometer showed that the largest of Jupiter's moons, Ganymede, possesses a surface magnetic field of 0.0072 gauss.[40] Tidal forces exerted by Jupiter and mean motion resonances between Ganymede and Jupiter's other large moons stir the electrolyte-filled liquid water far below Ganymede's frozen surface sufficiently to generate this weak magnetic field. No other solar system moon possesses a magnetic field.

By contrast, Earth's surface magnetic field strength has remained above 0.10 gauss for at least the past 3.7 billion years.[41] Measurements on magnetic minerals in Greenland rocks confirm this longevity. Studies of ancient zircons in Australia suggest that Earth's surface magnetic field 4.2–3.3 billion years ago varied between 0.05 and 0.40 gauss.[42] Further confirmation comes from evidence showing that Earth's atmosphere has retained nitrogen over the past 4.2 billion years.[43] If not for the existence of a strong magnetic field, the solar wind would have ionized and removed nitrogen from Earth's atmosphere.[44]

The flow of liquid ferrous metals in Earth's core both affects *and* is affected by the core's magnetic field. The flow is driven by convection and organized by Coriolis forces (the effects of spinning) resulting from Earth's rotation. The Coriolis forces organize the convection flows into rolls, or swirls, that generate

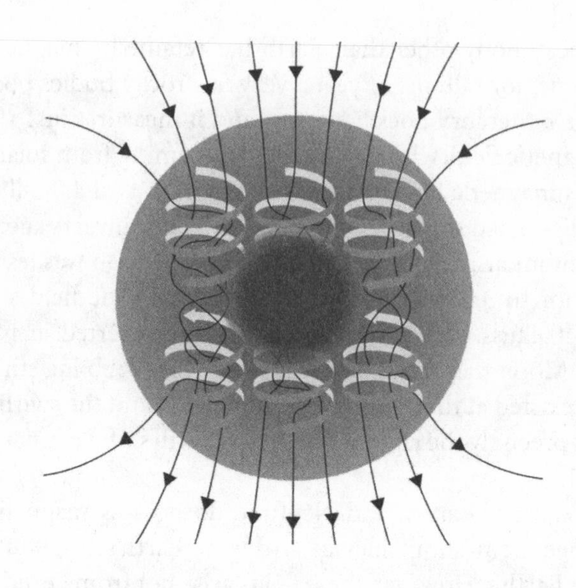

Figure 14.2: Dynamo Mechanism That Generates Earth's Magnetic Field
Credit: United States Geological Survey

circulating electric current—the dynamo mechanism (see figure 14.2). This electric current, generated in the dynamo, produces Earth's magnetic field.

Unique Dynamo History

Multiple extraordinary factors make the exceptional, enduring strength of Earth's dynamo possible. Apart from these factors, Earth's magnetic field would have gone the way of the other inner planets' magnetic fields—from weak to nonexistent. The first and foremost factor is that Earth is an "iron champion" among rocky planets.

Iron, of course, is one of only a few easily magnetized elements, and Earth contains an enormous quantity of it. In fact, by mass, iron is Earth's most abundant element. While iron comprises 5.19% (by mass) of all the heavy elements (elements heavier than helium) in the universe and an exceptional 6.50% of the solar system's heavy elements, iron makes up 19.53% of Earth's heavy elements.

However, its abundance alone cannot fully account for the dynamo in Earth's core and the strong and long-lasting magnetic field it generates, a protector of advanced life on Earth.

Seven additional factors play a significant role:

Factor #1. Most of Earth's iron, a little more than 75%, resides in the inner and outer core, a uniquely high percentage for known rocky planets. Apparently, the merger of proto-Earth with Theia that led to the Moon's formation, drove much of both bodies' iron into Earth's core. Early bombardment by large asteroids added to that quantity.

Meanwhile, Earth's mantle, unlike the mantle of any other known rocky planet, delivered even more iron to the core. Given the pressure, temperature, and elemental composition of Earth's lower mantle, iron there forms small, interconnected pockets of liquid alloy. These linked pockets become pathways whereby iron alloys flow gradually into the upper portion of the outer core.[45] This unique delivery system helps explain why Earth's iron core has remained as large as it is to this day.

Factor #2. As previously noted, the temperature difference between the bottom and top of Earth's outer core is 1400 K. This enormous temperature difference is the primary driver of powerful convective currents throughout the outer core, fueling the dynamo.

Factor #3. As solidification of the inner core progresses, it gradually squeezes out light elements, driving them into the outer core. Once there, these lighter elements rise upward toward the mantle and, in that process, generate additional convective currents—the second strongest contribution to outer core convection. During the inner core's early history, this upward rise of light elements in the outer core played a bigger role than it does today in sustaining the dynamo's convective currents.[46]

Factor #4. The tidal force the Moon exerts on Earth also contributes to ongoing convection. The extremely high (and likely unique among planet-moon systems) Moon-to-Earth mass ratio leads to a notable difference between the gravitational force the Moon exerts on the portion of Earth nearest the Moon and the portion most distant from the Moon. The closer the two bodies to one another, the more significant this tidal effect.

The Moon currently orbits at such a distance from Earth that the lunar tidal contribution to convection currents in Earth's outer core no longer plays a major role. However, during Earth's early history when the Moon orbited more closely to Earth, the lunar tidal contribution would have been 10–1,000 times greater than it is now.[47]

Factor #5. Earth's startlingly high abundance of radioisotopes with long half-lives also contributes heat flow that sustains Earth's dynamo. Some of this abundance had its origin in the solar nebula's superendowment with thorium and uranium.[48] As part of the solar nebula, primitive meteorites were likewise superendowed, and they were the building blocks of planets. Because of the difference in the way Earth formed, it became hyperendowed with uranium and thorium. The abundance of uranium and thorium in Earth's crust exceeds that of primitive meteorites by an astonishing 154 and 184 times, respectively.[49]

Assuming that deep ocean basalts are a useful proxy for the upper mantle, the relative abundance of uranium and thorium in the upper mantle is approximately the same as for the crust. Analysis of data from the Borexino neutrino observatory (see chapter 9) determined that the present flow of radiogenic heat from uranium-238 and thorium-232 in Earth's mantle is 24.6 ± 10.4 terawatts, and the quantity of uranium-238 and thorium-232 in Earth's mantle is much higher than the amount in its core.[50]

As with the contribution from lunar tides, internal radiogenic heat would have contributed much more to Earth's liquid core convection during Earth's early history. Four billion years ago, Earth's internal radiogenic heat level would have been more than 4 times greater (see chapter 15).

Factor #6. The collision event that enlarged Earth, enhanced Earth's abundance of heavy elements, and formed the Moon also dramatically accelerated Earth's rotation rate. It sped up to a high of 2–4 hours per day. Thanks to Earth's rapid rotation rate, Coriolis forces organized convection flows in the liquid core into rolls. These rolls generated circulating electric currents that produced Earth's magnetic field. The currents would have been more potent 1–4 billion years ago than they are today. Over the 4.47 billion years since then, tidal forces exerted by the Moon, and to a lesser degree by the Sun, have slowed Earth's rotation rate to 24 hours. However, despite the decrease in Earth's rotation rate by 6–12 times, the current rate is still sufficient, given the more potent outer core convection flows, to produce the necessary Coriolis forces.

Factor #7. During the first billion years of Earth's history, a molten silicate layer surrounded Earth's core. Molecular dynamics simulations demonstrate that the electrical conductivity of this silicate layer was more than 100 times greater than that of the silicate mantle today.[51] Such high electrical conductivity would have been more than adequate to generate a dynamo in the molten silicate layer, a dynamo that contributed substantially to Earth's magnetic field from 4.2 to 3.7 billion years ago.

A review of these seven known sources of convection shows that as some sources of the dynamo's energy abated, other sources increased to compensate. Some exquisite orchestration lies behind the extraordinary strength and duration (4.2 billion years) of Earth's magnetic field.

Unique Magnetic History

The complex histories of the inner and outer cores resulted in a complex history of Earth's magnetic field. From 4.2–2.0 billion years ago, in the absence of a solid inner core, Earth's magnetic field was both weaker and more variable than it is today. During the era 4.2–1.3 billion years ago, when the surface magnetic field ranged from just 0.05 to 0.40 gauss, the field was predominantly multipolar rather than dipolar. Geomagnetic reversals, flips of magnetic north to magnetic south and vice versa, likely occurred more frequently and for shorter durations. Field reversals occur about 6 times more rapidly, on average, in a liquid core than in a solid core.[52]

From 4.2 billion to 1.3–1.0 billion years ago, Earth's magnetic field followed a trend of gradual weakening. Some increase in field strength and variability occurred when the solid core of bcc iron alloy began to grow.[53] The field remained strong for a while thereafter.

Numerical convection and dynamo models for the period when Earth's core was fully liquid (prior to 1.3–1.0 billion years ago) show that Earth's magnetic field was largely dominated by multipolar (nondipolar) components.[54] From at least a billion years ago until 0.56 billion years ago, Earth had a small solid inner core comprised primarily of bcc iron alloys. Solid phase bcc iron has a viscosity (resistance to deformation or flow) resembling that of a viscous liquid. Thus, from 1.3–1.0 billion years ago to 0.56 billion years ago, Earth's magnetic field transitioned from predominantly multipolar to predominantly dipolar, and yet it remained relatively weak.

Unfortunately, the paleointensity record from 1.0–0.65 billion years ago is sparse. Research does show that beginning about 0.635 billion years ago, Earth's geodynamo entered an anomalous epoch, a period characterized by a scattering of both the intensity and direction of Earth's magnetic field.

Three independent studies reveal that the thermal conductivity of Earth's core was high from 0.60–0.565 billion years ago.[55] High thermal conductivity implies that less heat was available to drive convection and, thus, to induce a strong magnetic field. Paleomagnetic data reveal that by 0.565 billion years ago, Earth's magnetic field strength had dropped to only one-tenth the present-day value.[56] Further, the field had become multipolar and manifested a hyperreversal frequency.

At this point, 0.565 billion years ago, Earth's magnetic field was on the verge of disappearing altogether. If it had disappeared, solar radiation would have eroded away Earth's atmosphere and hydrosphere, and deadly solar and cosmic radiation would have blasted Earth's surface. Earth would have been permanently "sterilized" of all life.

However, the emergence of the solid inner core of hcp iron alloy shortly before 0.56 billion years ago "occurred right in the nick of time to recharge the geodynamo and save Earth's magnetic field."[57] From that time onward, Earth's magnetic field has remained predominantly strong and dipolar. The one exception is a brief episode between the end of the Cambrian Period (0.485 billion years ago) and the end of the Devonian Period (0.359 billion years ago) when Earth's magnetic field was characterized mostly by reversal hyperactivity and complex low-intensity fields.[58]

Despite the complex history of Earth's magnetic field, Earth's predominantly strong, dipolar magnetic field over the past 0.56 billion years made the existence of terrestrial animals, vascular plants, human beings, and global civilization possible. Nevertheless, a question remains: How was complex life able to survive during brief episodes of weak magnetic field strengths?

Magnetic Reversals and Life

Since the hcp iron alloy solid core began to form 0.56 billion years ago, a few hundred magnetic reversals have occurred.[59] Before that time, magnetic reversals were far more frequent. These reversals occur randomly and with no discernible periodicity. Once a full reversal begins, it may take anywhere from 1,000 to 12,000 years to complete. The reversal takes less time at low latitudes than at high latitudes.[60]

During a magnetic reversal, the magnetic field strength weakens. It declines to a level between 40% and 5% of its prereversal strength before bouncing back.[61] The farther it drops, the briefer it remains at that low level. This weakening results from temporary transitions from a dipolar to a multipolar magnetic field (see figure 14.3).

The question of how life survived from 3.8–0.56 billion years ago—when Earth's magnetic field was weaker than it is now or during brief episodes of weakening since then—has been answered by Harvard University astronomer Manasvi Lingam.[62]

Lingam first demonstrated that even during that early era when Earth's geodynamo was predominantly multipolar, rather than dipolar, it remained strong enough to prevent the loss of Earth's surface water and atmosphere and

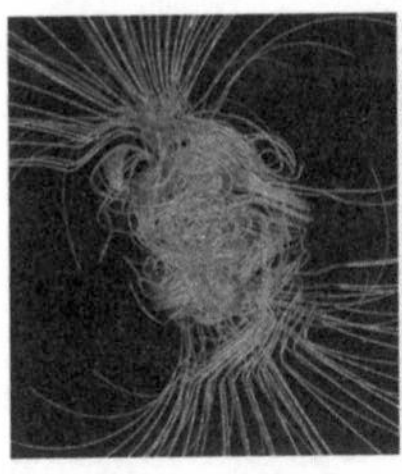
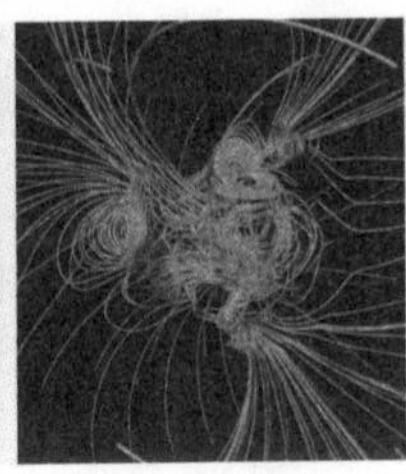
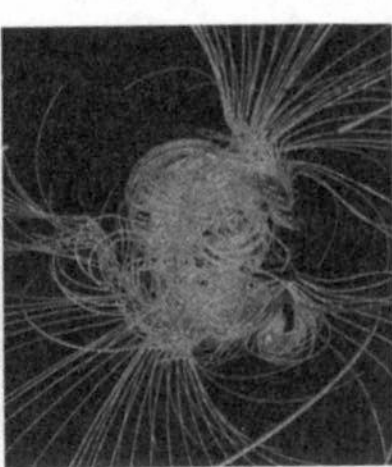

Figure 14.3: Reversal of Earth's Magnetic Field
The images show (L–R) how Earth's magnetic field undergoes a progressive polarity shift. The shifts are indicated by switching positions of the gold and blue lines (colors visible online at reasons.org/audiobooks and in the e-book). *Images credit: NASA; Diagram credit: Hugh Ross*

to preserve the microbial life (the totality of Earth's biodiversity) that existed at that time.

Lingam then determined the consequences of later brief drops down to as low as 10% of present strength level. He showed that, even for the longest of these episodes, the dose of radiation received by Earth's life increased by no more than a factor of three and, typically, only by double or less. This temporary increase in exposure, Lingam showed, fell below the exposure threshold that would cause the extinction of any plant or animal species.

Lingam also calculated that the atmospheric escape rate for water increased by no more than a factor of two during the brief episodes when Earth's magnetic field strength dropped to 10% of its present level. He showed that given the relative brevity of these episodes, this doubling of atmospheric escape rates would result in only a minor loss of water from Earth's surface.

Exoplanet Magnetic Fields

A team of astronomers from the University of Hawaii and the University of California, Berkeley, developed a detailed model to ascertain how long dynamos would endure, if they formed at all, in rocky planets of varying masses and distances from their host star.[63] They demonstrated the validity of their model by successfully reproducing the properties of both Earth's and Venus's interiors and magnetic fields. Their model established, for example, that Venus's dehydrated, high-viscosity (high resistance to deformation or flow) mantle either shut down its dynamo very early, or the dynamo never operated at all.

The team's model predicted that, at a fixed planet mass, the bigger the planet's core, the longer enduring the planet's dynamo would be and the stronger its magnetic field. The model also showed that the higher a planet's mantle viscosity, the briefer its dynamo history, and the higher the thermal conductivity of the planet's core, the briefer the planet's dynamo history. Other factors influencing a planet's dynamo history included the core's thermal expansivity, the initial core temperature, and the heat flow across the core-mantle boundary.

The model established that for rocky planets larger than 3.0 Earth masses, the core never cools sufficiently for iron to condense. That is, not even a tiny solid inner core will form. While ongoing cooling in the liquid core can generate a dynamo, it will be weak due to the small temperature contrast between the core and the mantle. Furthermore, the temperature contrast between the core and mantle will continually decrease and quickly shut down the dynamo.

For planets between 2.0 and 3.0 Earth masses, the solid inner core, once formed, will not grow. Consequently, in each case the dynamo will be weak and eventually shut down.

Regardless of their mass, planets lacking mobile "lids"—that is, plate tectonics—and planets lacking both a silicate mantle and a near pure iron core, will have, at best, a weak dynamo. Any dynamo that does form will shut down within a couple of billion years.

With the data from their model, this team of astronomers showed that for a planet to possess a dynamo of sufficient strength and longevity to generate the kind of magnetic field advanced life needs, the following properties and/or values must fit within extremely narrow ranges:

- planetary mass
- core mass
- mobile "lids"
- mantle viscosity
- core thermal conductivity
- core thermal expansivity
- heat flow rate across the core-mantle boundary

- initial core temperature
- inner core composition
- outer core composition

The long-term shutdown of a planet's dynamo renders that planet uninhabitable. Two additional habitability requirements apply to planets with magnetic fields weaker than 10% of Earth's present field strength or that experience short-term total shutdowns.

If such a planet orbits a star less massive than the Sun (such stars comprise 95% of the total star population[64]) at a distance that allows for the existence of liquid surface water, it will be exposed to more frequent and intense stellar flares and to stronger stellar winds than Earth experiences. Such exposure will rapidly deplete surface water and deliver a far stronger radiation dose to the planetary surface. This stronger radiation would be especially detrimental to advanced plants and animals. If such a planet were to have a lower atmospheric pressure than Earth's, the result would be the same: rapid water depletion and a stronger dose of radiation.

As important for life as a planet's fine-tuned core appears to be, the specific features of a planet's mantle and crust appear equally significant, if not more so. The mantle must modulate the flow of energy from the core to the surface in a manner that favors the survival of life, especially of advanced life on a planet's surface. The next chapter describes the features of Earth's mantle.

Chapter 15

Earth's Mantle

Chapter summary: *Earth's mantle, likely the only one of its kind in the solar system or anywhere else in the universe, plays a critical role in making Earth habitable. Its multilayered structure, elemental and molecular composition, and heat flow capacity combine to help provide and sustain two essential life-support requirements: a strong and long-lasting magnetic field, as well as strong and long-lasting plate tectonic activity. If the mantle characteristics were to vary by more than a few percent, the possibility for advanced life on Earth would be severely diminished, if not destroyed.*

Earth's mantle remains the most mysterious and least understood of Earth's interior components. Researchers have only limited ways to study it. However, what we do know about it reveals the importance of its precise characteristics for making life on Earth possible, especially complex, enduring life.

In simplest terms, Earth's mantle refers to the layer between the outer core and the crust. Its inner boundary is at 3,480 kilometers from Earth's center, and its outer boundary, just beneath the crust, measures 6,345 kilometers from Earth's center. The mantle, comprised almost entirely of silicate rock, takes up 82.5% of Earth's volume and 67.1% of Earth's mass. It has been studied predominantly via tens of thousands of seismic measurements.

Mantle Structure

Earth's mantle as depicted in most textbooks needs revision. It is not a viscous layer thoroughly homogenized by widespread aggressive convection like a jar of homogenized creamy-style peanut butter. While the energy transport in the mantle is predominantly convection, its components, though well mixed, are not *thoroughly* mixed, at least not consistently throughout Earth's history.

In their analysis of 7,000 seismic readings from magnitude 6.5+ earthquakes that occurred between 1990 and 2018 across the Pacific Ocean, a team of geophysicists detected two distinct structures just above the core-mantle boundary.[1] Two large blobs, each measuring about 1,000 kilometers across and about 25 kilometers thick, along with several much smaller ones, stood out. The composition and density of these blobs differed distinctly from both the molten iron-nickel alloy at the top of the outer core and the slushy rock at the bottom of the mantle.

One of the two large blobs sits under the Hawaiian Islands and the other, under the Marquesas Islands. Both blobs are associated with hot vertical plumes emerging from the lower mantle and rising through the upper mantle and crust to form the volcanoes responsible for formation of the Hawaiian and Marquesas Islands. This island-building process, which has been progressing for the past 28 million years for the Hawaiian Islands and 5 million years for the Marquesas Islands, continues to this day. It could potentially continue for another several million years.

An even larger database of seismic readings reveals sharp seismic velocity discontinuities, one at 660 kilometers and another at 440 kilometers below Earth's surface. Increasing pressure produced by increasing depth appears to cause these discontinuities. The discontinuities at 660 kilometers arise from the transformation of ringwoodite, a higher-pressure phase of magnesium orthosilicate, into bridgmanite (a high-density form of magnesium iron silicate), or into magnesium silicate ($MgSiO_3$) and periclase. (Periclase is a cubic form of magnesium oxide (MgO). The discontinuities at 410 kilometers result from transformation of olivine, the low-pressure phase of magnesium orthosilicate (Mg_2SiO_4), into wadsleyite, a high-pressure phase of magnesium orthosilicate.

Geophysicists refer to the portion of the mantle between 660 and 410 kilometers below Earth's surface as the mantle transition zone (MTZ), the mantle above the MTZ as the upper mantle, and the mantle below the MTZ as the lower mantle. The thermal gradient (temperature variation with respect to depth) at the MTZ varies substantially with time. This variation causes the mantle to switch between a layered state, in which convection across the MTZ is weak, and an unlayered state, in which mass can transfer across the MTZ with little or no resistance.

When the mantle is in an unlayered state, plumes rise directly from the core-mantle boundary to the crust, and the mantle shows little chemical stratification. When the mantle is in a layered state, rising plumes stall at the MTZ and then spawn new plumes that continue to rise to the crust. In these instances, the lower mantle manifests a higher silicon-to-magnesium ratio than the upper mantle.

Seismic observations show that some tectonic plates that have been subducted into the mantle stagnate at depths between about 700 and 1,000 kilometers while others sink unimpeded to near the bottom of the lower mantle. This variability implies that a moderate compositional gradient (some layering) across mantle depths can and does persist even while whole-mantle convection continues.[2] This gradient helps regulate the heat flow across the mantle, keeping it within the life-favoring range.

Internal Heat Flow

Heat flow in the outer core is the primary contributor to the convection that sustains Earth's life-essential magnetic field. This heat flow would be inadequate, however, if not for the just-right heat transfer from the outer core to the lower mantle, from the lower mantle to the upper mantle, from the upper mantle to the crust, and, finally, from the crust to Earth's surface, atmosphere, and interplanetary space. To a large degree, mantle dynamics control the core's thermal history and Earth's magnetic field.

Recent research shows Earth to be a "champion" in yet another of its features (beyond its iron abundance). Among all known rocky planets (those in the solar system and in exoplanetary systems) roughly similar in size and age, Earth stands out as the internal heat flow champion. What is known of these other planets would lead scientists to expect much less heat transfer from Earth's core all the way up through the mantle to the crust. In the case of Mars, for example, heat flow from the interior to the surface measures only 7 milliwatts per square meter.[3] This low heat flow explains why Mars is missing at least two life-essential features: a strong, long-lasting magnetic field and long-lasting plate tectonic activity.

According to some 70,000 measurements, every square meter of Earth's continental surface is warmed, on average, by 92 milliwatts flowing from Earth's interior.[4] Every square meter of ocean surface is warmed by 67 milliwatts.[5] Heat flows more readily through continental crust material, mostly silicates, than it does through oceanic crust material, mostly basalts.

On Earth's surface, incident radiation from the Sun dominates heat flowing from Earth's interior. The Sun warms every square meter of Earth's surface by an average of 340.2 watts.[6] By comparison, internal heat flow accounts for only 0.024% of Earth's surface warmth. No wonder it goes unnoticed.

The Sun's incident radiation, though much stronger, penetrates only a few tens of meters into Earth's crust. Below that, internal heat flow from Earth's core and through its mantle dominates solar heat. As noted, without that extremely high internal heat flow to help power Earth's dynamo, Earth would be lifeless today.

Heat Flow Sources

One of the two major sources of Earth's interior heat is the radioactive decay of long-half-life radioisotopes. This radiogenic heat accounts for 58% of the current total heat flow.[7] The second major source is referred to as primordial heat—heat lost in the ongoing cooling from the intensely hot accretion (gravity-induced accumulation of matter) at Earth's formation.

Earth has a remarkably high level of primordial heat because of its unique formation. Like all rocky planets, it began to form through the accretion of planetesimals, dust, and gas, a process that generated high internal heat. However, Earth's accretion history did not end there.

Earth experienced three additional accretion events, all major and highly unusual. The most significant occurred a little less than 100 million years after Earth began to take shape. That is when Theia (a planet 11–15% of Earth's original mass) collided and merged with the primordial Earth, increasing Earth's mass, producing the Moon, and substantially intensifying Earth's accretion heat. Shortly after this event, Earth received what astronomers refer to as a "late veneer"—a barrage of large asteroids and comets.[8] Then, about 3.9 billion years ago, Earth experienced the Late Heavy Bombardment, a second pounding by large asteroids and comets.[9] These events heightened Earth's primordial accretion heat far beyond the norm for rocky planets of its size.

Earth's level of radiogenic heat may be considered even more remarkable. Compared to the calculated average abundance of these radiogenic elements in rocky exoplanets, Earth possesses 90 times more potassium-40, 340 times more uranium (uranium-238 and uranium-235, combined), and 610 times more thorium-232.[10] Given the timing and complex processes by which the solar system formed, all the solar planets became unusually enriched with these elements.[11] However, Earth received a superendowment far beyond the level of other solar system planets.[12] More importantly, this endowment penetrated to great depths, not just into the crust where it would dissipate rapidly, as it did on Mars 4 billion years ago. What we know about Earth's interior heat sources today helps us understand Earth's internal convection and conduction modes.

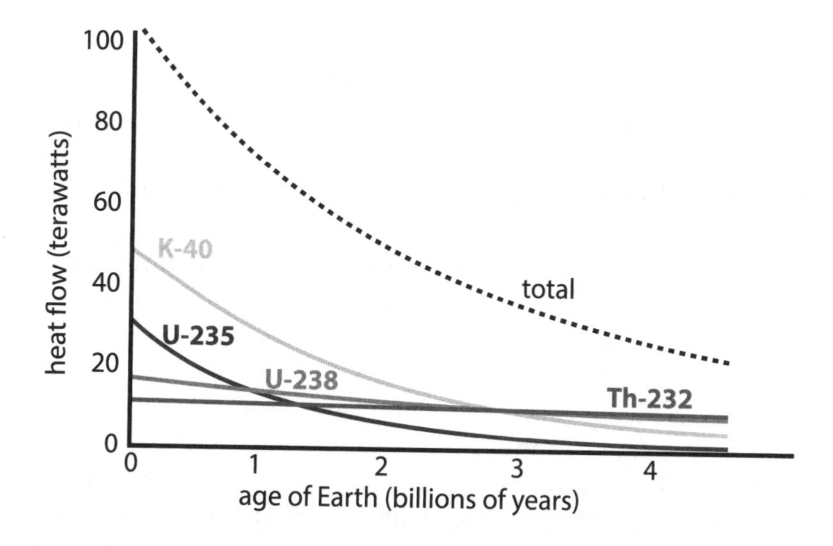

Figure 15.1: Radiogenic Heat Flow History from Earth's Interior Radioisotopes
Credit: Hugh Ross

Heat Flow Pathways

With the knowledge available in the mid-nineteenth century, Britain's famed physicist, Lord Kelvin, proposed that all of Earth's internal heat came from a single accretion event. His peers agreed and joined him in assuming that heat flowed from Earth's interior via conductive cooling only.[13] Both the proposition and the assumption have since proved incorrect.

Convection plays a much more important role in heat transport than conduction in both Earth's mantle and liquid core. For Earth's crust, the dominant heat transport mode is volcanic advection (flows of molten lava and volcanic gases). For the outer core and mantle, convection is the dominant mode, while conduction still dominates in the inner core. The operation of convection, a process that slows heat flow, is an important reason Earth's internal heat flow has been sustained over billions of years.

Earth's Interior Heat Flow History

Interior heat flow from both accretion and radiogenic heat has varied to some degree over time. The heat left over from accretion still gradually dissipates as it flows from Earth's deep interior through the mantle, through the crust, to the surface and beyond.

When Earth was less than 100 million years old, most of its radiogenic heat came from multiple short-half-life radioisotopes. Since then, just four radioisotopes—potassium-40, uranium-235, uranium-238, and thorium-232—have accounted for more than 99% of Earth's radiogenic heat. While the quantities of these radioisotopes in Earth's interior have declined, the amount of heat from them still plays a significant role in driving convection. Figure 15.1 shows the relative contributions of these radioisotopes to Earth's internal heat flow throughout the past 4.5 billion years.

Heat Flow and Viscosity

Today, the mantle temperature just under Earth's oceanic crust is 1,410°C.[14] This high temperature means upper mantle material has a low viscosity (like heated honey). Due to this low viscosity, tectonic plates in Earth's crust have been able to move, relative to one another, throughout the past 3.8 billion years. This tectonic activity, as it began, transformed Earth from a water world to a planet with both oceans and continents on its surface.

The combination of surface continents, oceans, and enduring, powerful tectonic activity has contributed to Earth's habitability in multiple ways. It allowed for continual recycling of life-essential nutrients. It allowed for biogeochemical cycles that compensated in a crucial way for the Sun's increasing brightness (see chapter 16 and figure 16.2). Without Earth's just-right and enduring interior heat flow, only microbial life could have existed anywhere on Earth and for no more than some millions of years, if at all.

The current cooling rate of Earth's mantle is 70–130°C per billion years.[15] This cooling proceeds so slowly as to pose no short-term threat to life. The cooling implies, however, that Earth's mantle will become more viscous through time. Eventually, its viscosity will be high enough to shut down plate tectonic activity. When that happens, Earth will no longer be able to support life.

As for time estimates, within several million years from now, subduction tectonics (whereby one tectonic plate slides under another and sinks into the mantle) will begin to decline with increasing rapidity. Less than a billion years from now, all tectonic activity on Earth will cease. Until then, Earth's internal temperature, low viscosity upper mantle, and heat flow will keep things shaking as it continues to allow plate tectonic activity, which, though threatening occasionally to human life on a local level, is needed for survival of all life on a global scale.

Mantle Influence on Magnetic Field

In several respects, what happens in the mantle controls what occurs in Earth's outer core. By its structure, composition, and dynamics, the mantle determines the rate of heat flow outward from Earth's core. The flow of core heat into the mantle, in turn, plays a significant role in driving the outer core convection that is crucial for maintaining the operation of Earth's magnetic field.

As explained in chapter 14, another important factor that drives outer core convection is the floating up of light elements—oxygen, silicon, sulfur, and carbon squeezed from the inner core, up through the outer core, and into the mantle. These light elements are continuously deposited from the outer core into a layer at the base of the mantle. Only aggressive mantle convection keeps these elements from accumulating at the bottom of the mantle and blocking any further flow of light elements out from the core. Such blockage, if it were to occur, would weaken or terminate Earth's magnetic field.[16]

Mantle convection works effectively in this process due to the cooling influence of plate tectonics. The 2,080 K temperature gradient between the core-mantle boundary and the mantle-crust boundary (cooled by plate tectonics)[17] draws heat from the core-mantle boundary with strength and efficiency. This heat draw is strong enough, but not too strong, to ensure that outer core convection can sustain Earth's magnetic field for billions of years at the level necessary to protect Earth's life. For the heat draw to be just right, the mantle must be comprised of layers, each with just-right density and composition, throughout nearly all of the past 4.2 billion years.[18]

A geophysics research team led by Paul Tackley and Takashi Nakagawa concluded that "there is only a limited parameter range in which the heat extracted from the core is large enough at all times for a geodynamo to exist, but small enough that the core did not cool more than observed" and, thereby, shut down the geodynamo.[19] Mantle structure, composition, and history shape the core's thermal properties and thermal evolution.

The most significant factor in shaping these characteristics is the presence of a specific just-right quantity of water within the mantle.[20] Even a small amount of water in the mantle decreases mantle viscosity by more than a thousand times. It also lowers the temperature at which mantle minerals melt, alters the depth of the MTZ where vital phase transition of mantle minerals occurs, and increases the buoyancy of subducted slabs. A slight change in the quantity of water in the mantle would eventually disrupt Earth's dynamo and weaken or destroy the magnetic shield protecting life.

How plate tectonics drives surface water, atmospheric gases, and surface minerals through Earth's crust into the asthenosphere and mantle, and causes much of them to return, also plays a crucial role in making Earth habitable throughout the past 3.8 billion years. The next chapter addresses these interior features and the history of Earth's "lids."

Chapter 16

Earth's Crustal Interior

Chapter summary: *Unique characteristics at the interface between Earth's mantle and rocky crust have made Earth's life-essential plate tectonic activity possible throughout the past several billion years. This tectonic activity has sustained a deep carbon cycle, a deep water cycle, and a deep oxygen cycle, all of which must fall within specific narrow ranges to produce and maintain the atmosphere and hydrosphere Earth's avian and mammalian life depends upon—even more so to produce the resources needed for global high-technology civilization. These three cycles also account for Earth's historic snowball events, without which Earth's atmosphere would lack the oxygen and carbon dioxide levels vital for advanced life.*

All of Earth's life resides in, on, or slightly above Earth's crust, a layer that comprises a mere 1.0% of Earth's total volume. The average thickness of continental crust is 41 kilometers (25 miles) and of oceanic crust, 7 kilometers (4.5 miles).[1] This thickness and the fact that the crust is cracked proves essential for habitability. Sixteen major plates, or "lids," ride atop Earth's mantle (see figure 16.1), and scientists refer to their dynamical movement as plate tectonics.

For most people, the mention of plate tectonics conjures images of all the devastation caused by earthquakes, tsunamis, and volcanoes. Research has made clear, however, that life depends on the enormous benefits plate tectonic activity provides. Without plate tectonics, Earth would lack surface landmasses, nutrient recycling, an oxygen-rich atmosphere, and other essentials for life. Without strong, enduring plate tectonics, Earth would lack the quantity, configuration, and distribution of landmasses, and the relief features on the landmasses needed for advanced life.

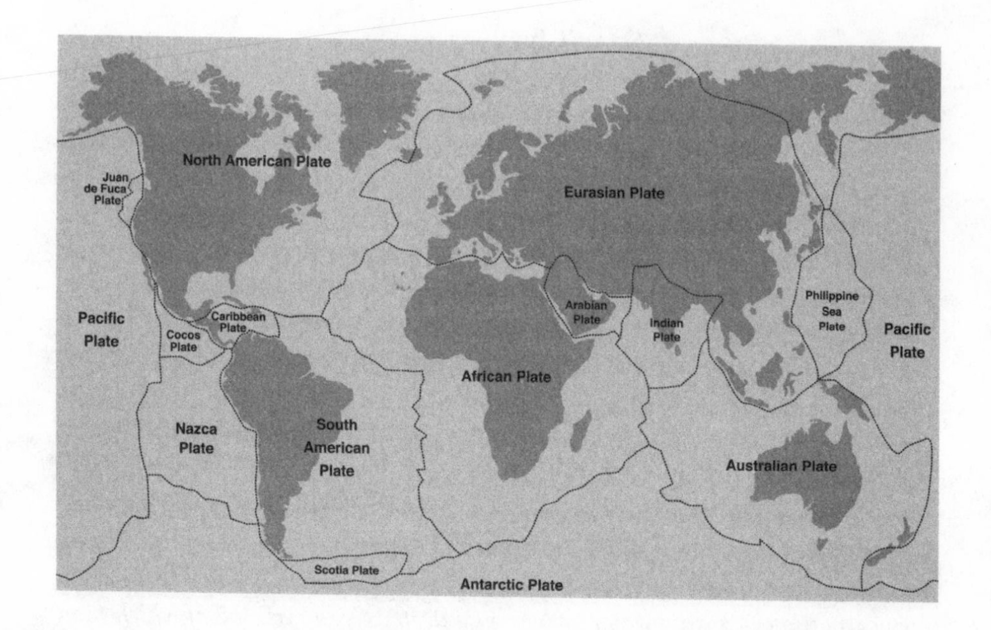

Figure 16.1: Earth's Current Principal Tectonic Plates
The shaded regions with borders represent 17 major tectonic plates. Arrows represent the ongoing movements of tectonic plates relative to one another. *Credit: U.S. Geological Survey*

The Underlying Asthenosphere

Just beneath Earth's rocky crust, or lithosphere, lies the uppermost layer of Earth's mantle, a relatively thin layer between 40 and 150 kilometers thick (depending on geographic location), known as the asthenosphere. The lithosphere's solid, brittle crustal plates ride atop the asthenosphere layer as they continually move relative to one another.

Between the core-mantle boundary and the mantle-crust boundary, where the asthenosphere resides, Earth's interior temperature cools from 3,490 ± 290°C (3,760 ± 290 K) down to 1,410°C (1,680 K). Though it may seem strange, the melting temperature of material in the mantle drops more rapidly in moving from the bottom to the top of the mantle than does the mantle temperature.[2] This lower melting point serves to greatly lower the viscosity of the asthenosphere.

One contributing factor to the mantle melting temperature dropping more rapidly than the mantle temperature is Earth's extraordinarily high interior density. Earth is the densest planet in the solar system, much denser than rocky exoplanets orbiting their host stars at distances greater than 50 million kilometers (third of an astronomical unit). A second contributing factor is the presence of water in the mantle, which can drastically decrease mantle viscosity and thereby lower the temperature at which mantle minerals melt. This effect weakens with depth since the quantity of water in the mantle declines with depth.

The third and most important factor for sustaining plate movements is what happens geochemically because of water's presence in the upper mantle. The two predominant mineral groups in Earth's mantle are the olivines and pyroxenes. Both olivines and pyroxenes can take hydrated forms. Their hydrated forms significantly impact the viscosity levels of mantle layers and regions.

A special feature of Earth's upper mantle is that it contains a large quantity of aluminous orthopyroxene ($xAlSi_2O_6$), a mineral compound in which X is either another aluminum atom or the atom of another metal. Under the temperature and pressure conditions of the upper mantle, aluminous orthopyroxene is highly effective in lowering viscosity (via its contribution to water solubility) near the mantle top but exhibits a sharp decrease in water solubility with depth.[3] This sharp decrease in water solubility (through the formation of hydrates) means that the asthenosphere is much wetter than both the mantle layers below it and the plates above it. Thus, the viscosity of mantle material attains a minimum level nearest the asthenosphere-crust boundary.

This counterintuitive feature of Earth's mantle, its increasing ductility (ability to sustain plastic deformation) with nearness to Earth's crust, accounts for the sustenance of tectonic activity throughout the past 4 billion years. Another contributor is the ongoing melting of a hydrous silicate in the upper asthenosphere. This mineral has a drying effect on the crust, making the crust more rigid and brittle. In fact, without this desiccation (drying out), Earth's system of plate tectonics would not exist.

These features, among others, appear so intricate and specific that Earth may well be the only rocky planet on which plate tectonic activity, at a survivable level for life, has been operating for an extended period, much less approaching 4 billion years.[4] For planets larger than Earth, the asthenosphere will form at too deep a level for the necessary crustal plates to exist and move relative to one another. For planets smaller than Earth, the asthenosphere will reside at too shallow a level, resulting in too rapid a dissipation of interior heat and too much movement.

What's more, enduring plate tectonic activity can only occur on a planet where water is available to the asthenosphere for a very long time. And, for the asthenosphere to be sufficiently wet, it must contain aluminum in high abundance. Compared to other rocky bodies (bodies devoid of light gases) in the universe, Earth has a rare wealth of aluminum. Earth's crust has 31.9 times, and Earth's mantle 8.3 times, as much aluminum as these other bodies.[5]

Earth's solid crustal plates float about on the slow-flowing asthenosphere that, although slow, moves at a much faster rate than the rest of the mantle. This capacity of tectonic plates to move relative to one another atop a ductile asthenosphere makes three major systems possible: the building of continental landmasses to replace those that have eroded away, the recycling of life-essential nutrients throughout Earth's ecosystems, and the development of mountain ranges both on the continents and in the oceans to maintain life-essential climate and weather patterns.

For the movement of tectonic plates to remain at the level of a few centimeters per year, on average, the asthenosphere's temperature and pressure must fall within extremely narrow ranges. Temperature and pressure are major factors in determining how ductile the asthenosphere will be. The asthenosphere's temperature and pressure in combination with the crust's thickness, composition, and plate structure also control how much heat is released from the mantle through the crust and out to the hydrosphere, atmosphere, and interplanetary space. This heat flow, as noted in chapters 14 and 15, regulates the inner and outer core properties and determines whether Earth maintains a strong, steady magnetic field capable of shielding advanced life.

As geochemical and thermal processes continue in the asthenosphere, its ductility varies somewhat with geographical location and time. This variation explains, in part, why some tectonic plates move faster than others and why any plate's velocity may vary over time. Even this variability in tectonic plate velocity plays a crucial role in forming the different kinds of topographical structures, including mountain chains, plateaus, and plains, that provide for the needs of advanced life.

Tectonic Plates

Earth's crust is broken up into a few dozen major and minor tectonic plates. Currently, 10 of these plates measure in excess of 10,000,000 square kilometers; 13 tectonic plates, between 1–10 million square kilometers; and 57 microplates, less than 1 million square kilometers.[7] Continental plates, made up of silicates, have a mean density of 2.83 grams/cubic centimeter (g/cc). Oceanic

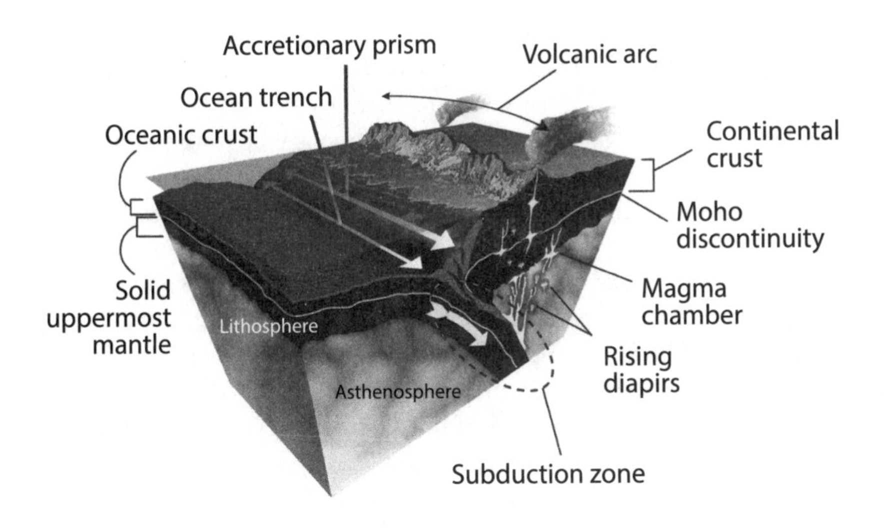

Figure 16.2: Tectonic Plate Subduction
The collision of an oceanic crustal plate with a continental crustal plate typically results in the oceanic plate sliding underneath the continental plate into the mantle. *Credit: Subduction-en.svg from Wikimedia Commons by K. D. Schroeder, CC-BY-SA 4.0.*

plates, composed of basalts rich in magnesium and iron, have a mean density of 2.9 g/cc.

When these plates collide, a process of subduction sometimes occurs, whereby one tectonic plate slides under another and is driven into Earth's slightly denser (3.3 g/cc) mantle, as figure 16.2 illustrates. In this process of subduction, the intrusion of plates into the mantle facilitates three significant cycles on which life crucially depends—water, carbon, and oxygen cycles.

Deep Water Cycle

Earth's water cycle receives more attention than any other planetary feature as the key to our planet's habitability. This cycle is among the earliest science lessons in children's education: water flows from the atmosphere into rivers, lakes, oceans, and life-forms and returns via rivers, lakes, oceans, and life-forms to the atmosphere in a beautifully balanced way. This cycle includes distribution, transportation, and transformation of precisely balanced proportions of water vapor, liquid water, and frozen water throughout Earth's environment.

The water cycle people know little about—the deep water cycle—proves equally important for life. This cycle entails the flow of water from the crust, ocean, atmosphere, and life-forms into the mantle and back again. One reason the deep water cycle has garnered so little attention is that, until recently, scientists lacked tools to investigate it in detail.

An international, interdisciplinary research team known as the VoiLA (Volatiles in the Lesser Antilles) team conducted research in the eastern Caribbean's Lesser Antilles Arc (LAA), a volcanic arc that forms the eastern boundary of the Caribbean Plate. The team used the connection between boron quantities and boron isotope ratios to demonstrate how serpentine, a hydrated rock/mineral, subducted into the upper mantle through plate tectonic activity contributes to the dynamics of the deep water cycle. (See sidebar, "The Boron-Serpentine Connection to the Deep Water Cycle.")

The VoiLA team established that upon reaching the subduction zone—the LAA in this case—the sinking plate heats up and its water is squeezed into a smaller volume. This heating and squeezing gradually releases water from the serpentine minerals. The release of water lowers the melting point of the surrounding rock, transforming it into magma. This magma, being more buoyant, floats upward, causing frequent eruptions in the volcanic chain.

As part of the cycle, the release of water and formation of magma dramatically reduce the buildup of crustal stresses along the LAA. Thus, the current LAA is characterized by many relatively small earthquakes, volcanic eruptions of lesser intensity, and no noticeable tsunamis. By contrast, other regions such as the Pacific Ocean rim, where the subducting plates are interacting with the faster-spreading Pacific plate, experience more intensive activity.

With a lesser release of water and slower formation of magma in the uppermost mantle and lowermost crust, earthquakes, tsunamis, and volcanic eruptions along the Ring of Fire—a 40,000-kilometer horseshoe-shaped arc of volcanoes along the Pacific Ocean's basin rim—occur less frequently per unit area, but prove more destructive. Nevertheless, if not for the efficiency of the deep water cycle along the Ring of Fire, earthquakes, tsunamis, and volcanic eruptions there would prove far more destructive than they are, eliminating the possibility of human civilization in Pacific Ocean rim regions.

Unlike the surface water cycle, the deep water cycle is not in perfect balance. Yet, a compensating factor is at work. The addition of water to the upper mantle lowers its viscosity, while the cooling of mantle material raises its viscosity. Thus, as radiogenic heat and primordial accretion heat have declined over time (see chapter 14), the gradual addition of water to the mantle has helped compensate

The Boron-Serpentine Connection to the Deep Water Cycle

In 2020, the VoiLA team published the results of an extensive investigation that began by demonstrating that boron and the isotope boron-11 are excellent proxies for fluid (or fluid-like) materials in Earth's surface tectonic plates that subduction delivers into the mantle (see figure 16.2).[8] Boron is fluid-mobile. Thus, a high ratio of boron to fluid-immobile elements, such as titanium or zirconium, in the mantle layer indicates the presence of a subducting plate's fluid material. A high boron-11 to boron-10 ratio indicates the presence of serpentine in the mantle and, if high enough, measures the quantity of serpentine in a particular mantle layer or region.

Serpentine is a hydrated form of olivine, and olivine is a magnesium iron silicate, the dominant mineral in Earth's upper mantle. When a large-scale tectonic fault provides a pathway for seawater to enter the mantle, this seawater hydrates olivine to form serpentine.[9] Serpentine can hold up to 13%, by weight, of water.

Having established this base of understanding, the VoiLA team took measurements of boron and boron isotope ratios from core drills into ocean floor sediments surrounding the LAA. This site was chosen because it is one of only two subduction zones where a subducting plate is currently forming by slow, rather than rapid, seafloor spreading. In such a plate, geophysicists expect hydration of olivine to occur more pervasively and water release from the mantle to the crust surface to prove more pronounced.

The boron quantities and boron isotope ratios measured by the VoiLA Team established that serpentine is, in fact, abundant in the sinking tectonic plate associated with the LAA.[10] Their work yielded the best and most unambiguous evidence to date that the amount of water in the serpentine minerals within the LAA's sinking plate directly correlates with the degree and kind of volcanic and associated earthquake activity in the LAA.

for the heat loss, ensuring that upper mantle viscosity is low enough to keep tectonic plates active not only in nutrient recycling but also in building up new continental crust to replace loss of continental crust due to erosion.

The deep water cycle also serves to remove slightly more volatiles (water, carbon dioxide, methane, and other gases) from Earth's atmosphere and hydrosphere (Earth's oceans, seas, lakes, rivers, icefields, and glaciers) than it returns. In view of the greenhouse effect of these volatiles, this slight ongoing imbalance helps compensate for the continually increasing solar luminosity (see figure 16.3).

Shallow and Deep Carbon Cycles

Like all stars, the Sun has brightened since the time its nuclear furnace ignited. During the last 3.8 billion years, the period in which life has continuously existed on Earth, the Sun's luminosity has increased by 20–23%[11] (see figure 16.3). An increase of such magnitude would have been catastrophic to, and perhaps prohibitive of, life if not for the gradual removal of greenhouse gases via the deep water cycle, as well as two carbon cycles.

Carbon-based molecules in Earth's atmosphere, the most abundant of which are carbon dioxide and methane, act as blankets keeping Earth's surface warm. For Earth's surface temperature to remain optimal for life, it is necessary for the warming effect of these greenhouse gases to *decrease* at a rate that steadily compensates for the Sun's increasing brightness. The needed compensation has occurred and is occurring through the workings of both the shallow carbon cycle and the deep carbon cycle.

The shallow carbon cycle refers to the movement of carbon throughout Earth's atmosphere, hydrosphere, and crust. This cycle has long been well understood, qualitatively and quantitatively. Some life-forms remove carbon from the atmosphere, through photosynthesis, for example, while other life-forms add carbon through the respiration of oxygen. On or in Earth's crust, the decay of dead life-forms normally releases carbon back to the atmosphere. In Earth's oceans, when dissolved silica reacts with alkali metal cations (positively charged ions of elements such as lithium, sodium, and potassium, among others) to form certain types of clay (other than those derived from kaolinite), carbon dioxide is released into the oceans and atmosphere and, as a by-product, marine pH is stabilized.[13]

The shallow carbon cycle removes carbon from the atmosphere primarily through silicate weathering and burial of organic carbon. Rainfall on exposed silicates (the main constituents of continental landmasses) acts as a catalyst in chemically transforming atmospheric carbon dioxide and silicates into carbonates and sand. Different life-forms will expose varying amounts of silicate surface to rain and, thus, influence this terrestrial silicate weathering rate.[14] The

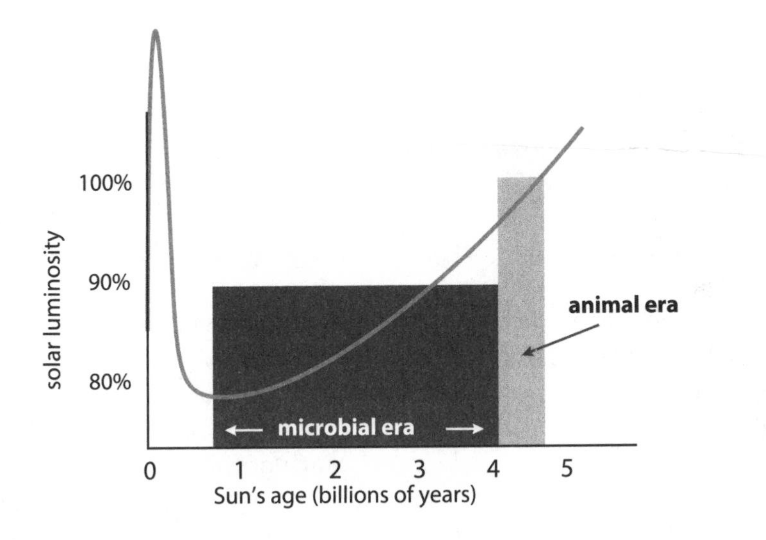

Figure 16.3: Sun's Luminosity throughout Its History
Credit: Hugh Ross

roots of trees, for example, break up silicate rock, resulting in exposure of more silicate rock surfaces to falling rain.

Marine silicate weathering and oceanic crust weathering also help remove atmospheric carbon.[15] The carbon dioxide released from organic matter embedded in seafloor sediments and atmospheric carbon dioxide dissolved in seawater react with the silicates in the sediments to form carbonates and sand.[16]

As oxygen levels in Earth's atmosphere increased throughout Earth's history (see "Deep Oxygen Cycle"), so did the quantity of dissolved oxygen in Earth's oceans. This ocean oxygenation led to a decrease in production of nonkaolinite clays and an increase in marine silicate weathering.[17] Thus, the rate of carbon dioxide removal from Earth's atmosphere accelerated throughout life's history, helping to compensate for the Sun's ongoing brightening.

Rapid burial of living and dead organisms by floods, landslides, volcanic eruptions, and earthquakes prevents the tissues and organs of dead organisms from decaying and thereby releasing carbon dioxide and methane into the atmosphere. Tectonic forces operating in Earth's crust, over time, convert this buried organic material into limestone, coal, and petroleum. The same tectonic forces will, on occasion, expose underground limestone, coal, and petroleum to the surface where they erode, decay, and, in the process, release carbon dioxide and methane to the atmosphere.

Geochemists can now measure the total quantity of carbon removed from and added to Earth's atmosphere by the shallow carbon cycle throughout life's history. While the quantities removed and added vary through time, slightly more carbon has been removed, on average, than added. This net carbon removal from Earth's atmosphere compensates for much, though not all, of the Sun's ongoing luminosity increase.

The deep carbon cycle is necessary to compensate for the remaining luminosity increase—that which is not compensated for by the deep water and deep oxygen cycles. As seawater circulates over seafloor basalts, it contacts hydrothermal systems and reacts. In this reaction, basalts release calcium ions, which precipitate calcium carbonate.[18] Much of this calcium carbonate ends up being subducted into the mantle, thus removing carbon from Earth's hydrosphere. Likewise, much of the carbonate material manufactured by marine silicate weathering ends up being tectonically subducted into the mantle.

Ongoing subduction of tectonic plates into the mantle continues to remove carbon from the atmosphere and hydrosphere. Meanwhile, carbon is returned from the mantle to the atmosphere and hydrosphere, at times, through volcanic eruptions. Measurements show that the amount of carbon returned this way falls slightly below the amount removed from Earth's atmosphere and transported back into the crust and mantle.[19] As it turns out, this slight imbalance contributes to perfectly compensating for the Sun's increasing luminosity, and life throughout the past 3.8 billion years is the beneficiary.

Deep Oxygen Cycle

Photosynthesis is a chemical process whereby vegetation uses captured sunlight to convert carbon dioxide and water into sugars and oxygen. Similar chemical reactions operate in subducted oceanic tectonic plates that use organic carbon compounds to produce oxygen.

Given that living things prefer carbon-12 to carbon-13, researchers have been able to determine, via carbon isotope ratio analysis, that no less than one-fifth and possibly as much as one-half of the organic carbon subducted from the crust and delivered to the mantle remains there. It is not returned to Earth's surface and crust through volcanic eruptions.[20]

This unrecycled organic carbon undergoes a graphitization process, with oxygen as a by-product. Here is the chemistry behind graphitization:[21]

> As an oceanic tectonic plate slides underneath a continental plate, water and dissolved carbon dioxide in deep seawater are subducted into the mantle with it. Some of this water and carbon dioxide reacts to form formaldehyde and molecular oxygen ($H_2O + CO_2 \quad CH_2O + O_2$). As the formaldehyde sinks deeper into the mantle, it decomposes into water and carbon ($CH_2O \quad H_2O + C$). This carbon (C), in the form of graphite, encounters increasing pressure and temperature as it descends to mantle depths of 150–800 kilometers (93–500 miles). At such depths, pressure and temperature transform graphite into diamonds.

A similar set of reactions occurs when carbonates (where CO_3 takes the place of CO_2) are subducted into the mantle. One outcome of this chemistry is the production of molecular oxygen (O_2).

Evidence for the operation of this deep oxygen cycle comes from the diamonds extracted from kimberlite and lamproite pipes—deep narrow cones of solidified magma that connect partially melted mantle (below 150 kilometers) with dormant or active volcanoes. Kimberlite pipes are found exclusively in rocks that date back to the Archean eon (2.5–4.0 billion years ago). Lamproite pipes are found in rocks of various ages.

Natural diamonds are found only in kimberlite and lamproite rocks. Laboratory experiments affirm that graphite is transformed into diamonds under the pressure and temperature conditions existing at mantle depths of 150–800 kilometers.[22] These experiments also show that at pressure and temperature conditions representative of mantle depths greater than 800 kilometers, diamonds rapidly degrade into graphite.

If not for the subduction of organic carbon into Earth's mantle at just-right times in just-right amounts in Earth's history, the quantity of oxygen in Earth's atmosphere would be insufficient to sustain animal life, especially avian and mammalian. The burial of an enormous amount of organic carbon is widely cited as a cause of the sudden rise in Earth's atmospheric oxygen 2.45–2.32 billion years ago, an occurrence referred to as the Great Oxidation Event.[23] Only this extra boost of oxygen, added to the oxygen produced by photosynthetic life, could overcome the oxygen loss from oxygenation (rusting) of metals in Earth's crust and mantle.

Another event, known as the Great Unconformity, provided yet another significant oxygen boost. Just prior to the Avalon explosion—575 million years ago when the first animals appeared—a combination of continental crust erosion and oceanic sediment subduction of unprecedented magnitude occurred.[24] This event is associated with a set of large global oxygen isotope excursions (deviations from the norm).[25]

Like the Great Oxidation Event, the Great Unconformity injected an enormous quantity of oxygen into the atmosphere through a massive and efficient subduction of organic carbon into Earth's mantle. When this event occurred, the oxygen quantity in Earth's atmosphere jumped from 1% or less up to 8%. Just before the time of the Cambrian explosion 543 million years ago, another major continental erosion event coupled with oceanic sediment subduction led to a jump in the atmospheric oxygen level from 8 to 10%.

The 8% level is the minimum required for the existence of large-bodied animals that lack digestive tracts and internal organs (the Avalon animals, e.g., sponges and jellyfish). The 10% level is the minimum required for animals with complex internal organs (the Cambrian animals). One of the great marvels of life history is that Avalon and Cambrian animals representing several Avalon phyla and 30+ Cambrian phyla appeared in what may be considered a geologic "instant" after each of these oxygen levels was attained.[26]

Snowball Events

What led to these enormous boosts in atmospheric oxygen has long been a mystery, but recent studies in tectonics history have finally revealed answers. Just prior to the Great Oxygenation Event and the Great Unconformity, unparalleled tectonic and erosion events scoured massive amounts of landmass off the continents and dumped them onto oceanic tectonic plates. Through this deposition, vast amounts of organic carbon were subducted into the mantle. This subduction led to a dramatic rise in oxygen and a drastic drop in atmospheric carbon dioxide.

The enormous loss of an important greenhouse gas brought on significant global cooling. The temperature drop became so extreme as to give rise to "snowball events," epochs in Earth's history when thick ice sheets covered more than 80% of Earth's surface for several million years. Only greatly accelerated rates of oceanic plate subduction can account for such dramatic decreases in atmospheric carbon dioxide, increases in atmospheric oxygen, and subsequent temperature drops to snowball levels.

This exceptional acceleration required an unusual cascade of circumstances. Igneous rocks that characterize oceanic plates contain few hydrated minerals and, therefore, move slowly. Sedimentary plates, on the other hand, are wet with abundant hydrated minerals and, therefore, move relatively rapidly. Sediments at the juncture of two tectonic plates act as a lubricant to facilitate the sliding of one plate beneath another.

As cooling continued and continental ice sheets grew thicker and more extensive, the weight and flow of ice precipitated massive tectonic and erosion events that greatly enhanced the weathering and erosion of the continents. As a result, even more sediments were deposited onto the continental shelves (the shallow water seafloors off the coasts of continents). The extra load of sediments further lubricated the interfaces between descending and overriding tectonic plates and, at the same time, accelerated continental collisions, which led to the formation of long ranges of high mountains such as the Andes. The ongoing formation of long ranges of high, steep-sided mountains accelerated erosion, delivering an even greater load of sediments to the interfaces between tectonic plates. Consequently, snowball events spurred the removal of a large fraction of carbon dioxide from the atmosphere and injected an equally large fraction of oxygen into the atmosphere.

Snowball events have occurred four times in Earth's history:

- Huronian Glaciation, 2,450–2,320 million years ago
- Sturtian Glaciation, 715–680 million years ago
- Marinoan Glaciation, 650–635 million years ago
- Gaskiers Glaciation, 579.9–579.6 million years ago

Geophysicists Stephan Sobolev and Michael Brown explained in a paper published in *Nature* that these four snowball events played a crucial role in sustaining the more than three-billion-year history of Earth's plate tectonic activity.[27] They played an equally crucial role in helping to compensate for the brightening Sun and in boosting atmospheric oxygen, but they would have been disastrous to life had they been timed slightly differently.

If the snowball events had occurred any earlier in Earth's history, the Sun would have been too dim to prevent Earth's entire surface from being covered by thick ice sheets. Any life on Earth would have been extinguished, and ice would have remained on Earth for far longer time periods. On the other hand, if the snowball events had occurred later, the brighter Sun would have shortened the duration of each event and limited the ice coverage. Less atmospheric oxygen would have been produced, and more carbon dioxide would have remained in Earth's atmosphere, making Earth's surface too hot for life. Furthermore, the level of plate tectonic activity would have been diminished.

Thus, either all Earth's life would have been permanently exterminated or the abundance, diversity, and complexity of Earth's life would have been severely diminished.

The four snowball events are the greatest "catastrophes" Earth's life has experienced in its history. Yet without them, or apart from their precise timing, it seems more than doubtful anyone would be here to learn about them.

Layers of Certainty

Though for millennia humans could only theorize about what existed in the depths below their feet, knowledge of the materials, structure, and depths of diverse layers and dynamic interactions are now being revealed through modern scientific endeavors. The discoveries don't only reveal what is below and how it has existed and persisted through the history of the planet. They provide a logical reason behind what otherwise appear to be natural disasters, the transforming of cataclysmic events into necessary measures for the ongoing transformation of Earth's atmosphere that life requires. More scientific discovery is giving greater revelation to the inner workings of the Earth's crust and its connection to the life-forms that depend on its composition and function.

Just-Right Interiors Everywhere

The interior features of the universe, the Laniakea Supercluster, Virgo Cluster, Local Group, Milky Way Galaxy, local galactic neighborhood, Sun, solar system, Moon, and Earth that converge to make the existence of humans and global civilization possible boggle the imagination. On every size scale observed, interior fine-tuning appears both essential and favorable to a vast diversity of life—and the entire age of the universe is required for all these interior features to come together.

How much longer can they be sustained? What does the evident precision imply about the universe, Earth, and human life? What profound questions does this towering cumulation of coincidences raise? These topics are the focus of the concluding chapter.

Chapter 17

Interior Design Implications

The latest scientific literature provides an increasing wealth of evidence for the explanatory and predictive power of a robust anthropic principle. Previous studies of the principle have focused predominantly on the physics and physical features of the universe.[1] For this book I chose to explore recent discoveries about the interior characteristics of the universe and its component parts, the features that relate specifically to making human existence and flourishing possible. The intent is to inspire, as well as to inform.

My hope is that evidence for the exquisite fine-tuning observed at all astronomical levels, from the farthest reaches of the cosmos to the ground beneath our feet, arouses a profound sense of awe and wonder. My greater hope is that this awe and wonder will inspire readers to ponder the deep questions raised by a close-up glimpse of nature's unfolding story.

How Much Preparation

The interior designs described in each chapter resemble, in some ways, a home's interior designs. They reflect thoughtful planning and preparation, and they tend to change somewhat over time. To provide for the residents' comfort and well-being for as long as they may stay, designs require an investment of resources and time.

In one major respect, however, this home analogy breaks down. In nearly all cases, the time of construction and preparation for habitation represents a small fraction of the total time in which a home can or will be occupied—even if it doesn't feel that way to persons waiting for what may seem endless construction delays. For the universe, however, the reverse is true. The time window for human habitability and thriving civilization represents only the narrowest sliver of the universe's total longevity.

As a number of environmental crises make abundantly clear today, the time window for global high-technology civilization may be as brief as a few tens of thousands of years, at most, though more likely a bit closer to ten thousand.[2]

More Fine-Tuning or Less?

Those who pay attention to the scientific literature can attest to the progress of research. Daily, new data accumulates, more than any one researcher in the investigative quest can keep track of or digest. The challenge I faced in writing this book was determining which of the compelling anthropocentric design evidences to include and which to let go, for brevity's sake.

Design, to use the word so commonly seen in the literature, increasingly appears ubiquitous. There appears to be no end to the evidence of fine-tuning and design coming from scientific discovery. Yet, design was evident even a few thousand years ago, as recorded in ancient writings about a man named Job, who commented on the long list of evidences drawn from observation of nature's realm. His comment still echoes today: "These are but the outer fringe of his works."[3] Job rightly discerned a Designer behind all the evidence in the natural realm. Considering all the scientific exploration humans have done over the past four thousand years, we've gained deeper glimpses of the Fine Tuner's works, though only glimpses, with infinitely more to see and understand.

Questions to Ponder

I'd like to pose a few questions that the findings presented in this book lead to:

1. How firmly would you say the anthropic principle has been established, to date?
2. How useful do you think the anthropic principle can be in guiding future scientific research?
3. How "anthropic" does the principle now seem, in light of increasing evidence?
4. What are we to make of the apparently narrow time window during which the fine-tuned features that permit our existence—and the existence of our global civilization—opens and closes?
5. What can we deduce from the fine-tuning about the attributes of the Tuner?
6. Can we discern the Tuner's purpose(s) for crafting the universe as it is?

Discerning Purpose

A famous and wise king once said that in addition to providing for our existence and well-being for a time on this Earth, "[The Tuner] has also planted eternity in every human heart."[4] Could this "seed" explain why atheists, agnostics, deists, and others who acknowledge no personal Creator behind all the visible design features nevertheless tend to affirm, and rightly so, that their lives have ultimate meaning and purpose or that humanity has hope?

Something else is written on the heart of human beings: an awareness that something is missing, something is wrong, something that no amount of self-improvement or self-distraction can ever fully quell.[5]

What if the One whose planning, power, and design that made our existence possible also made a way for us to discover the purpose in our life? Isn't it reasonable that such an exceptional Tuner cares enough to also provide humans a way to discover these answers, to figure out what's been missing? Though the answers to humanity's questions about the workings of the universe, the Milky Way Galaxy, black holes, the solar system, and Earth's interior once seemed impossible to know, they are now undeniably discernible.

Isn't it reasonable to imagine that the One whose planning, power, and fine-tuned precision made our human existence possible also cares enough to provide for us that which we cannot provide for ourselves—a way to access that perfect, enduring, peaceful, purposeful, relational "home" *beyond* the constraints of the universe, the true home every human heart yearns for? Doesn't this offer seem too good and too convincing for anyone who has seriously examined the evidence to turn down? In all my studies of science, my readings of global wisdom literature, and my philosophical ponderings, I've become convinced that the Way to this eternal home is the Person who fine-tuned the universe and Earth. The Way has a name, and that name can be found in the pages of the New Testament.[6]

Appendix

Solar Elemental Abundance—Rocky Planet Configuration Link

Appendix summary: *The solar system is unique among all known planetary systems in that its rocky planets orbit so distantly from its host star. The Sun's rocky planets are also exceptionally dense and massive. The unique properties of the Sun that contribute to making life possible on one of its system's rocky planets can now be explained by an unusually large transfer of angular momentum and refractory elements from the Sun to its rocky planets.*

The Sun's relative abundance of elements is unlike that of any other known star. Likewise, the Sun's array of rocky planets is unlike that of any other known planetary system. Several astronomical studies, when considered together, now explain the link between the Sun's unique abundance of elements and the unique configuration of its rocky planets.

In one study, a team of astronomers led by Jorge Meléndez compared the Sun's elemental abundance with that of 21 stars closely resembling the Sun.[1] They found that the Sun is 20% more depleted than typical in its ratio of refractory elements to volatile elements. A follow-up study of 79 Sunlike stars affirmed this finding.[2]

In particular, the quantity of lithium observed on a star's surface (photosphere) holds special importance. It serves as a sensitive indicator of the star's interior characteristics and composition. Stars like the Sun are unable to manufacture lithium in their nuclear cores. What lithium they acquired in their formation process came from the nucleosynthesis that occurred during the first few minutes after the cosmic origin event. Reactions operating within the stellar core and radiative zone act to destroy the lithium.

Elemental analysis of primitive solar system meteorites indicates lithium was relatively abundant in the gas cloud out of which the Sun and its planetary system formed. However, the amount of lithium on the Sun's surface[3] is far below that of the primordial solar system, roughly 170 times below that level.[4] This large difference is exceptional, given the Sun's relative youth—just 4.567 billion years of age.[5]

Some degree of lithium depletion is expected because temperatures as (relatively) low as 2.5 million K (equivalent to 2.5 million degrees Celsius above absolute zero) will destroy lithium. For Sunlike stars, such temperatures are encountered at the top of the innermost radiative zone, just below the base of the convective zone.

Meanwhile, astronomical observations have established a strong inverse correlation between stellar rotation rate and lithium depletion. Stellar rotation affects the mixing efficiency of stellar matter at the boundary between the convective and radiative zones. The higher the rotation rate, the more effectively stellar material in the convection zone, in the form of penetrating plumes, is blocked from entering the radiative zone.

The influence of the Sun's changing rotation rate on plume penetration explains the helioseismology data (see chapter 9 and figure 9.2).[6] It also explains observations of the Sun's magnetic field and the Sun's magnetic activity.[7]

Stellar rotation rates decrease as stars age. For stars of similar mass to the Sun, the observed rate of rotation accurately reveals the age of the star. The older the star and the slower its rotation, the less lithium that remains in the star's photosphere (surface).

The Sun differs, however, from the typical relationship between a star's age and surface lithium abundance. A team of astronomers led by Marília Carlos measured the surface lithium abundance in 77 stars that most closely matched the Sun's effective temperature, surface gravity, and metallicity.[8] Their research affirmed a strong linear correlation between stellar age and surface lithium depletion, but the Sun's surface lithium abundance proved far lower than that of any star in its age range of 4.1–5.1 billion years.

Carlos's team noted that the most lithium-depleted stars in their sample of solar-like stars also had the fewest refractory elements. In this respect they resembled the Sun. But this finding led to a question: How can such relatively metal-rich stars be so poor in terms of refractory elements?

In 2004, another team of astronomers, led by Garik Israelian, compared the surface lithium abundance of 79 stars that host planets with 38 stars that host none.[9] They noticed greater lithium depletion in planet-hosting stars with effective temperatures between 5,600–5,850 K, closely matching the Sun's effective temperature of 5,772 K. This severe lithium depletion, they explained, is the expected outcome of the transfer of angular momentum from a star to its protoplanetary disk and eventual planets. Such angular momentum transfer will have a braking effect on rotation in the planet-hosting star's convective zone, thus deepening the zone and leading to greater penetration of plumes into the radiative zone.

In 2006, a parallel study by astronomers Yu-Qin Chen and Gang Zhao affirmed that planet-hosting solar-type stars manifest greater lithium depletion than stars without planets.[10] In a 2009 follow-up study of 451 stars with effective temperatures similar to the Sun's, Israelian and his colleagues found that 50% of solar-analogue stars with no detected planets have, on average, 10 times more surface lithium than solar-analogue, planet-bearing stars.[11]

In 2019, Carlos's team clarified that the key difference maker is not just whether a star hosts planets, but what *kinds* of planets it hosts.[12] Compared to the 3,573 other currently known planetary systems,[13] the solar system is unique in that it hosts large high-density rocky planets orbiting at relatively large distances. The solar system began with five rocky planets, one of which, Theia, merged with the primordial Earth. The four that remain, Mercury, Venus, Earth, and Mars, are relatively dense at 5.427, 5.243, 5.514, and 3.934 grams per cubic centimeter (g/cc), respectively. They orbit the Sun at distances of 57.9, 108.2, 149.6, and 227.9 million kilometers, respectively. Their masses equal 0.3301, 4.8675, 5.9724, and 0.6417 trillion trillion kilograms, respectively. These values can be compared and contrasted with the averages for known extrasolar rocky planets: 4.171 g/cc, 7.96-million-kilometer orbital distance, and 3.169 trillion trillion kilograms.[14]

The solar system has the second highest total mass of rocky planets of any known planetary system, exceeded only by the TRAPPIST-1 system.[15] The seven TRAPPIST-1 planets, however, orbit their host star at distances ranging from only 1.73–9.27 million kilometers, where the most massive planet in the system is only 15% more massive than Earth and 275 times less massive than Jupiter. Furthermore, five of the seven TRAPPIST-1 planets are not actually rocky. They possess very thick "envelopes of volatiles in the form of thick atmospheres, oceans, or ice."[16] Therefore, the solar system differs from other known planetary systems in both the quantity of refractory elements and of angular momentum transferred from the host star to its system of rocky planets. (The angular momentum transfer is roughly determined by the masses and orbital distances of the planets.)

Astronomers now understand that the Sun's exceptionally low abundance of lithium and refractory elements likely explains the Sun's unique system of rocky planets (see chapter 10). One team of astronomers concluded their research paper by saying the peculiar solar elemental composition "would imply that solar-like stars with planetary systems similar to our own are a relatively rare occurrence."[17]

The Sun is the only star known to possess rocky planets that orbit at distances ranging from 50 million to 250 million kilometers. Typically, the closer a planet is to its host star, the more its light elements evaporate due to the heat and radiation of the star. Thus, the farther a planet is from its host star, the less dense it will be. Yet, despite the much greater orbital distances of the Sun's rocky planets by comparison with rocky exoplanets, the Sun's rocky planets are denser on average (see chapter 10). This anomalous density is explained by the massive transfer of refractory elements from the Sun to its rocky planets. The much greater orbital distances of our solar system planets and the transfer of an unusually high abundance of refractory elements contribute in a major way to the possible existence of advanced life on one of the Sun's rocky planets.

The Sun's low abundance of lithium and refractory elements, together with the Sun's mass and age, help keep the Sun's flaring activity level so extremely low.[18] These solar features help account for the Sun's current exceptionally low levels of short ultraviolet and x-ray radiation. Global, high-technology civilization on Earth is a possibility only because the levels and intensities of flares, and of short ultraviolet and x-ray radiation, are extremely low.

Notes

Chapter 1: The Anthropic Principle

1. "Neil deGrasse Tyson, (caught on camera): The Universe Is Trying to Kill You," interview outtake, Big Think Mentor, June 27, 2013, bigthink.com/big-think-mentor/neil-degrasse-tyson-caught-on-camera-the-universe-is-trying-to-kill-you.
2. Fraser Cain (host) with Phil Plait (guest), "The Universe Is Trying to Kill You," *Astronomy Cast*, ep. 343, May 2014, astronomycast.com/2014/05/ep-343-the-universe-is-trying-to-kill-you/.
3. If the universe has a flat geometry, or if dark energy is a positive constant (both affirmed by measurements—see chapter 2), then the universe will continue to expand. As it expands it cools and the energy flow from hot to cold bodies in the universe diminishes. Eventually, the flow of heat from hot to cold bodies becomes so minuscule that work and life is no longer possible.
4. Philippe Claeys, Jean-Georges Casier, and Stanley V. Margolis, "Microtektites and Mass Extinctions: Evidence for a Late Devonian Asteroid Impact," *Science* 257, no. 5073 (August 21, 1992): 1102–1104, doi:10.1126/science.257.5073.1102; Kurt H. Kjær et al., "A Large Impact Crater beneath Hiawatha Glacier in Northwest Greenland," *Science Advances* 4, no. 11 (November 14, 2018): id. eaar8173, doi:10.1126/sciadv.aar8173; Joseph Scott Stuart and Richard P. Binzel, "Bias-Corrected Population, Size, Distribution, and Impact Hazard for the Near-Earth Objects," *Icarus* 170, no. 2 (August 2004): 295–311, doi:10.1016/j.icarus.2004.03.018.
5. Manasvi Lingam and Abraham Loeb, "Risks for Life on Habitable Planets from Superflares of Their Host Stars," *Astrophysical Journal* 848, no. 1 (October 10, 2017): id. 41, doi:10.3847/1538-4357/aa8e96.
6. Brandon Carter, "Large Number Coincidences and the Anthropic Principle in Cosmology," in M. S. Longair, ed., *Confrontation of Cosmological Theories with Observational Data*, IAU Symposium 63, Copernicus Symposium II, Krakow, Poland, September 10–12, 1973 (Dordrecht, Netherlands: D. Reidel Publishing, 1974), 291–298; John D. Barrow and Frank J. Tipler, *The Anthropic Cosmological Principle* (New York: Oxford University Press, 1986).
7. Marcelo Gleiser has appeared in many television documentaries and written three best-selling books: *The Dancing Universe: From Creation Myths to the Big Bang* (Hanover, NH: Dartmouth College Press, 1998); *The Prophet and the Astronomer: Apocalyptic Science and the End of the World* (New York: W. W. Norton, 2003); and *A Tear at the Edge of Creation: A Radical New Vision for Life in an Imperfect Universe* (New York: Free Press, 2010). In his native country, he is as famous as Carl Sagan ever was in the United States.

8. Marcelo Gleiser, "Drake Equation for the Multiverse: From the String Landscape to Complex Life," *International Journal of Modern Physics D* 19, no. 08n10 (August 2010): 1299–1308, doi:10.1142/S0218271810017949.
9. Gleiser, "Drake Equation," 1299.
10. Geraint F. Lewis and Luke A. Barnes, "The Trouble with 'Puddle Thinking': A User's Guide to the Anthropic Principle," *Proceedings and Journal of the Royal Society of New South Wales* 154, part 1 (June 2021): 6–11, ISSN 0035-9173/21/010006-06.
11. Richard Swinburne, "Argument from the Fine-Tuning of the Universe," in *Physical Cosmology and Philosophy*, ed. John Leslie (New York: Macmillan, 1990), 165; William Lane Craig, "Barrow and Tipler on the Anthropic Principle vs. Divine Design," *British Journal for the Philosophy of Science* 38, no. 3 (September 1988): 389–395, doi:10.1093/bjps/39.3.389.
12. Hugh Ross, *The Creator and the Cosmos: How the Latest Scientific Discoveries Reveal God*, 4th ed. (Covina, CA: RTB Press, 2018), 181–198.

Chapter 2: Exterior Design Features

1. Hugh Ross, *The Creator and the Cosmos: How the Latest Scientific Discoveries Reveal God*, 4th ed. (Covina, CA: RTB Press, 2018); Hugh Ross, *Why the Universe Is the Way It Is* (Grand Rapids, MI: Baker Books, 2008); Hugh Ross, *Improbable Planet: How Earth Became Humanity's Home* (Grand Rapids, MI: Baker Books, 2016); Hugh Ross, *More Than a Theory: Revealing a Testable Model for Creation* (Grand Rapids, MI: Baker Books, 2009); Hugh Ross, *Hidden Treasures in the Book of Job: How the Oldest Book in the Bible Answers Today's Scientific Questions* (Grand Rapids, MI: Baker Books, 2011).
2. Stephen Hawking and Roger Penrose, "The Singularities of Gravitational Collapse and Cosmology," *Proceedings of the Royal Society A* 314, no. 1519 (January 27, 1970): 529–548, doi:10.1098/rspa.1970.0021; Arvind Borde, Alan H. Guth, and Alexander Vilenkin, "Inflationary Spacetimes Are Incomplete in Past Directions," *Physical Review Letters* 90, no. 15 (April 18, 2003): id. 151031, doi:10.1103/PhysRevLett.90.151301; Aron C. Wall, "The Generalized Second Law Implies a Quantum Singularity Theorem," *Classical and Quantum Gravity* 30 (July 12, 2013): id. 165003, doi:10.1088/0264-9381/30/16/165003; Ross, *Creator and the Cosmos*, 111–122.
3. Masataka Fukugita and P. J. E. Peebles, "The Cosmic Energy Inventory," *Astrophysical Journal* 616, no. 2 (December 1, 2004): 643–668, doi:10.1086/425155; Gary Hinshaw et al., "Nine-Year *Wilkinson Microwave Anisotropy Probe (WMAP)* Observations: Cosmological Parameter Results," *Astrophysical Journal Supplement Series* 208, no. 2 (October 2013): id. 19, doi:10.1088/0067-0049/208/2/19; Planck Collaboration, "*Planck* 2018 Results. VI. Cosmological Parameters," *Astronomy and Astrophysics* 641 (September 2020): id. A6, doi:10.1051/0004-6361/201833910.
4. Hinshaw et al., "Nine-Year *(WMAP)* Observations," id. 19; Planck Collaboration, "*Planck* 2018 Results. VI.," id. A6; Ariel G. Sánchez et al., "The Clustering of Galaxies in the Completed SDSS-III Baryon Oscillation Spectroscopic Survey: Cosmological Implications of the Configuration-Space Clustering Wedges," *Monthly Notices of the Royal Astronomical Society* 464, no. 2 (January 2017): 1640–1658, doi.org/10.1093/mnras/stw2443; Lu Chen, Qing-Guo Huang, and Ke Wang, "New Cosmological Constraints with Extended-Baryon Oscillation Spectroscopic Survey DR14 Quasar Sample," *European Physical Journal C* 77, no. 11 (November 2017): id. 762, doi:10.1140/epjc/s10052-017-5344-1.
5. Ross, *Why the Universe Is the Way It Is*, 27–41; Ross, *Creator and the Cosmos*, 45–63.
6. Alexander von Boetticher et al., "The EBLM Project: III. A Saturn-Size Low-Mass Star

at the Hydrogen-Burning Limit," *Astronomy and Astrophysics* 604 (August 2017): id. L6, doi:10.1051/0004-6361/201731107.

7. Binsen Zhang et al., "The Distance and Size of the Red Hypergiant NML Cygni from VLBA and VLA Astrometry," *Astronomy and Astrophysics* 544 (August 2012): id. A42, doi:10.1051/0004-6361/201219587.
8. Simone Aiola et al., "The Atacama Cosmology Telescope: DR4 Maps and Cosmological Parameters," *Journal of Cosmology and Astroparticle Physics* 2020, no. 12 (December 2020): id. 047, doi:10.1088/1475-7516/2020/12/047; Hinshaw et al., "Nine-Year *(WMAP)* Observations," id. 19; Planck Collaboration, "*Planck* 2015 Results. XIII. Cosmological Parameters," *Astronomy and Astrophysics* 594 (October 2016): id. A13, p. 47, doi:10.1051/0004-6361/201525830.
9. Ross, *Improbable Planet*, 166–168.
10. Ross, *Why the Universe Is the Way It Is*, 43–56.
11. Hinshaw et al., "Nine-Year *(WMAP)* Observations," id. 19; Planck Collaboration, "*Planck* 2015 Results. XIII.," id. A13; Sánchez et al., "Clustering of Galaxies," doi:10.1093/mnras/stw2443; Aiola et al., "Atacama Cosmology Telescope," id. 047.
12. Sánchez et al., "Clustering of Galaxies," 1640–1658; Beth A. Reid et al., "Cosmological Constraints from the Clustering of the Sloan Digital Sky Survey DR7 Luminous Red Galaxies," *Monthly Notices of the Royal Astronomical Society* 404, no. 1 (May 2010): 60–85, doi:10.1111/j.1365-2966.2010.16276.x; Max Tegmark et al., "Cosmological Constraints from the SDSS Luminous Red Galaxies," *Physical Review D* 74, no. 12 (December 15, 2006): id. 123507, doi:10.1103/PhysRevD.74.123507.
13. Planck Collaboration, "*Planck* 2018 Results. VI.," id. A6.
14. Hinshaw et al., "Nine-Year *(WMAP)* Observations," id. 19.
15. Aiola et al., "Atacama Cosmology Telescope," id. 047.
16. Narges Rashidi and Kourosh Nozari, "Gauss-Bonnet Inflation after Planck2018," *Astrophysical Journal* 890, no. 1 (February 10, 2020): id. 58, doi:10.3847/1538-4357/ab6a10; Planck Collaboration, "*Planck* 2018 Results. X. Constraints on Inflation," *Astronomy and Astrophysics* 641 (September 2020): id. A10, doi:10.1051/0004-6361/201833887; Hinshaw et al., "Nine-Year *(WMAP)* Observations," id. 19; Aiola et al., "Atacama Cosmology Telescope," id. 047; Chen, Huang, and Wang, "New Cosmological Constraints," id. 762.
17. Kevin Dowd et al., "How Unlucky Is 25-Sigma?," preprint, submitted March 29, 2011, arxiv.org/abs/1103.5672.
18. Dowd et al., "How Unlucky."
19. Ross, *Creator and the Cosmos*, 68–72, 111–113, 145–149.
20. Ross, *Improbable Planet*, 24–27, 29–42, 166–168.
21. Hugh Ross, "RTB Design Compendium (2009)," *Today's New Reason to Believe* (blog), Reasons to Believe, November 16, 2010, reasons.org/fine-tuning.

Chapter 3: Large-Scale Cosmic Structures

1. Paul Davies, *The Goldilocks Enigma: Why Our Universe Is Just Right for Life* (Boston: First Mariner Books, 2006), 43–45.
2. Robert Kirshner of Harvard was the first astronomer to refer to the sudden appearance of cosmic homogeneity and uniformity as one observes at greater and greater cosmological distances as the "End of Greatness." See Robert P. Kirshner, *The Extravagant Universe: Exploding Stars, Dark Energy and the Accelerating Cosmos* (Princeton: Princeton University Press, 2002), 71.

3. Suman Sarkar and Biswajit Pandey, "Unravelling the Cosmic Web: An Analysis of the Sloan Digital Sky Survey Data Release 14 with the Local Dimension," *Monthly Notices of the Royal Astronomical Society* 485, no. 4 (June 2019): 4743–4753, doi:10.1093/mnras/stz499; Morag I. Scrimgeour et al., "The WiggleZ Dark Energy Survey: The Transition to Large-Scale Cosmic Homogeneity," *Monthly Notices of the Royal Astronomical Society* 425, no. 1 (September 2012): 116–134, doi:10.1111/j.1365-2966.2012.21402.x; Felipe Avila et al., "The Angular Scale of Homogeneity in the Local Universe with the SDSS Blue Galaxies," *Monthly Notices of the Royal Astronomical Society* 488, no. 1 (September 2019): 1481–1487, doi:10.1093/mnras/stz1765.
4. Fly through the Cosmic Web (March 10, 2011), youtube.com/watch?v=CMiYj6wIinE; OpenCL NBody Cosmic web 1 (July 31, 2013), youtube.com/watch?v=o0_HBsuZUIk; The Cosmic Web, or: What does the universe look like at a VERY large scale? (November 6, 2010), youtube.com/watch?v=74IsySs3RGU.
5. R. Brent Tully et al., "The Laniakea Supercluster of Galaxies," *Nature* 513, no. 7516 (September 4, 2014): 71–73, doi:10.1038/nature13674.
6. R. Brent Tully et al., "*Cosmicflows–2*: The Data," *Astronomical Journal* 146, no. 4 (October 1, 2013): id. 86, doi:10.1088/0004-6256/146/4/86.
7. R. Brent Tully, Hélène M. Courtois, and Jenny G. Sorce, "Cosmicflows–3," *Astronomical Journal* 152, no. 2 (August 1, 2016): id. 50, doi:10.3847/0004-6256/152/2/50.
8. Gayoung Chon, Hans Böhringer, and Saleem Zaroubi, "On the Definition of Superclusters," *Astronomy and Astrophysics* 575 (March 2015): id. L14, doi:10.1051/0004-6361/201425591.
9. Chon, Böhringer, and Zaroubi, "On the Defintion of Superclusters."
10. Pei-Li Ho and Lin-Wen Chen, "The Star Formation Activity in the Shapley Supercluster," in *Galaxy Mergers in the Evolving Universe*, ASP Conference Series 477, ed. Wei-Hsin Sun et al. (San Francisco: Astronomical Society of the Pacific, 2012), 281–282, aspbooks.org/publications/477/281.pdf; Dominique Proust et al., "The Shapley Supercluster: The Largest Matter Concentration in the Local Universe," *The Messenger* 124 (June 2006): 30–31, eso.org/sci/publications/messenger/archive/no.124-jun06/messenger-no124-30-31.pdf.
11. Proust et al., "Shapley Supercluster," 30.
12. Proust et al., "Shapley Supercluster," 30.
13. Chris P. Haines et al., "Shapley Supercluster Survey: Mapping the Filamentary Network Connecting the Clusters," *Monthly Notices of the Royal Astronomical Society* 481, no. 1 (November 2018): 1055–1074, doi:10.1093/mnras/sty2338.
14. Paola Merluzzi et al., "Shapley Supercluster Survey: Galaxy Evolution from Filaments to Cluster Cores," *Monthly Notices of the Royal Astronomical Society* 446, no. 1 (January 2015): 803–822, doi:10.1093/mnras/stu2085.
15. Haines et al., "Shapley Supercluster Survey," 1055.
16. Ho and Chen, "Star Formation Activity," 281–282.
17. Sandro Bardelli et al., "A Study of the Core of the Shapley Concentration. II. ROSAT Observation of A 3558," *Astronomy and Astrophysics* 305 (January 1996): 435–449, arxiv.org/abs/astro-ph/9506019.
18. R. C. Kraan-Korteweg, A. P. Fairall, and C. Balkowski, "Extragalactic Large-Scale Structures behind the Southern Milky Way. – I. Redshifts Obtained at the SAAO in the Hydra/Antlia Extension," *Astronomy and Astrophysics* 297 (May 1995): 617–635. Preprint available at arxiv.org/pdf/astro-ph/9411089.pdf.
19. A. Finoguenov et al., "A Puzzling Merger in A3266: The Hydrodynamic Picture from *XMM-Newton*," *Astrophysical Journal* 643, no. 2 (June 1, 2006): 790–796, doi:10.1086/503285.

20. Hélène M. Courtois et al., "Cosmography of the Local Universe," *Astronomical Journal* 146, no. 3 (September 2013): id. 69, doi:10.1088/0004-6256/146/3/69.
21. Planck Collaboration, "*Planck* 2013 Results. XXVII. Doppler Boosting of the CMB: Eppur Si Muove," *Astronomy and Astrophysics* 571 (November 2014): id. A27, doi:10.1051/0004-6361/201321556.
22. Roberto Scaramella, Giampaolo Vettolani, and Giovanni Zamorani, "The Distribution of Clusters of Galaxies within 300 Mpc h^{-1} and the Crossover to an Isotropic and Homogeneous Universe," *Astrophysical Journal Letters* 376 (July 20, 1991): L1–L4, doi:10.1086/186089; Tod R. Lauer and Marc Postman, "The Motion of the Local Group with Respect to the 15,000 Kilometer per Second Abell Cluster Inertial Frame," *Astrophysical Journal* 425, no. 2 (April 20, 1994): 418–438, doi:10.1086/173997.
23. Bohdan Paczynski and Tsvi Piran, "A Dipole Moment of the Microwave Background as a Cosmological Effect," *Astrophysical Journal* 364 (December 1, 1990): 341–348, doi:10.1086/169417.
24. M. Jaroszynski and B. Paczynski, "The Cosmic Microwave Background Dipole Cannot Be the Result of the Cosmological Entropy Gradient," *Astrophysical Journal* 448 (August 1, 1995): 488–493, doi:10.1086/175979.
25. Dale D. Kocevski, Christopher R. Mullis, and Harald Ebeling, "The Dipole Anisotropy of the First All-Sky X-Ray Cluster Sample," *Astrophysical Journal* 608, no. 2 (June 20, 2004): 721–730, doi:10.1086/420694.
26. Kocevski, Mullis, and Ebeling, "Dipole Anistropy," 721.
27. Dale D. Kocevski and Harald Ebeling, "On the Origin of the Local Group's Peculiar Velocity," *Astrophysical Journal* 645, no. 2 (July 10, 2006): 1043–1053, doi:10.1086/503666; Khaled Said, Renée C. Kraan-Korteweg, and Lister Staveley-Smith, "The HI Mass Function in the Parkes HI Zone of Avoidance Survey," *Monthly Notices of the Royal Astronomical* Society 486, no. 2 (July 2019): 1796–1804, doi:10.1093/mnras/stz956.
28. T. Mutabazi et al., "The Norma Cluster (ACO 3627) – III. The Distance and Peculiar Velocity via the Near-Infrared K_s-band Fundamental Plane," *Monthly Notices of the Royal Astronomical Society* 439, no. 4 (April 21, 2014): 3666–3682, doi:10.1093/mnras/stu217; Guilhem Lavaux et al., "Cosmic Flow from Two Micron All-Sky Redshift Survey: The Origin of Cosmic Microwave Background Dipole and Implications for CDM Cosmology," *Astrophysical Journal* 709, no. 1 (January 20, 2010): 483–498, doi:10.1088/0004-637X/709/1/483; D. J. Radburn-Smith et al., "Structures in the Great Attractor Region," *Monthly Notices of the Royal Astronomical Society* 369, no. 3 (July 2006): 1131–1142, doi:10.1111/j.1365-2966.2006.10347.x.
29. Kocevski, Mullis, and Ebeling, "Dipole Anisotropy," 721–730; Lavaux et al., "Cosmic Flow from Two Micron All-Sky Redshift Survey," 483–498.
30. R. Brent Tully et al., "Cosmicflows–3: Cosmography of the Local Void," *Astrophysical Journal* 880, no. 1 (July 20, 2019): id. 24, doi:10.3847/1538-4357/ab2597; R. Brent Tully et al., "Our Peculiar Motion Away from the Local Void," *Astrophysical Journal* 676, no. 1 (March 20, 2008): 184, doi:10.1086/527428.
31. Jeffrey E. McClintock and Ronald A. Remillard, "Black Hole Binaries," in *Compact Stellar X-ray Sources*, eds. W. H. G. Lewin and M. van der Klis (Cambridge: Cambridge University Press, 2004), 157, arxiv.org/pdf/astro-ph/0306213.pdf, 10–11.
32. Ohad Shemmer et al., "Near-Infrared Spectroscopy of High-Redshift Active Galactic Nuclei. I. A Metallicity-Accretion Rate Relationship," *Astrophysical Journal* 614, no. 2 (October 20, 2004): 547–557, doi:10.1086/423607.

33. Shemmer et al., "Near-Infrared Spectroscopy," 553.
34. Shemmer et al., "Near-Infrared Spectroscopy," 548.
35. Gabriele Ghisellini et al., "The Blazar S5 0014+813: A Real or Apparent Monster?," *Monthly Notices of the Royal Astronomical Society: Letters* 399, no. 1 (October 2009): L24–L28, doi:10.1111/j.1745-3933.2009.00716.x; F. G. Saturni et al., "Restframe UV-to-Optical Spectroscopy of APM 08279+5255. BL Classification and Black Hole Mass Estimates," *Astronomy and Astrophysics* 617 (September 2018): id. A118, doi:10.1051/0004-6361/201832794.
36. M. J. Valtonen, S. Ciprini, and H. J. Lehto, "On the Masses of OJ287 Black Holes," *Monthly Notices of the Royal Astronomical Society* 427, no. 1 (November 21, 2012): 77–83, doi:10.1111/j.1365-2966.2012.21861.x; Roger W. Romani et al., "A Multi-Wavelength Study of the Host Environment of SMBHB 4C+37.11," *Astrophysical Journal* 780, no. 2 (January 10, 2014): id. 149, doi:10.1088/0004-637X/780/2/149.
37. R. P. Saglia et al., "The Sinfoni Black Hole Survey: The Black Hole Fundamental Plane Revisited and the Paths of (Co)Evolution of Supermassive Black Holes and Bulges," *Astrophysical Journal* 818, no. 1 (February 10, 2016): id. 47, doi:10.3847/0004-637X/818/1/47; Nicholas J. McConnell and Chung-Pei Ma, "Revisiting the Scaling Relations of Black Hole Masses and Host Galaxy Properties," *Astrophysical Journal* 764, no. 2 (February 20, 2013): id. 184, doi:10.1088/0004-637X/764/2/184; John Kormendy and Luis C. Ho, "Coevolution (Or Not) of Supermassive Black Holes and Host Galaxies," *Annual Review of Astronomy and Astrophysics* 51 (August 2013): 511–653, doi:10.1146/annurev-astro-082708-101811.

Chapter 4: The Laniakea Supercluster

1. Jeremy L. Tinker et al., "The Correlation between Halo Mass and Stellar Mass for the Most Massive Galaxies in the Universe," *Astrophysical Journal* 839, no. 2 (April 20, 2017): id. 121, doi:10.3847/1538-4357/aa6845.
2. Christopher S. Reynolds, "Observing Black Holes Spin," *Nature Astronomy* 3, no. 1 (January 8, 2019): 41–47, doi:10.1038/s41550-018-0665-z.
3. Reynolds, "Observing Black Holes Spin," 41–47.
4. Event Horizon Telescope Collaboration, "First M87 Event Horizon Telescope Results. VI. The Shadow of the Supermassive Black Hole," *Astrophysical Journal Letters* 875, no. 1 (April 10, 2019): id. L1, doi:10.3847/2041-8213/ab0ec7; Event Horizon Telescope Collaboration, "First M87 Event Horizon Telescope Results. VI. The Shadow and Mass of the Central Black Hole," *Astrophysical Journal Letters* 875, no. 1 (April 10, 2019): id. L6, doi:10.3847/2041-8213/ab1141.
5. Hooman Davoudiasl and Peter B. Denton, "Ultralight Boson Dark Matter and Event Horizon Telescope Observations of M87*," *Physical Review Letters* 123, no. 2 (July 12, 2019): id. 021102, doi:10.1103/PhysRevLett.123.021102; Event Horizon Telescope Collaboration, "First M87 Event Horizon Telescope Results. VI.," id. L6.
6. Tiziana Di Matteo et al., "Accretion onto the Supermassive Black Hole in M87," *Astrophysical Journal* 582, no. 1 (January 1, 2003): 133–140, doi:10.1086/344504; A. Neronov and Felix A. Aharonian, "Production of TeV Gamma Radiation in the Vicinity of the Supermassive Black Hole in the Giant Radio Galaxy M87," *Astrophysical Journal* 671, no. 1 (December 10, 2007): 85–96, doi:10.1086/522199; Amir Levinson and Frank Rieger, "Variable TeV Emission as a Manifestation of Jet Formation in M87?," *Astrophysical Journal* 730, no. 2 (April 1, 2011): id. 123, doi:10.1088/0004-637X/730/2/123; K. Hada et al., "A Strong Radio Brightening at the Jet Base of M87 during the Elevated Very-High-Energy γ-Ray State in

2012," *Proceedings of the International Astronomical Union* 10, S313 (March 2015): 340–345, doi:10.1017/S174392131500246X.

7. John Linsley, "Evidence for a Primary Cosmic-Ray Particle with Energy 10^{20} eV," *Physical Review Letters* 10, no. 4 (February 15, 1963): 146–168, doi:10.1103/PhysRevLett.10.146.
8. Kenneth Greisen, "End to the Cosmic-Ray Spectrum?," *Physical Review Letters* 16, no. 17 (April 25, 1966): 748–750, doi:10.1103/PhysRevLett.16.748; G. T. Zatsepin and V. A. Kuz'min, "Upper Limit of the Spectrum of Cosmic Rays," *Journal of Experimental and Theoretical Physics Letters* 4 (August 1966): 78–80. Original Russian paper published in *ZhETF Pis'ma* 4, no. 3 (August 1, 1966): 114–117, jetpletters.ac.ru/ps/1624/article_24846.pdf.
9. Laura J. Watson, Daniel J. Mortlock, and Andrew H. Jaffe, "A Bayesian Analysis of the 27 Highest Energy Cosmic Rays Detected by the Pierre Auger Observatory," *Monthly Notices of the Royal Astronomical Society* 418, no. 1 (November 21, 2011): 206–213, doi:10.1111/j.1365-2966.2011.19476.x.
10. D. J. Bird et al., "Detection of a Cosmic Ray with Measured Energy Well beyond the Expected Spectral Cutoff due to Cosmic Microwave Radiation," *Astrophysical Journal* 441 (March 1, 1995): 144–150, doi:10.1086/175344.
11. Pierre Auger Collaboration et al., "Observation of a Large-Scale Anisotropy in the Arrival Directions of Cosmic Rays above 8 x 10^{18} eV," *Science* 357, no. 6357 (September 22, 2017): 1266–1270, doi:10.1126/science.aan4338; Pierre Auger Collaboration et al., "Large-Scale Cosmic-Ray Anisotropies above 4 EeV Measured by the Pierre Auger Observatory," *Astrophysical Journal* 868, no. 1 (November 20, 2018): id. 4, doi:10.3847/1538-4357/aae689.
12. Jihyun Kim et al., "Filaments of Galaxies as a Clue to the Origin of Ultrahigh-Energy Cosmic Rays," *Science Advances* 5, no. 1 (January 2, 2019): eaau8227, doi:10.1126/sciadv.aau8227.
13. Kim et al., "Filaments of Galaxies," 1.
14. Suk Kim et al., "Large-Scale Filamentary Structures around the Virgo Cluster Revisited," *Astrophysical Journal* 833, no. 2 (December 20, 2016): id. 207, doi:10.3847/1538-4357/833/2/207; Kim et al., "Filaments of Galaxies."
15. Kim et al., "Filaments of Galaxies," 1.
16. S. Britzen et al., "A New View on the M 87 Jet Origin: Turbulent Loading Leading to Large-Scale Episodic Wiggling," *Astronomy and Astrophysics* 601 (May 2017): id. A52, doi:10.1051/0004-6361/201629469.
17. Michael Loewenstein et al., "*Chandra* Limits on X-Ray Emission Associated with the Supermassive Black Holes in Three Giant Elliptical Galaxies," *Astrophysical Journal Letters* 555, no. 1 (July 1, 2001): L21–L24, doi:10.1086/323157; Juntai Shen and Karl Gebhardt, "The Supermassive Black Hole and Dark Matter Halo of NGC 4649 (M60)," *Astrophysical Journal* 711, no. 1 (March 1, 2010): 484–494, doi:10.1088/0004-637X/711/1/484.
18. Shen and Gebhardt, "Supermassive Black Hole and Dark Matter Halo," 484–494.
19. Loewenstein et al., "*Chandra* Limits on X-Ray Emission," L21–L24; G. A. Bower et al., "Kinematics of the Nuclear Ionized Gas in the Radio Galaxy M84 (NGC 4374)*," *Astrophysical Journal* 492, no. 2 (January 10, 1998): L111–L114, doi:10.1086/311109.
20. Karl Gebhardt et al., "The Black Hole Mass and Extreme Orbital Structure in NGC 1399," *Astrophysical Journal* 671, no. 2 (December 20, 2007): 1321–1328, doi:10.1086/522938.

Chapter 5: The Virgo Cluster Interior

1. Regina Barber DeGraaff et al., "A Galaxy in Transition: Structure, Globular Clusters, and

Distance to the Star-Forming S0 Galaxy NGC 1533 in Dorado," *Astrophysical Journal* 671, no. 2 (December 2007): 1624–1639, doi:10.1086/523640.
2. Simona Mei et al., "The ACS Virgo Cluster Survey. XIII. SBF Distance Catalog and the Three-Dimensional Structure of the Virgo Cluster*," *Astrophysical Journal* 655, no. 1 (January 20, 2007): 144–162, doi:10.1086/509598.
3. Michael A. Beasley et al., "Evidence for the Disky Origin of Luminous Virgo Dwarf Ellipticals from the Kinematics of Their Globular Cluster Systems*," *Astronomical Journal* 137, no. 6 (June 2009): 5146–5153, doi:10.1088/0004-6256/137/6/5146; Thorsten Lisker, Eva K. Grebel, and Bruno Binggeli, "Virgo Cluster Early-Type Dwarf Galaxies with the Sloan Digital Sky Survey. I. On the Possible Disk Nature of Bright Early-Type Dwarfs," *Astronomical Journal* 132, no. 2 (August 1, 2006): 497–513, doi:10.1086/505045; F. D. Barazza, B. Binggeli, and H. Jergen, "More Evidence for Hidden Spiral and Bar Features in Bright Early-Type Dwarf Galaxies*," *Astronomy and Astrophysics* 391, no. 3 (September 2002): 823–831, doi:10.1051/0004-6361:20020875; John Kormendy, "Families of Ellipsoidal Stellar Systems and the Formation of Dwarf Elliptical Galaxies," *Astrophysical Journal* 295 (August 1, 1985): 73–79, doi:10.1086/163350.
4. Gagandeep S. Anand et al., "The Distance and Motion of the Maffei Group," *Astrophysical Journal Letters* 872, no. 1 (February 10, 2019): id. L4, doi:10.3847/2041-8213/aafee6.
5. Robin L. Fingerhut et al., "The Extinction and Distance of Maffei 2 and a New View of the IC 342/Maffei Group," *Astrophysical Journal* 655, no. 2 (February 1, 2007): 814, doi:10.1086/509862.
6. N. A. Tikhonov and O. A. Galazutdinova, "Does the IC 342/Maffei Galaxy Group Really Exist?," *Astrophysical Bulletin* 73, no. 3 (July 2018): 279–292, doi:10.1134/S1990341318030021.
7. Julianne J. Dalcanton et al., "The ACS Nearby Galaxy Survey Treasury," *Astrophysical Journal Supplement Series* 183, no. 1 (July 2009): 67–108, doi:10.1088/0067-0049/183/1/67.
8. I. D. Karachentsev et al., "Distances to Nearby Galaxies in Sculptor*," *Astronomy and Astrophysics* 404, no. 1 (June 11, 2003): 93–111, doi:10.1051/0004-6361:20030170.
9. Karachentsev et al., "Distances to Nearby Galaxies," 93–111.
10. Gretchen L. H. Harris, Marina Rejkuba, and William E. Harris, "The Distance to NGC 5128 (Centaurus A)," *Publications of the Astronomical Society of Australia* 27, no. 4 (2010): 457–462, doi:10.1071/AS09061.
11. Norbert Bartel, Michael F. Bietenholz, and Michael P. Rupen, "The Core-Jet Radio Source at the Center of M81," *Symposium – International Astronomical Union* 205 (2001): 42, doi:10.1017/S0074180900220378.
12. R. Brent Tully, Hélène M. Courtois, and Jenny G. Sorce, "Cosmicflows-3," *Astronomical Journal* 152, no. 2 (August 1, 2016): id. 50, doi:10.3847/0004-6256/152/2/50.
13. John L. Tonry et al., "The SBF Survey of Galaxy Distances. IV. SBF Magnitudes, Colors, and Distances," *Astrophysical Journal* 546, no. 2 (January 10, 2001): 681–693, doi:10.1086/318301.
14. Benjamin J. Shappee and K. Z. Stanek, "A New Cepheid Distance to the Giant Spiral M101 Based on Image Subtraction of *Hubble Space Telescope*/Advanced Camera for Surveys Observations," *Astrophysical Journal* 733, no. 2 (June 1, 2011): id. 124, doi:10.1088/0004-637X/733/2/124.

Chapter 6: The Local Group Interior

1. I. D. Karachentsev, "The Local Group and Other Neighboring Galaxy Groups," *Astronomical Journal* 129, no. 1 (January 2005): 178–188, doi:10.1086/426368.
2. Joachim Janz et al., "How Elevated Is the Dynamical-to-Stellar Mass Ratio of the

Ultracompact Dwarf S999?," *Monthly Notices of the Royal Astronomical Society* 449, no. 2 (May 2015): 1716–1730, doi:10.1093/mnras/stv389; Christopher P. Ahn et al., "Detection of Supermassive Black Holes in Two Virgo Ultracompact Dwarf Galaxies," *Astrophysical Journal* 839, no. 2 (April 20, 2017): id. 72, doi:10.3847/1538-4357/aa6972.

3. Steffen Mieske et al., "On Central Black Holes in Ultra-Compact Dwarf Galaxies," *Astronomy and Astrophysics* 558 (October 2013): id. A14, doi:10.1051/0004-6361/201322167; Anil C. Seth et al., "A Supermassive Black Hole in an Ultra-Compact Dwarf Galaxy," *Nature* 513, no. 7518 (September 18, 2014): 398–400, doi:10.1038/nature13762; Ahn et al., "Detection of Supermassive Black Holes," id. 72; Henriette Wirth and Kenji Bekki, "Formation of Massive Black Holes in Ultracompact Dwarf Galaxies: Migration of Primordial Intermediate-Mass Black Holes in *N*-Body Simulation," *Monthly Notices of the Royal Astronomical Society* 496, no. 1 (July 2020): 921–932, doi:10.1093/mnras/staa1603.
4. Zhao-Zhou Li et al., "Constraining the Milky Way Mass Profile with Phase-Space Distribution of Satellite Galaxies," *Astrophysical Journal* 894, no. 1 (May 1, 2020): id. 10, doi:10.3847/1538-4357/ab84f0; T. K. Fritz et al., "The Mass of Our Galaxy from Satellite Proper Motions in the *Gaia* Era," *Monthly Notices of the Royal Astronomical Society* 494, no. 4 (June 2020): 5178–5193, doi:10.1093/mnras/staa1040; Thomas M. Callingham et al., "The Mass of the Milky Way from Satellite Dynamics," *Monthly Notices of the Royal Astronomical Society* 484, no. 4 (April 2019): 5453–5467; doi:10.1093/mnras/stz365; Ekta Patel et al., "Estimating the Mass of the Milky Way Using the Ensemble of Classical Satellite Galaxies," *Astrophysical Journal* 857, no. 2 (April 20, 2018): id. 78, doi:10.3847/1538-4357/aab78f; Denis Erkal, Vasily A. Belokurov, and Daniel L. Parkin, "Equilibrium Models of the Milky Way Mass Are Biased High by the LMC," *Monthly Notices of the Royal Astronomical Society* 498, no. 4 (November 2020): 5574–5580, doi:10.1093/mnras/staa2840; Prajwal Raj Kafle et al., "On the Shoulders of Giants: Properties of the Stellar Halo and the Milky Way Mass Distribution," *Astrophysical Journal* 794, no. 1 (October 10, 2014): id. 59, doi:10.1088/0004-637X/794/1/59; Paul J. McMillan, "The Mass Distribution and Gravitational Potential of the Milky Way," *Monthly Notices of the Royal Astronomical Society* 465, no. 1 (February 11, 2017): 76–94, doi:10.1093/mnras/stw2759; Prajwal Raj Kafle et al., "Kinematics of the Stellar Halo and the Mass Distribution of the Milky Way Using Blue Horizontal Branch Stars," *Astrophysical Journal* 761, no. 2 (December 20, 2012): id. 98, doi:10.1088/0004-637X/761/2/98; Robert J. J. Grand et al., "The Effects of Dynamical Substructure on Milky Way Mass Estimates from the High-Velocity Tail of the Local Stellar Halo," *Monthly Notices of the Royal Astronomical Society: Letters* 487, no. 1 (July 2019): L72–L76, doi:10.1093/mnrasl/slz092.
5. J. Veljanoski et al., "Newly Discovered Globular Clusters in NGC 147 and NGC 185 from PAndAS," *Monthly Notices of the Royal Astronomical Society* 435, no. 4 (November 11, 2013): 3654–3666, doi:10.1093/mnras/stt1557; Kohei Hayashi and Masashi Chiba, "The Prolate Dark Matter Halo of the Andromeda Galaxy," *Astrophysical Journal* 789, no. 1 (July 1, 2014): id. 62, doi:10.1088/0004-637X/789/1/62.
6. Ekta Patel et al., "ΛCDM Predictions for the Satellite Population of M33," *Monthly Notices of the Royal Astronomical Society* 480, no. 2 (October 2018): 1883–1897, doi:10.1093/mnras/sty1946; P. R. Hague and M. I. Wilkinson, "The Degeneracy of M33 Mass Modeling and Its Physical Implications," *Astrophysical Journal* 800, no. 1 (February 10, 2015): id. 15, doi:10.1088/0004-637X/800/1/15; Edvige Corbelli, "Dark Matter and Visible Baryons in M33," *Monthly Notices of the Royal Astronomical Society* 342, no. 1 (June 2003): 199–207, doi:10.1046/j.1365-8711.2003.06531.x; A. S. Saburova and A. V. Zasov, "On the Mass and

Density of the Stellar Disk of M33," *Astronomy Letters* 38, no. 3 (March 2012): 139–146, doi:10.1134/S1063773712030048.

7. Denis Erkal et al., "The Total Mass of the Large Magellanic Cloud from the Perturbation on the Orphan Stream," *Monthly Notices of the Royal Astronomical Society* 487, no. 2 (August 2019): 2685–2700, doi:10.1093/mnras/stz1371.
8. Jorge Perñarrubia et al., "A Timing Constraint on the (Total) Mass of the Large Magellanic Cloud," *Monthly Notices of the Royal Astronomical Society: Letters* 456, no. 1 (February 11, 2016): L54–L58, doi:10.1093/mnrasl/slv160.
9. Chervin F. P. Laporte et al., "Response of the Milky Way's Disc to the Large Magellanic Cloud in a First Infall Scenario," *Monthly Notices of the Royal Astronomical Society* 473, no. 1 (January 2018): 1218–1230, doi:10.1093/mnras/stx2146.
10. Marius Cautun et al., "The Aftermath of the Great Collision between Our Galaxy and the Large Magellanic Cloud," *Monthly Notices of the Royal Astronomical Society* 483, no. 2 (February 2019): 2185–2196, doi:10.1093/mnras/sty3084.
11. Peter S. Behroozi, Risa H. Wechsler, and Charlie Conroy, "The Average Star Formation Histories of Galaxies in Dark Matter Halos from $z = 0$–8," *Astrophysical Journal* 770, no. 1 (June 10, 2013): id. 57, doi:10.1088/0004-637X/770/1/57.
12. A. J. Deason et al., "Satellites of LMC-Mass Dwarfs: Close Friendships Ruined by Milky Way Mass Haloes," *Monthly Notices of the Royal Astronomical Society* 453, no. 4 (November 11, 2015): 3568–3574, doi:10.1093/mnras/stv1939.
13. Kenji Bekki and Snežana Stanimirović, "The Total Mass and Dark Halo Properties of the Small Magellanic Cloud," *Monthly Notices of the Royal Astronomical Society* 395, no. 1 (May 2009): 342–350, doi:10.1111/j.1365-2966.2009.14514.x.
14. J. I. Read and D. Erkal, "Abundance Matching with the Mean Star Formation Rate: There Is No Missing Satellite Problem in the Milky Way above $M_{200} \sim 10^9$ M," *Monthly Notices of the Royal Astronomical Society* 487, no. 4 (August 2019): 5799–5812, doi:10.1093/mnras/stz1320.
15. David L. Block et al., "An Almost Head-On Collision as the Origin of Two Off-Centre Rings in the Andromeda Galaxy," *Nature* 443, no. 7113 (November 2006): 832–834, doi:10.1038/nature05184; Gary A. Welch and Leslie J. Sage, "The Interstellar Medium of M32," *Astrophysical Journal* 557, no. 2 (August 20, 2000): 671–680, doi:10.1086/322266.
16. K. M. Howley et al., "Internal Stellar Kinematics of M32 from the SPLASH Survey: Dark Halo Constraints," *Astrophysical Journal* 765, no. 1 (March 1, 2013): id. 65, doi:10.1088/0004-637X/765/1/65.
17. Garry W. Angus et al., "The Potential Role of NGC 205 in Generating Andromeda's Vast Thin Corotating Plane of Satellite Galaxies," *Monthly Notices of the Royal Astronomical Society* 462, no. 3 (November 1, 2016): 3221–3242, doi:10.1093/mnras/stw1822; I. De Looze et al., "*Herschel** and JCMT Observations of the Early-Type Dwarf Galaxy NGC 205," *Monthly Notices of the Royal Astronomical Society* 423, no. 3 (July 2012): 2359–2373, doi:10.1111/j.1365-2966.2012.21044.x.
18. Mario Mateo, "Dwarf Galaxies of the Local Group," *Annual Reviews of Astronomy and Astrophysics* 36 (September 1998): 435–506, doi:10.1146/annurev.astro.36.1.435.
19. Richard Powell, "The Universe within 5 Million Light Years: The Galaxies of the Local Group," An Atlas of the Universe, last updated July 30, 2006, atlasoftheuniverse.com/localgr.html.
20. Joshua D. Simon and Marla Geha, "The Kinematics of the Ultra-Faint Milky Way Satellites: Solving the Missing Satellite Problem," *Astrophysical Journal* 670, no. 1 (November 20,

2007): 313–331, doi:10.1086/521816.

21. Alan W. McConnachie, "The Observed Properties of Dwarf Galaxies in and around the Local Group," *Astronomical Journal* 144, no. 1 (July 1, 2012): id. 4, doi:10.1088/0004-6256/144/1/4.
22. Joshua Simon, "Observing Dwarf Galaxies in the Local Universe," *American Physical Society, April Meeting 2016* 61, no. 6 (presentation, Salt Lake City, UT, April 16–19, 2016): abstract id. E4.00002, meetings.aps.org/Meeting/APR16/Session/E4.2.
23. Azadeh Fattahi et al., "Tidal Stripping and the Structure of Dwarf Galaxies in the Local Group," *Monthly Notices of the Royal Astronomical Society* 476, no. 3 (May 2018): 3816–3836, doi:10.1093/mnras/sty408; Qi Guo et al., "Further Evidence for a Population of Dark-Matter-Deficient Dwarf Galaxies," *Nature Astronomy* 3 (March 2020): 246–251, doi:10.1038/s41550-019-0930-9; Andrew R. Wetzel, Erik J. Tollerud, and Daniel R. Weisz, "Rapid Environmental Quenching of Satellite Dwarf Galaxies in the Local Group," *Astrophysical Journal Letters* 808, no. 1 (July 20, 2015): id. L27, doi:10.1088/2041-8205/808/1/L27; Christopher T. Garling et al., "The Case for Strangulation in Low-Mass Hosts: DDO 113," *Monthly Notices of the Royal Astronomical Society* 492, no. 2 (February 2020): 1713–1730, doi:10.1093/mnras/stz3526.
24. Michelle L. M. Collins, "A Detailed Study of Andromeda XIX, an Extreme Local Analogue of Ultradiffuse Galaxies," *Monthly Notices of the Royal Astronomical Society* 491, no. 3 (January 2020): 3496–3514, doi:10.1093/mnras/stz3252; F. Annibali et al., "The Smallest Scale of Hierarchy Survey (SSH) – I. Survey Description," *Monthly Notices of the Royal Astronomical Society* 491, no. 4 (February 2020): 5101–5125, doi:10.1093/mnras/stz3185.
25. Azadeh Fattahi, Julio F. Navarro, and Carlos S. Frenk, "The Missing Dwarf Galaxies of the Local Group," *Monthly Notices of the Royal Astronomical Society* 493, no. 2 (April 2020): 2596–2605, doi:10.1093/mnras/staa375; Simon and Geha, "Ultra-Faint Milky Way Satellites," 313–331.
26. Annibali et al., "Smallest Scale of Hierarchy Survey," 5101–5125.
27. Shany Danieli, Pieter van Dokkum, and Charlie Conroy, "Hunting Faint Dwarf Galaxies in the Field Using Integrated Light Surveys," *Astrophysical Journal* 856, no. 1 (March 20, 2018): id. 69, doi:10.3847/1538-4357/aaadfb; Fattahi, Navarro, and Frenk, "Missing Dwarf Galaxies," 2596–2605.
28. Azadeh Fattahi et al., "Galaxy Pairs in the Local Group," *Monthly Notices of the Royal Astronomical Society: Letters* 431, no. 1 (May 1, 2013): L73–L77, doi:10.1093/mnrasl/slt011.
29. Alejandro Benítez-Llambay et al., "Dwarf Galaxies and the Cosmic Web," *Astrophysical Journal Letters* 763, no. 2 (February 1, 2013): id. L41, doi:10.1088/2041-8205/763/2/L41.
30. M. Bellazzini et al., "Dwarfs Walking in a Row: The Filamentary Nature of the NGC 3109 Association," *Astronomy and Astrophysics: Letters* 559 (November 2013): id. L11, doi:10.1051/0004-6361/201322744.
31. Alis Deason, Andrew Wetzel, and Shea Garrison-Kimmel, "Satellite Dwarf Galaxies in a Hierarchical Universe: The Prevalence of Dwarf-Dwarf Major Mergers," *Astrophysical Journal* 794, no. 2 (October 20, 2014): id. 115, doi:10.1088/0004-637X/794/2/115.
32. Lulu Liu et al., "How Common Are the Magellanic Clouds?," *Astrophysical Journal* 733, no. 1 (May 20, 2011): id. 62, doi:10.1088/0004-637X/733/1/62.
33. Liu et al., "How Common Are the Magellanic Clouds?," p. 3.
34. Grzegorz Pietrzynski et al., "A Distance to the Large Magellanic Cloud that Is Precise to One Percent," *Nature* 567, no. 7747 (March 14, 2019): 200–203, doi:10.1038/s41586-019-0999-4.
35. A. S. G. Robotham et al., "Galaxy and Mass Assembly (GAMA): In Search of Milky Way Magellanic Cloud Analogues," *Monthly Notices of the Royal Astronomical Society* 424, no. 2

(August 1, 2012): 1448–1453, doi:10.1111/j.1365-2966.2012.21332.x.

36. Dariusz Graczyk et al., "A Distance Determination to the Small Magellanic Cloud with an Accuracy of Better than Two Percent Based on Late-Type Eclipsing Binary Stars," *Astrophysical Journal* 904, no. 1 (November 20, 2020): id. 13, doi:10.3847/1538-4357/abbb2b.
37. Sanjaya Paudel and C. Sengupta, "UGC 4703 Interacting Pair Near the Isolated Spiral Galaxy NGC 2718: A Milky Way Magellanic Cloud Analog," *Astrophysical Journal Letters* 849, no. 2 (November 10, 2017): id. L28, doi:10.3847/2041-8213/aa95bf.
38. Pietrzynski et al., "A Distance to the Large Magellanic Cloud."
39. Kenji Bekki et al., "Explaining the Mysterious Age Gap of Globular Clusters in the Large Magellanic Cloud," *Astrophysical Journal Letters* 610, no. 2 (August 1, 2004): L93–L96, doi:10.1086/423372.
40. Jonathan Diaz and Kenji Bekki, "Constraining the Orbital History of the Magellanic Clouds: A New Bound Scenario Suggested by the Tidal Origin of the Magellanic Stream," *Monthly Notices of the Royal Astronomical Society* 413, no. 3 (May 2011): 2015–2020, doi:10.1111/j.1365-2966.2011.18289.x; Kenji Bekki, "When Was the Large Magellanic Cloud Accreted on to the Galaxy?," *Monthly Notices of the Royal Astronomical Society* 416, no. 3 (September 2011): 2359–2367, doi:10.1111/j.1365-2966.2011.19211.x.
41. K. Bechtol et al., "Eight New Milky Way Companions Discovered in First-Year Dark Energy Survey Data," *Astrophysical Journal* 807, no. 1 (July 1, 2015): id. 50, doi:10.1088/0004-637X/807/1/50; Sergey E. Koposov et al., "Beasts of the Southern Wild: Discovery of Nine Ultra Faint Satellites in the Vicinity of the Magellanic Clouds," *Astrophysical Journal* 805, no. 2 (June 1, 2015): id. 130, doi:10.1088/0004-637X/805/2/130.
42. A. J. Deason et al., "Satellites of LMC-Mass Dwarfs: Close Friendships Ruined by Milky Way Mass Haloes," *Monthly Notices of the Royal Astronomical Society* 453, no. 4 (November 11, 2015): 3568–3574, doi:10.1093/mnras/stv1939.
43. Igor A. Zinchenko et al., "On the Influence of Minor Mergers on the Radial Abundance Gradient in Disks of Milky-Way-Like Galaxies," *Astrophysical Journal* 806, no. 2 (June 20, 2015): id. 267, doi:10.1088/0004-637X/806/2/267.
44. F. Hammer et al., "The Milky Way, an Exceptionally Quiet Galaxy: Implications for the Formation of Spiral Galaxies," *Astrophysical Journal* 662, no. 1 (June 10, 2007): 322–334, doi:10.1086/516727; Rahul Shetty and Eve C. Ostriker, "Global Modeling of Spur Formation in Spiral Galaxies," *Astrophysical Journal* 647, no. 2 (August 20, 2006): 997–1017, doi:10.1086/505594; Woong-Tae Kim and Eve C. Ostriker, "Formation of Spiral-Arm Spurs and Bound Clouds in Vertically Stratified Galactic Gas Disks," *Astrophysical Journal* 646, no. 1 (July 20, 2006): 213–231, doi:10.1086/504677; C. L. Dobbs and I. A. Bonnell, "Spurs and Feathering in Spiral Galaxies," *Monthly Notices of the Royal Astronomical Society* 367, no. 3 (April 2006): 873–878, doi:10.1111/j.1365-2966.2006.10146.x; E. A. Filistov, "Polygonal Structure of Spiral Galaxies," *Astronomy Reports* 56, no. 1 (January 2012): 9–15, doi:10.1134/S1063772912010027.
45. Robotham et al., "Galaxy and Mass Assembly," 1448–1453; D. Crnojević et al., "How Unique Is the Local Group? A Comparison to the Nearby Centaurus A Group," in *Galactic Archaeology: Near-Field Cosmology and the Formation of the Milky Way*, ed. Wakō Aoki, ASP Conference Series, vol. 458 (San Francisco: Astronomical Society of the Pacific, 2012), 321, aspbooks.org/publications/458/321.pdf.
46. Gopalakrishnan Indu and Annapurni Subramaniam, "HI Kinematics of the Large Magellanic Cloud Revisited: Evidence of Possible Infall and Outflow," *Astronomy and*

Astrophysics 573 (January 2015): id. A136, doi:10.1051/0004-6361/201321133; Stephen A. Pardy, Elena D'Onghia, and Andrew J. Fox, "Models of Tidally Induced Gas Filaments in the Magellanic Stream," *Astrophysical Journal* 857, no. 2 (April 20, 2018): id. 101, doi:10.3847/1538-4357/aab95b; S. Lucchini et al., "The Magellanic Corona as the Key to the Formation of the Magellanic Stream," *Nature* 585, no. 7824 (September 10, 2020): 203–206, doi: 10.1038/s41586-020-2663-4; S. Lucchini et al, "The Magellanic Corona as the Key to the Formation of the Magellanic Stream," *Bulletin of the American Astronomical Society* 53 (January 2021): e-id 2021ni434p06.

47. Deason et al., "Satellites of LMC-Class Dwarfs," 3568–3574; Dali Zhang, Yu Luo, and Xi Kang, "The Effect of the Large Magellanic Cloud on the Satellite Galaxy Population in Milky Way Analogous Galaxies," *Monthly Notices of the Royal Astronomical Society* 486, no. 2 (June 2019): 2440–2448, doi:10.1093/mnras/stz957; Lucchini et al., "Magellanic Corona as the Key"; Eugene Vasiliev, Vasily Belokurov, and Denis Erkal, "Tango for Three: Sagittarius, LMC, and the Milky Way," *Monthly Notices of the Royal Astronomical Society* 501, no. 2 (February 2021): 2279–2304, doi:10.1093/mnras/staa3673.
48. Cautun et al., "Aftermath of the Great Collision," 2185–2196.
49. Denis Erkal et al., "A Hypervelocity Star with a Magellanic Origin," *Monthly Notices of the Royal Astronomical Society* 483, no. 2 (February 2019): 2007–2013, doi:10.1093/mnras/sty2674; Alessia Gualandris and Simon Portegies Zwart, "A Hypervelocity Star from the Large Magellanic Cloud," *Monthly Notices of the Royal Astronomical Society: Letters* 376, no. 1 (March 2007): L29–L33, doi:10.1111/j.1745-3933.2007.00280.x.
50. H. Boyce et al., "An Upper Limit on the Mass of a Central Black Hole in the Large Magellanic Cloud from the Stellar Rotation Field," *Astrophysical Journal* 846, no. 1 (September 1, 2017): id. 14, doi:10.3847/1538-4357/aa830c.
51. Robert M. Salow and Thomas S. Statler, "Self-Gravitating Eccentric Disk Models for the Double Nucleus of M31," *Astrophysical Journal* 611, no. 1 (August 10, 2004): 245–269, doi:10.1086/422163.
52. R. B. Menezes, J. E. Steiner, and T. V. Ricci, "Discovery of an Hα Emitting Disk around the Supermassive Black Hole of M31," *Astrophysical Journal Letters* 762, no. 2 (January 10, 2013): id. L29, doi:10.1088/2041-8205/762/2/L29.
53. Ralf Bender et al., "*HST* STIS Spectroscopy of the Triple Nucleus of M31: Two Nested Disks in Keplerian Rotation around a Supermassive Black Hole," *Astrophysical Journal* 631, no. 1 (September 20, 2005): 280–300, doi:10.1086/432434.
54. Zhiyuan Li et al., "The Murmur of the Hidden Monster: *Chandra*'s Decadal View of the Supermassive Black Hole in M31," *Astrophysical Journal Letters* 728, no. 1 (February 10, 2011): id. L10, doi:1088/2041-8205/728/1/L10.
55. Li et al., "Murmur of the Hidden Monster," p. 1.
56. Roeland P. van der Marel et al., "Improved Evidence for a Black Hole in M32 from *HST*/FOS Spectra. II. Axisymmetric Dynamical Models*," *Astrophysical Journal* 493, no. 2 (February 1, 1998): 613–631, doi:10.1086/305147.
57. Sijia Peng et al., "Resolving the Nuclear Radio Emission from M32 with the Very Large Array," *Astrophysical Journal* 894, no. 1 (May 1, 2020): id. 61, doi:10.3847/1538-4357/ab855d.
58. M. Loewenstein et al., "On the Nature of the X-Ray Emission from M32," *Astrophysical Journal* 497, no. 2 (April 20, 1998): 681–688, doi:10.1086/305504.
59. Block et al., "An Almost Head-On Collision," 832–834.
60. Karl Gebhardt et al., "M33: A Galaxy with No Supermassive Black Hole*," *Astronomical*

Journal 122, no. 5 (November 1, 2001): 2469–2476, doi:10.1086/323481; David Merritt, Laura Ferrarese, and Charles L. Joseph, "No Supermassive Black Hole in M33?," *Science* 293, no. 5532 (August 10, 2001): 1116–1118, doi:10.1126/science.1063896.

61. Monica Valluri et al., "The Low End of the Supermassive Black Hole Mass Function: Constraining the Mass of a Nuclear Black Hole in NGC 205 via Stellar Kinematics," *Astrophysical Journal* 628, no. 1 (July 20, 2005): 137–152, doi:10.1086/430752.
62. Anil C. Seth et al., "The NGC 404 Nucleus: Star Cluster and Possible Intermediate-Mass Black Hole," *Astrophysical Journal* 714, no. 1 (May 1, 2010): 713–731, doi:10.1088/0004-637X/714/1/713.
63. Nadine Neumayer et al., "SINFONI on the Nucleus of Centaurus A," *The Messenger* 139 (March 2010): 36–41.
64. Marina Rejkuba, "The Distance to the Giant Elliptical Galaxy NGC 5128*," *Astronomy and Astrophysics* 413, no. 3 (January 2004): 903–912, doi:10.1051/0004-6361:20034031.

Chapter 7: The Milky Way Galaxy Interior

1. Zhao-Zhou Li et al., "Constraining the Milky Way Mass Profile with Phase-Space Distribution of Satellite Galaxies," *Astrophysical Journal* 894, no. 1 (May 1, 2020): id. 10, doi:10.3847/1538-4357/ab84f0; T. K. Fritz et al., "The Mass of Our Galaxy from Satellite Proper Motions in the *Gaia* Era," *Monthly Notices of the Royal Astronomical Society* 494, no. 4 (June 2020): 5178–5193, doi:10.1093/mnras/staa1040; Thomas M. Callingham et al., "The Mass of the Milky Way from Satellite Dynamics," *Monthly Notices of the Royal Astronomical Society* 484, no. 4 (April 2019): 5453–5467; doi:10.1093/mnras/stz365; Ekta Patel et al., "Estimating the Mass of the Milky Way Using the Ensemble of Classical Satellite Galaxies," *Astrophysical Journal* 857, no. 2 (April 20, 2018): id. 78, doi:10.3847/1538-4357/aab78f; Denis Erkal, Vasily A. Belokurov, and Daniel L. Parkin, "Equilibrium Models of the Milky Way Mass Are Biased High by the LMC," *Monthly Notices of the Royal Astronomical Society* 498, no. 4 (November 2020): 5574–5580, doi: 10.1093/mnras/staa2840; Prajwal Raj Kafle et al., "On the Shoulders of Giants: Properties of the Stellar Halo and the Milky Way Mass Distribution," *Astrophysical Journal* 794, no. 1 (October 10, 2014): id. 59, doi:10.1088/0004-637X/794/1/59; Paul J. McMillan, "The Mass Distribution and Gravitational Potential of the Milky Way," *Monthly Notices of the Royal Astronomical Society* 465, no. 1 (February 11, 2017): 76–94, doi:10.1093/mnras/stw2759; Prajwal Raj Kafle et al., "Kinematics of the Stellar Halo and the Mass Distribution of the Milky Way Using Blue Horizontal Branch Stars," *Astrophysical Journal* 761, no. 2 (December 20, 2012): id. 98, doi:10.1088/0004-637X/761/2/98; Robert J. J. Grand et al., "The Effects of Dynamical Substructure on Milky Way Mass Estimates from the High-Velocity Tail of the Local Stellar Halo," *Monthly Notices of the Royal Astronomical Society: Letters* 487, no. 1 (July 2019): L72–L76, doi:10.1093/mnrasl/slz092.
2. McMillan, "Mass Distribution and Gravitational Potential," 76–94.
3. Jonathan Sick et al., "The Stellar Mass of M31 as Inferred by the Andromeda Optical and Infrared Disk Survey," *Proceedings of the International Astronomical Union* 10, no. S311 (July 2014): 82–85, doi:10.1017/S1743921315003440.
4. Matteo Mazzarini et al., "Simulations of Satellite Tidal Debris in the Milky Way Halo," *Astronomy and Astrophysics* 636 (April 2020): id. A106, doi:10.1051/0004-6361/202037558.
5. Dorota M. Skowron et al., "A Three-Dimensional Map of the Milky Way Using Classical Cepheid Variable Stars," *Science* 365, no. 6452 (August 2, 2019): 478–482, doi:10.1126/science.aau3181.

6. M. López-Corredoira et al., "Disk Stars in the Milky Way Detected beyond 25 kpc from Its Center," *Astronomy and Astrophysics: Letters* 612 (April 2018): id. L8, doi:10.1051/0004-6361/201832880.
7. E. S. Levine, Leo Blitz, and Carl Heiles, "The Spiral Structure of the Outer Milky Way in Hydrogen," *Science* 312, no. 5781 (June 23, 2006): 1773–1777, doi:10.1126/science.1128455.
8. T. Piffl et al., "Constraining the Galaxy's Dark Halo with RAVE Stars," *Monthly Notices of the Royal Astronomical Society* 445, no. 3 (December 11, 2014): 3133–3151, doi:10.1093/mnras/stu1948.
9. Alis J. Deason et al., "The Edge of the Galaxy," *Monthly Notices of the Royal Astronomical Society* 496, no. 3 (August 2020): 3929–3942, doi:10.1093/mnras/staa1711.
10. Piffl et al., "Constraining the Galaxy's Dark Halo," 3133–3151.
11. Planck Collaboration, "Planck 2018 Results. VI. Cosmological Parameters," submitted to *Astronomy and Astrophysics*, preprint, submitted July 17, 2018, revised September 20, 2019, arxiv.org/abs/1807.06209v2.
12. O. Cavichia, R. D. D. Costa, and W. J. Maciel, "Planetary Nebulae in the Inner Milky Way II. The Bulge-Disk Transition," *Revista Mexicana de Astronomía y Astrofísica* 47 (April 2011): 49–61, scielo.org.mx/pdf/rmaa/v47n1/v47n1a4.pdf.
13. Matthieu Portail et al., "Dynamical Modelling of the Galactic Bulge and Bar: The Milky Way's Pattern Speed, Stellar and Dark Matter Mass Distribution," *Monthly Notices of the Royal Astronomical Society* 465, no. 2 (February 2017): 1621–1644, doi:10.1093/mnras/stw2819.
14. Elena Valenti et al., "Stellar Density Profile and Mass of the Milky Way Bulge from VVV Data*," *Astronomy and Astrophysics: Letters* 587 (March 2016): id. L6, doi:10.1051/0004-6361/201527500.
15. Paul J. McMillan, "Mass Models of the Milky Way," *Monthly Notices of the Royal Astronomical Society* 414, no. 3 (July 2011): 2446–2457, doi:10.1111/j.1365-2966.2011.18564.x.
16. Carlos Allende Prieto, "The Stellar Population of the Thin Disk," *Proceedings of the International Astronomical Union* 5, no. S265 (August 2009): 304–312, doi:10.1017/S1743921310000785; Mario Jurić et al., "The Milky Way Tomography with SDSS. I. Stellar Number Density Distribution," *Astrophysical Journal* 673, no. 2 (February 1, 2008): 864–914, doi:10.1086/523619.
17. Jurić et al., "Milky Way Tomography," 864–914.
18. Jurić et al., "Milky Way Tomography."
19. Chengdong Li and Gang Zhao, "The Evolution of the Galactic Thick Disk with the LAMOST Survey," *Astrophysical Journal* 850, no. 1 (November 20, 2017): id. 25, doi:10.3847/1538-4357/aa93f4.
20. V. Grisoni et al., "The AMBRE Project: Chemical Evolution Models for the Milky Way Thick and Thin Discs," *Monthly Notices of the Royal Astronomical Society* 472, no. 3 (December 2017): 3637–3647, doi:10.1093/mnras/stx2201.
21. Grisoni et al., "The AMBRE Project," 3637–3647; Sanjib Sharma et al., "The K2-HERMES Survey: Age and Metallicity of the Thick Disc," *Monthly Notices of the Royal Astronomical Society* 490, no. 4 (December 2019): 5335–5352, doi:10.1093/mnras/stz2861.
22. Grisoni et al., "The AMBRE Project," 3637–3647.
23. A. C. Robin et al., "Constraining the Thick Disc Formation Scenario of the Milky Way," *Astronomy and Astrophysics* 569 (September 2014): id. A13, doi:10.1051/0004-6361/201423415.
24. M. Haywood et al., "Clues to the Formation of the Milky Way's Thick Disk," *Astronomy and Astrophysics* 579 (July 2015): id. A5, doi:10.1051/0004-6361/201425459; Li and Zhao,

"Evolution of the Galactic Thick Disk" id. 25.
25. The GRAVITY Collaboration, "A Geometric Distance Measurement to the Galactic Center Black Hole with 0.3% Uncertainty," *Astronomy and Astrophysics* 625 (May 2019): id. L10, doi:10.1051/0004-6361/201935656.
26. J. Ted Mackereth and Jo Bovy, "Weighing the Stellar Constituents of the Galactic Halo with APOGEE Red Giant Stars," *Monthly Notices of the Royal Astronomical Society* 492, no. 3 (March 2020): 3631–3546, doi:10.1093/mnras/staa047; Alis J. Deason, Vasily Belokurov, and Jason L. Sanders, "The Total Stellar Halo Mass of the Milky Way," *Monthly Notices of the Royal Astronomical Society* 490, no. 3 (December 2019): 3426–3439, doi:10.1093/mnras/stz2793.
27. Tetsuya Fukushima et al., "The Stellar Halo of the Milky Way Traced by Blue Horizontal-Branch Stars in the Subaru Hyper Suprime-Cam Survey," *Publications of the Astronomical Society of Japan* 71, no. 4 (August 2019): id. 72, doi:10.1093/pasj/psz052; Jurić et al., "Milky Way Tomography," 864–914.
28. Fukushima et al., "Stellar Halo of the Milky Way."
29. L. I. Mashonkina et al., "Abundances of α-Process Elements in Thin-Disk, Thick-Disk, and Halo Stars of the Galaxy: Non-LTE Analysis," *Astronomy Reports* 63, no. 9 (September 2019): 726–738, doi:10.1134/S1063772919090063.
30. Ricardo P. Schiavon et al., "The Building Blocks of the Milky Way Halo Using APOGEE and Gaia or Is the Galaxy a Typical Galaxy?," *Proceedings of the International Astronomical Union* 14, no. S351 (2019): 170–173, doi:10.1017/S1743921319007889.
31. Chris B. Brook et al., "Explaining the Chemical Trajectories of Accreted and *in-situ* Halo Stars of the Milky Way," *Monthly Notices of the Royal Astronomical Society* 495, no. 3 (July 2020): 2645–2651, doi:10.1093/mnras/staa992.
32. Lydia M. Elias et al., "Cosmological Insights into the Assembly of the Radial and Compact Stellar Halo of the Milky Way" *Monthly Notices of the Royal Astronomical Society* 495, no. 1 (June 2020): 29–39, doi:10.1093/mnras/staa1090.
33. G. C. Myeong et al., "Evidence for Two Early Accretion Events that Built the Milky Way Stellar Halo," *Monthly Notices of the Royal Astronomical Society* 488, no. 1 (September 2019): 1235–1247, doi:10.1093/mnras/stz1770.
34. Chervin F. P. Laporte et al., "Response of the Milky Way's Disc to the Large Magellanic Cloud in a First Infall Scenario," *Monthly Notices of the Royal Astronomical Society* 473, no. 1 (January 2018): 1218–1230, doi:10.1093/mnras/stx2146; Kenji Bekki, "The Influences of the Magellanic Clouds on the Galaxy: Pole Shift, Warp and Star Formation History," *Monthly Notices of the Royal Astronomical Society* 422, no. 3 (May 2012): 1957–1974, doi:10.1111/j.1365-2966.2012.20621.x.
35. François Hammer et al., "The Milky Way, an Exceptionally Quiet Galaxy: Implications for the Formation of Spiral Galaxies," *Astrophysical Journal* 662, no. 1 (June 10, 2007): 322–334, doi:10.1086/516727.
36. Hammer et al., "Exceptionally Quiet Galaxy," 322–334.
37. Hammer et al., "Exceptionally Quiet Galaxy."
38. Kambiz Fathi, "Scale Length of Disk Galaxies," *Proceedings of the International Astronomical Union* 6, no. S277 (2010): 317–320, doi:10.1017/S1743921311023027.
39. Paul J. McMillan, "Mass Models of the Milky Way," *Monthly Notices of the Royal Astronomical Society* 414, no. 3 (July 2011): 2446–2457, doi:10.1111/j.1365-2966.2011.18564.x.
40. Pauline Barmby et al., "Dusty Waves on a Starry Sea: The Mid-Infrared View of M31," *Astrophysical Journal* 650, no. 1 (October 10, 2006): L45–L49, doi:10.1086/508626.

41. Hammer et al., "Exceptionally Quiet Galaxy," 322–334.
42. Daniela Carollo et al., "Two Stellar Components in the Halo of the Milky Way," *Nature* 450, no. 7172 (December 13, 2007): 1020–1025, doi:10.1038/nature06460.
43. Hammer et al., "Exceptionally Quiet Galaxy," 322–334.
44. Charlie Conroy et al., "Resolving the Metallicity Distribution of the Stellar Halo with the H3 Survey," *Astrophysical Journal* 887, no. 2 (December 20, 2019): id. 237, doi:10.3847/1538-4357/ab5710; Branimir Sesar, Mario Jurić, and Željko Ivezić, "The Shape and Profile of the Milky Way Halo as Seen by the Canada-France-Hawaii Telescope Legacy Survey," *Astrophysical Journal* 731, no. 1 (April 10, 2011): id. 4, doi:10.1088/0004-637X/731/1/4.
45. Karoline M. Gilbert et al., "Global Properties of M31's Stellar Halo from the SPLASH Survey. II. Metallicity Profile," *Astrophysical Journal* 796, no. 2 (December 1, 2014): id. 76, doi:10.1088/0004-637X/796/2/76; Rodrigo A. Ibata et al., "The Large-Scale Structure of the Halo of the Andromeda Galaxy. I. Global Stellar Density, Morphology and Metallicity Properties," *Astrophysical Journal* 780, no. 2 (January 10, 2014): id. 128, doi:10.1088/0004-637X/780/2/128.
46. M. Mouhcine et al., "The Metallicities of Luminous, Massive Field Galaxies at Intermediate Redshifts," *Monthly Notices of the Royal Astronomical Society* 369, no. 2 (June 2006): 891–908, doi:10.1111/j.1365-2966.2006.10360.x.
47. Sesar, Jurić, and Ivezić, "Shape and Profile of the Milky Way Halo," id. 4.
48. A. J. Deason et al., "Touching the Void: A Striking Drop in Stellar Halo Density beyond 50 kpc," *Astrophysical Journal* 787, no. 1 (May 20, 2014): id. 30, doi:10.1088/0004-637X/787/1/30.
49. Andreea S. Font et al., "The ARTEMIS Simulations: Stellar Haloes of Milky Way-Mass Galaxies," *Monthly Notices of the Royal Astronomical Society* 498, no. 2 (October 2020): 1765, doi:10.1093/mnras/staa2463.
50. Andreea S. Font et al., "Dynamics and Stellar Content of the Giant Southern Stream in M31. II. Interpretation," *Astronomical Journal* 131, no. 3 (March 1, 2006): 1436–1444, doi:10.1086/499564; Andreea S. Font et al., "Phase-Space Distributions of Chemical Abundances in Milky Way-Type Galaxy Halos," *Astrophysical Journal* 646, no. 2 (August 1, 2006): 886–898, doi:10.1086/505131.
51. Igor A. Zinchenko et al., "On the Influence of Minor Mergers on the Radial Abundance Gradient in Disks of Milky Way-Like Galaxies," *Astrophysical Journal* 806, no. 2 (June 20, 2015): id. 267, doi:10.1088/0004-637X/806/2/267.
52. Christopher J. Conselice et al., "A Direct Measurement of Major Galaxy Mergers at $z < \sim 3$," *Astronomical Journal* 126, no. 3 (September 1, 2003): 1183–1207, doi:10.1086/377318; David L. Block et al., "An Almost Head-On Collision as the Origin of Two Off-Centre Rings in the Andromeda Galaxy," *Nature* 443, no. 7113 (October 19, 2006): 832–834, doi:10.1038/nature05184; Gilbert et al., "Global Properties of M31's Stellar Halo."
53. Benjamin L. Davis, Alister W. Graham, and Ewan Cameron, "Black Hole Mass Scaling Relations for Spiral Galaxies. I. M_{BH}–M_*,sph," *Astrophysical Journal* 873, no. 1 (March 1, 2019): id. 85, doi:10.3847/1538-4357/aaf3b8.
54. Benjamin L. Davis, Alister W. Graham, and Marc S. Seigar, "Updating the (Supermassive Black Hole Mass)–(Spiral Arm Pitch Angle) Relation: A Strong Correlation for Galaxies with Pseudobulges," *Monthly Notices of the Royal Astronomical Society* 471, no. 2 (October 2017): 2187–2203, doi:10.1093/mnras/stx1794; Davis, Graham, and Cameron, "Black Hole Mass Scaling."
55. Benjamin L. Davis, Alister W. Graham, and Françoise Combes, "A Consistent Set of Empirical Scaling Relations for Spiral Galaxies: The (V_{max}, M_{oM})–(s_0, M_{BH}, ϕ) Relations,"

Astrophysical Journal 877, no. 1 (May 20, 2019): id. 64, doi:10.3847/1538-4357/ab1aa4.

56. Si-Yue Yu and Luis C. Ho, "On the Correlation between Spiral Arm Pitch Angle and Galaxy Properties," *Astrophysical Journal* 871, no. 2 (February 1, 2019): id. 194, doi:10.3847/1538-4357/aaf895.
57. Ross E. Hart et al., "Galaxy Zoo and SPARCFIRE: Constraints on Spiral Arm Formation Mechanisms from Spiral Arm Number and Pitch Angles," *Monthly Notices of the Royal Astronomical Society* 472, no. 2 (December 2017): 2263–2279, doi:10.1093/mnras/stx2137.
58. M. J. Reid et al., "Trigonometric Parallaxes of Massive Star-Forming Regions. VI. Galactic Structure, Fundamental Parameters, and Non-Circular Motions," *Astrophysical Journal* 700, no. 1 (July 20, 2009): 137–148, doi:10.1088/0004-637X/700/1/137; V. V. Bobylev and A. T. Bajkova, "Estimation of the Pitch Angle of the Galactic Spiral Pattern," *Astronomy Letters* 39, no. 11 (November 2013): 759–764, doi:10.1134/S1063773713110017.
59. Zhang Ming, Han Jin-lin, and Peng Qiu-he, "A Study on the Sagittarius-Carina Arm and the Halo Mass of Our Galaxy," *Chinese Astronomy and Astrophysics* 26, no. 3 (July–September 2002): 267–275, doi:10.1016/S0275-1062(02)00066-8.
60. Bobylev and Bajkova, "Estimation of the Pitch Angle," 759–764.
61. I explain why the relatively brief existence of advanced life requires that less-advanced precede it, existing continuously for a minimum of a few billion years, in *Improbable Planet: How Earth Became Humanity's Home* (Grand Rapids, MI: Baker Books, 2016), 94–197.
62. Rita Tojeiro et al., "The Different Star Formation Histories of Blue and Red Spiral and Elliptical Galaxies," *Monthly Notices of the Royal Astronomical Society* 432, no. 1 (June 11, 2013): 359–373, doi:10.1093/mnras/stt484.
63. S. Benetti et al., "Supernova 2002bo: Inadequacy of the Single Parameter Description," *Monthly Notices of the Royal Astronomical Society* 348, no. 1 (February 2004): 261–278, doi:10.1111/j.1365-2966.2004.07357.x; A. Di Paola et al., "Discovery of the Heavily Obscured Supernova 2002cv," *Astronomy and Astrophysics* 393 (October 2002): L21–L24, doi:10.1051/0004-6361:20021168.
64. Simon J. Mutch, Darren J. Croton, and Gregory B. Poole, "The Mid-Life Crisis of the Milky Way and M31," *Astrophysical Journal* 736, no. 2 (August 1, 2011): id. 84, doi:10.1088/0004-637X/736/2/84.
65. Chris Flynn et al., "On the Mass-to-Light Ratio of the Local Galactic Disc and the Optical Luminosity of the Galaxy," *Monthly Notices of the Royal Astronomical Society* 372, no. 3 (November 2006): 1149–1160, doi:10.1111/j.1365-2966.2006.10911.x.
66. The GRAVITY Collaboration, "A Geometric Distance Measurement."
67. Rosa A. González-Lópezlira et al., "The Relation between Globular Cluster Systems and Supermassive Black Holes in Spiral Galaxies: The Case Study of NGC 4258," *Astrophysical Journal* 835, no. 2 (February 1, 2017): id. 184, doi:10.3847/1538-4357/835/2/184; Gretchen L. H. Harris, Gregory B. Poole, and William E. Harris, "Globular Clusters and Supermassive Black Holes in Galaxies: Further Analysis and a Larger Sample," *Monthly Notices of the Royal Astronomical Society* 438, no. 3 (March 1, 2014): 2117–2130, doi:10.1093/mnras/stt2337; Katherine L. Rhode, "Exploring the Correlations between Globular Cluster Populations and Supermassive Black Holes in Giant Galaxies," *Astronomical Journal* 144, no. 5 (November 1, 2012): id. 154, doi:10.1088/0004-6256/144/5/154.
68. Stefano de Nicola, Alessandro Marconi, and Giuseppe Longo, "The Fundamental Relation between Supermassive Black Holes and Their Host Galaxies," *Monthly Notices of the Royal Astronomical Society* 490, no. 1 (November 2019): 600–612, doi:10.1093/mnras/stz2472; G. Yang et al., "Evident Black Hole-Bulge Coevolution in the Distant Universe," *Monthly*

Notices of the Royal Astronomical Society 485, no. 3 (May 2019): 3721–3737, doi:10.1093/mnras/stz611; John Kormendy and Luis C. Ho, "Coevolution (Or Not) of Supermassive Black Holes and Host Galaxies," *Annual Review of Astronomy and Astrophysics* 51 (August 2013): 511–653, doi:10.1146/annurev-astro-082708-101811; Yohei Miki et al., "Hunting a Wandering Supermassive Black Hole in the M31 Halo Hermitage," *Astrophysical Journal* 783, no. 2 (March 10, 2014): id. 87, doi:10.1088/0004-637X/783/2/87.

69. Alessandro Marconi and Leslie K. Hunt, "The Relation between Black Hole Mass, Bulge Mass, and Near-Infrared Luminosity," *Astrophysical Journal* 589, no. 1 (May 20, 2003): L21–L24, doi:10.1086/375804.
70. Tuan Do et al., "Prospects for Measuring Supermassive Black Hole Masses with Future Extremely Large Telescopes," *Astronomical Journal* 147, no. 4 (April 1, 2014): id. 93, doi:10.1088/0004-6256/147/4/93; Kayhan Gültekin et al., "The M-σ and M-L Relations in Galactic Bulges, and Determinations of Their Intrinsic Scatter," *Astrophysical Journal* 698, no. 1 (June 10, 2009): 198–221, doi:10.1088/0004-637X/698/1/198.
71. Joel C. Berrier et al., "Further Evidence for a Supermassive Black Hole Mass-Pitch Angle Relation," *Astrophysical Journal* 769, no. 2 (June 1, 2013): id. 132, doi:10.1088/0004-637X/769/2/132; Marc S. Seigar et al., "Discovery of a Relationship between Spiral Arm Morphology and Supermassive Black Hole Mass in Disk Galaxies," *Astrophysical Journal* 678, no. 2 (May 10, 2008): L93–L96, doi:10.1086/588727.
72. Christopher Marsden et al., "The Case for the Fundamental M_{BH}-σ," *Frontiers in Physics* 8 (March 2020): id. 61, doi:10.3389/fphy.2020.00061; Alper K. Ates, Can Battal Kılınç, and Cafer Ibanoğlu, "On the M-σ Relationship and SMBH Mass Estimates of Selected Nearby Galaxies," *International Journal of Astronomy and Astrophysics* 2013, no. 3 (July 2013): 1–9, doi:10.4236/ijaa.2013.33A001.
73. Francesco Shankar et al., "Probing Black Hole Accretion Tracks, Scaling Relations, and Radiative Efficiencies from Stacked X-Ray Active Galactic Nuclei," *Monthly Notices of the Royal Astronomical Society* 493, no. 1 (March 2020): 1500–1511, doi:10.1093/mnras/stz3522.
74. Nandini Sahu, Alister W. Graham, and Benjamin L. Davis, "Revealing Hidden Substructures in the M_{BH}-σ Diagram, and Refining the Bend in the L–σ Relation," *Astrophysical Journal* 887, no. 1 (December 10, 2019): id. 10, doi:10.3847/1538-4357/ab50b7.
75. Turgay Caglar et al., "LLAMA: The M_{BH}-σ Relation of the Most Luminous Local AGNs," *Astronomy and Astrophysics* 634 (February 2020): id. A114, doi:10.1051/0004-6361/201936321.
76. Kastytis Zubovas and Andrew R. King, "The M–σ Relation in Different Environments," *Monthly Notices of the Royal Astronomical Society* 426, no. 4 (November 11, 2012): 2751–2757, doi:10.1111/j.1365-2966.2012.21845.x.
77. Burçin Mutlu-Pakdil, Marc S. Seigar, and Benjamin L. Davis, "The Local Black Hole Mass Function Derived from the M_{BH}-P and the M_{BH}-n Relations," *Astrophysical Journal* 830, no. 2 (October 20, 2016): id. 117, doi:10.3847/0004-637X/830/2/117; Y. Watabe et al., "Supermassive Black Hole Mass Regulated by Host Galaxy Morphology," *Monthly Notices of the Royal Astronomical Society* 400, no. 4 (December 2009): 1803–1807, doi:10.1111/j.1365-2966.2009.15345.x; Zubovas and King, "The M–σ Relation," 2751–2757.
78. Markus Hartman et al., "The Effect of Bars on the M-σ_e Relation: Offset, Scatter, and Residuals Correlations," *Monthly Notices of the Royal Astronomical Society* 441, no. 2 (June 2014): 1243–1259, doi:10.1093/mnras/stu627; Sergei Nayakshin, Chris Power, and Andrew R. King, "The Observed M–σ Relations Imply that Super-Massive Black Holes

Grow by Cold Chaotic Accretion," *Astrophysical Journal* 753, no. 1 (July 1, 2012): id. 15, doi:10.1088/0004-637X/753/1/15.
79. Rachael L. Beaton et al., "Unveiling the Boxy Bulge and Bar of the Andromeda Spiral Galaxy," *Astrophysical Journal* 658, no. 2 (April 1, 2007): L91–L94, doi:10.1086/514333.
80. Kastytis Zubovas, Sergei Nayakshin, and Sera Markoff, "Sgr A* Flares: Tidal Disruption of Asteroids and Planets?," *Monthly Notices of the Royal Astronomical Society* 421, no. 2 (April 10, 2012): 1315–1324, doi:10.1111/j.1365-2966.2011.20389.x.
81. Zubovas, Navakshin, and Markoff, "Sgr A* Flares," 1315–1324.
82. Sergei Nayakshin, Sergey Sazonov, and Rashid Sunyaev, "Are Supermassive Black Holes Shrouded by 'Super-Oort' Clouds of Comets and Asteroids?," *Monthly Notices of the Royal Astronomical Society* 419, no. 2 (January 11, 2012): 1238–1247, doi:10.1111/j.1365-2966.2011.19777.x.
83. Nayakshin, Sazonov, and Sunyaev, "Are Supermassive Black Holes Shrouded," 1238–1247.
84. Zubovas, Nayakshin, and Markoff, "Sgr A* Flares," 1315–1324.
85. Lia Corrales et al., "Perils at the Heart of the Milky Way: Systematic Effects for Studying Low-Luminosity Accretion onto Sgr A,*" *16th HEAD Meeting: Meeting Abstracts* (paper, American Astronomical Society, Sun Valley, Idaho, August 20–24, 2017,): id. 300.01, aas.org/sites/default/files/2019-11/head16-meeting-abstract-book.pdf.
86. N. Nicole Sanchez et al., "Preferential Accretion in the Supermassive Black Holes of Milky Way-Size Galaxies Due to Direct Feeding by Satellites," *Astrophysical Journal* 860, no. 1 (June 10, 2018): id. 20, doi:10.3847/1538-4357/aac015.
87. Meng Su, Tracy R. Slatyer, and Douglas P. Finkbeiner, "Giant Gamma-Ray Bubbles from *Fermi*-LAT: Active Galactic Nucleus Activity or Bipolar Galactic Wind?," *Astrophysical Journal* 724, no. 2 (December 1, 2010): 1044–1082, doi:10.1088/0004-637X/724/2/1044.
88. P. Predehl et al., "Detection of Large-Scale X-Ray Bubbles in the Milky Way Halo," *Nature* 588, no. 7837 (December 10, 2020): 227–231, doi:10.1038/s41586-020-2979-0.
89. G. Ponti et al., "An X-Ray Chimney Extending Hundreds of Parsecs Above and Below the Galactic Centre," *Nature* 567, no. 7748 (March 21, 2019): 347–350, doi:10.1038/s41586-019-1009-6.
90. Bruce G. Elmegreen, "GMC Origins and Turbulent Motions in Spiral and Dwarf Galaxies," *Proceedings of the International Astronomical Union* 8, no. S292 (2012): 35–38, doi:10.1017/S1743921313000197.
91. C. L. Dobbs and I. A. Bonnell, "Spurs and Feathering in Spiral Galaxies," *Monthly Notices of the Royal Astronomical Society* 367, no. 3 (April 2006): 873–878, doi:10.1111/j.1365-2966.2006.10146.x.
92. Rahul Shetty and Eve C. Ostriker, "Global Modeling of Spur Formation in Spiral Galaxies," *Astrophysical Journal* 647, no. 2 (August 20, 2006): 997–1017, doi:10.1086/505594; Woong-Tae Kim and Eve C. Ostriker, "Formation of Spiral-Arm Spurs and Bound Clouds in Vertically Stratified Galactic Gas Disks," *Astrophysical Journal* 646, no. 1 (July 20, 2006): 213–231, doi:10.1086/504677; Dobbs and Bonnell, "Spurs and Feathering in Spiral Galaxies," 873–878; S. Chakrabarti, G. Laughlin, F. H. Shu, "Branch, Spur, and Feather Formation in Spiral Galaxies," *Astrophysical Journal* 596, no. 1 (October 10, 2003): 220–239, doi:10.1086/377578; Woong-Tae Kim and Eve C. Ostriker, "Formation and Fragmentation of Gaseous Spurs in Spiral Galaxies," *Astrophysical Journal* 570, no. 1 (May 1, 2002): 132–151, doi:10.1086/339352.
93. F. Renaud et al., "Beads on a String and Spurs in Galactic Disks," in *Structure and Dynamics of Disk Galaxies*, ed. Marc S. Seigar and Patrick Treuthardt, ASP Conference Series, vol. 480

(San Francisco: Astronomical Society of the Pacific, 2014), 247–251.
94. Abraham Loeb, Rafael A. Batista, and David Sloan, "Relative Likelihood for Life as a Function of Cosmic Time," *Journal of Cosmology and Astroparticle Physics* 8 (August 2016): id. 040, doi:10.1088/1475-7516/2016/08/040; Hugh Ross, "Are We Alone in the Cosmos?," *Today's New Reason to Believe* (blog), August 29, 2016, Reasons to Believe, reasons.org/explore/blogs/todays-new-reason-to-believe/are-we-alone-in-the-cosmos.

Chapter 8: The Local Arm

1. Mark J. Reid et al., "Trigonometric Parallaxes of High-Mass Star-Forming Regions: Our View of the Milky Way," *Astrophysical Journal* 885, no. 2 (November 10, 2019): id. 131, doi:10.3847/1538-4357/ab4a11; Mark J. Reid et al., "Trigonometric Parallaxes of High Mass Star Forming Regions: The Structure and Kinematics of the Milky Way," *Astrophysical Journal* 783, no. 2 (March 10, 2014): id. 130, doi:10.1088/0004-637X/783/2/130; Y. W. Wu et al., "Trigonometric Parallaxes of Star-Forming Regions in the Sagittarius Spiral Arm," *Astronomy and Astrophysics* 566 (June 2014): id. A17, doi:10.1051/0004-6361/201322765; Nobuyuki Sakai et al., "Noncircular Motions in the Outer Perseus Spiral Arm," *Astrophysical Journal* 876, no. 1 (May 1, 2019): id. 30, doi:10.3847/1538-4357/ab12e0.
2. M. J. Reid et al., "Trigonometric Parallaxes of Massive Star-Forming Regions. VI. Galactic Structure, Fundamental Parameters, and Noncircular Motions," *Astrophysical Journal* 700, no. 1 (July 20, 2009): 138, doi:10.1088/0004-637X/700/1/137.
3. N. Lodieu et al., "A 3D View of the Hyades Stellar and Sub-Stellar Population," *Astronomy and Astrophysics* 623 (March 2019): id. A35, doi:10.1051/0004-6361/201834045; Carl Melis et al., "A VLBI Resolution of the Pleiades Distance Controversy," *Science* 345, no. 6200 (August 29, 2014): 1029–1032, doi:10.1126/science.1256101; F. van Leeuwen, "Parallaxes and Proper Motions for 20 Open Clusters as Based on the New Hipparcos Catalogue," *Astronomy and Astrophysics* 497, no. 1 (April 2009): 209–242, doi:10.1051/0004-6361/200811382.
4. Lodieu et al., "A 3D View of the Hyades."
5. Shih-Yun Tang et al., "Characterization of Stellar and Substellar Members in the Coma Berenices Star Cluster," *Astrophysical Journal* 862, no. 2 (August 1, 2018): id. 106, doi:10.3847/1538-4357/aacb7a.
6. H. Bouy et al., "The Seven Sisters DANCe," *Astronomy and Astrophysics* 577 (May 2015): id. A148, doi:10.1051/0004-6361/201425019; P. A. B. Galli et al., "A Revised Moving Cluster Distance to the Pleiades Open Cluster," *Astronomy and Astrophysics* 598 (February 2017): id. A48, doi:10.1051/0004-6361/201629239.
7. Masaru Shibata et al., "Constraint on the Maximum Mass of Neutron Stars Using GW170817 Event," *Physical Review D* 100, no. 2 (July 15, 2019): id. 023015, doi:10.1103/PhysRevD.100.023015.
8. Laura Kreidberg et al., "Mass Measurements of Black Holes in X-Ray Transients: Is There a Mass Gap?," *Astrophysical Journal* 757, no. 1 (September 20, 2012): id. 36, doi:10.1088/0004-637X/757/1/36; Dawn M. Gelino and Thomas E. Harrison, "GRO J0422+32: The Lowest Mass Black Hole?," *Astrophysical Journal* 599, no. 2 (December 20, 2003): 1254–1259, doi:10.1086/379311.
9. Łukasz Wyrzykowski and Ilya Mandel, "Constraining the Masses of Microlensing Black Holes and the Mass Gap with *Gaia* DR2," *Astronomy and Astrophysics* 636 (April 2020): id. A20, doi:10.1051/0004-6361/201935842.
10. Charles J. Hailey et al., "A Density Cusp of Quiescent X-Ray Binaries in the Central Parsec of the Galaxy," *Nature* 556, no. 7699 (April 5, 2018): 70–73, doi:10.1038/nature25029; Mark

R. Morris, "Bounteous Black Holes at the Galactic Center," *Nature* 556, no. 7701 (April 19, 2018): 319–320, doi:10.1038/d41586-018-04341-8.

11. Feryal Özel et al., "The Black Hole Mass Distribution in the Galaxy," *Astrophysical Journal* 725, no. 2 (December 20, 2010): 1918–2010, doi:10.1088/0004-637X/725/2/1918.
12. Kreidberg et al., "Mass Measurements of Black Holes"; Özel et al., "Black Hole Mass Distribution," 1918–2010.
13. James C. A. Miller-Jones et al., "Cygnus X-1 Contains a 21-Solar Mass Black Hole—Implications for Massive Star Winds," *Science* 371, no. 6533 (March 5, 2021): 1046–1049, doi:10.1126/science.abb3363.
14. Özel et al., "Black Hole Mass Distribution," 1918–2010.
15. Elena Gallo et al., "ALMA Observations of A0620-00: Fresh Clues on the Nature of Quiescent Black Hole X-Ray Binary Jets," *Monthly Notices of the Royal Astronomical Society* 488, no. 1 (September 2019): 191–197, doi:10.1093/mnras/stz1634.
16. Thomas Rivinius et al., "A Naked-Eye Triple System with a Nonaccreting Black Hole in the Inner Binary," *Astronomy and Astrophysics* 637 (May 2020): id. L3, doi:10.1051/0004-6361/202038020.
17. William E. Harris, "Catalog of Parameters for Milky Way Globular Clusters: The Database," McMaster University, last revised December 2010, physwww.mcmaster.ca/~harris/mwgc.dat.
18. H. Baumgardt et al., "No Evidence for Intermediate-Mass Black Holes in the Globular Clusters ω Cen and NGC 6624," *Monthly Notices of the Royal Astronomical Society* 488, no. 4 (October 2019): 5340–5351, doi:10.1093/mnras/stz2060; Ruggero de Vita, Michele Trenti, and Morgan MacLeod, "Wandering Off the Centre: A Characterization of the Random Motion of Intermediate-Mass Black Holes in Star Clusters," *Monthly Notices of the Royal Astronomical Society* 475, no. 2 (April 2018): 1574–1586, doi:10.1093/mnras/stx3261.
19. S. R. Kulkarni, Piet Hut, and Steve J. McMillan, "Stellar Black Holes in Globular Clusters," *Nature* 364, no. 6436 (July 29, 1993): 421–423, doi:10.1038/364421a0; Steinn Sigurdsson and Lars Hernquist, "Primordial Black Holes in Globular Clusters," *Nature* 364, no. 6436 (July 29, 1993): 423–425, doi:10.1038/364423a0.
20. Jay Strader et al., "Two Stellar-Mass Black Holes in the Globular Cluster M22," *Nature* 490, no. 7418 (October 4, 2012): 71–73, doi:10.1038/nature11490.
21. Yue Zhao et al., "The MAVERIC Survey: A Hidden Pulsar and a Black Hole Candidate in ATCA Radio Imaging of the Globular Cluster NGC 6397," *Monthly Notices of the Royal Astronomical Society* 493, no. 4 (April 2020): 6033–6049, doi:10.1093/mnras/staa631.
22. Helmut A. Abt, "The Age of the Local Interstellar Bubble," *Astronomical Journal* 141, no. 5 (May 1, 2011): id. 165, doi:10.1088/0004-6256/141/5/165.
23. N. Voglis, I. Stavropoulos, and C. Kalapotharakos, "Chaotic Motion and Spiral Structure in Self-Consistent Models of Rotating Galaxies," *Monthly Notices of the Royal Astronomical Society* 372, no. 2 (October 2006): 901–922, doi:10.1111/j.1365-2966.2006.10914.x.
24. W. S. Dias et al., "The Spiral Pattern Rotation Speed of the Galaxy and the Corotation Radius with *Gaia* DR2," *Monthly Notices of the Royal Astronomical Society* 486, no. 4 (July 2019): 5726–5736, doi:10.1093/mnras/stz1196.
25. Douglas A. Barros and Jacques R. D. Lépine, "A Minimum of Stellar Density at the Corotation Radius of the Milky Way Spiral Pattern," in *Structure and Dynamics of Disk Galaxies*, ed. Marc S. Seigar and Patrick Treuthardt, ASP Conference Series, vol. 480 (San Francisco: Astronomical Society of the Pacific, 2014), 23–29.
26. Research Consortium on Nearby Stars, RECONS Census of Objects Nearer than 10

Parsecs, Georgia State University, last updated April 12, 2018, joy.chara.gsu.edu/RECONS/census.posted.htm; "M Stars within 100 Light-Years," Sol Company, 2014 solstation.com/stars3/100-ms.htm.

27. Research Consortium, RECONS Census, joy.chara.gsu.edu/RECONS/census.posted.htm; "M Stars within 100 Light-Years," solstation.com/stars3/100-ms.htm.
28. Jonathan D. Slavin, "Structures in the Interstellar Medium Caused by Supernovae: The Local Bubble," in *Handbook of Supernovae*, ed. A. Alsabti and P. Murdin (Cham, Switzerland: Springer, 2017), 2287–2299, doi:10.1007/978-3-319-21846-5_14.
29. D. Breitschwerdt et al., "The Locations of Recent Supernovae Near the Sun from Modelling ^{60}Fe Transport," *Nature* 532, no. 7597 (April 6, 2016): 73–76, doi:10.1038/nature17424; B. Fuchs et al., "The Search for the Origin of the Local Bubble Redivivus," *Monthly Notices of the Royal Astronomical Society* 373, no. 3 (December 2006): 993–1003, doi:10.1111/j.1365-2966.2006.11044.x.
30. B. C. Thomas et al., "Terrestrial Effects of Nearby Supernovae in the Early Pleistocene," *Astrophysical Journal Letters* 826, no. 1 (July 20, 2016): id. L3, doi:10.3847/2041-8205/826/1/L3; A. L. Melott et al., "A Supernova at 50 pc: Effects on the Earth's Atmosphere and Biota," *Astrophysical Journal* 840, no. 2 (May 10, 2017): id. 105, doi:10.3847/1538-4357/aa6c57; Adrian L. Melott, Franciole Marinho, and Laura Paulucci, "Hypothesis: Muon Radiation Dose and Marine Megafaunal Extinction at the End-Pliocene Supernova," *Astrobiology* 19, no. 6 (June 2019): 825–830, doi:10.1089/ast.2018.1902.
31. V. Pelgrims et al., "Modeling the Magnetized Local Bubble from Dust Data," *Astronomy and Astrophysics* 636 (April 1, 2020): id. A17, doi:10.1051/0004-6361/201937157.
32. M. I. R. Alves et al., "The Local Bubble: A Magnetic Veil to Our Galaxy," *Astronomy and Astrophysics* 611 (April 2018): id. L5, doi:10.1051/0004-6361/201832637.
33. Slavin, "Structures in the Interstellar Medium," 2287–2299.
34. I. Gebauer et al., "The Local Bubble as a Cosmic-Ray Isotropizer," *ASTRA Proceedings* 2 (July 2015): 1–3, doi:10.5194/ap-2-1-2015.
35. Donald P. Cox and Louise Helenius, "Flux-Tube Dynamics and a Model for the Origin of the Local Fluff," *Astrophysical Journal* 583, no. 1 (January 20, 2003): 205–228, doi:10.1086/344926; Priscilla C. Frisch, "The Local Bubble and the Interstellar Material Near the Sun," *Space Science Reviews* 130 (June 2007): 1–4, doi:10.1007/s11214-007-9209-z.
36. Priscilla C. Frisch, "The Journey of the Sun," submitted for publication May 29, 1997, eprint, arXiv:astro-ph/9705231; Priscilla C. Frisch, "Characteristics of Nearby Interstellar Matter," *Space Science Reviews* 72, nos. 3–4 (May 1995): 499–592, doi:10.1007/BF00749006.
37. Priscilla C. Frisch, "Interstellar Matter and the Boundary Conditions of the Heliosphere," *Space Science Reviews* 86, nos. 1–4 (July 1998): 107–126, doi:10.1023/A:1005067511216.
38. B. Nordström et al., "The Geneva-Copenhagen Survey of the Solar Neighbourhood," *Astronomy and Astrophysics* 418, no. 3 (May 2004): 989–1019, doi:10.1051/0004-6361:20035959.
39. Bjarne Rosenkilde Jørgensen, "The G Dwarf Problem: Analysis of a New Data Set," Astr*onomy and Astrophysics* 363 (November 2000): 947, aa.springer.de/papers/0363003/2300947.pdf.
40. Nordström et al., "The Geneva-Copenhagen Survey," 989.
41. Nordström et al., 989–1019; Jørgensen, "The G Dwarf Problem," 947–957.
42. L. Casagrande et al., "New Constraints on the Chemical Evolution of the Solar Neighborhood and Galactic Disc(s)," *Astronomy and Astrophysics* 530 (June 2011): id. A138, doi:10.1051/0004-6361/201016276; M. Haywood, "Radial Mixing and the Transition between the Thick and Thin Galactic Discs," *Monthly Notices of the Royal Astronomical Society*

388, no. 3 (August 2008): 1175–1184, doi:10.1111/j.1365-2966.2008.13395.x.
43. Ralph Schönrich and James Binney, "Chemical Evolution with Radial Mixing," *Monthly Notices of the Royal Astronomical Society* 396, no. 1 (June 2009): 203–222, doi:10.1111/j.1365-2966.2009.14750.x.
44. Schönrich and Binney, "Chemical Evolution," 203–222.
45. I. Minchev and B. Famaey, "A New Mechanism for Radial Migration in Galactic Disks: Spiral-Bar Resonance Overlap," *Astrophysical Journal* 722, no. 1 (October 10, 2010): 112–121, doi:10.1088/0004-637X/722/1/112.
46. Yue Wang and Gang Zhao, "The Influence of Radial Stellar Migration on the Chemical Evolution of the Milky Way," *Astrophysical Journal* 769, no. 1 (May 20, 2013): id. 4, doi:10.1088/0004-637X/769/1/4.
47. Or Graur et al., "LOSS Revisited. I. Unraveling Correlations between Supernova Rates and Galaxy Properties, as Measured in a Reanalysis of the Lick Observatory Supernova Search," *Astrophysical Journal* 837, no. 2 (March 10, 2017): id. 120, doi:10.3847/1538-4357/aa5eb8; Weidong Li et al., "Nearby Supernova Rates from the Lick Observatory Supernova Search – III. The Rate-Size Relation, and the Rates as a Function of Galaxy Hubble Type and Colour," *Monthly Notices of the Royal Astronomical Society* 412, no. 3 (April 2011): 1473–1507, doi:10.1111/j.1365-2966.2011.18162.x; Or Graur, Federica B. Bianco, and Maryam Modjaz, "A Unified Explanation for the Supernova Rate-Galaxy Mass Dependence Based on Supernovae Discovered in Sloan Galaxy Spectra," *Monthly Notices of the Royal Astronomical Society* 450, no. 1 (June 11, 2015): 905–925, doi:10.1093/mnras/stv713.
48. Richard B. Firestone, "Observation of 23 Supernovae That Exploded <300 pc from Earth during the Past 300 kyr," *Astrophysical Journal* 789, no. 1 (July 1, 2014): id. 29, doi:10.1088/0004-637X/789/1/29.

Chapter 9: Interior Features of the Sun

1. M. Agostini et al. (Borexino Collaboration), "Simultaneous Precision Spectroscopy of *pp*, ^{7}Be, and *pep* Solar Neutrinos with Borexino Phase-II," *Physical Review D* 100, no. 8 (October 15, 2019): id. 082004, doi:10.1103/PhysRevD.100.082004.
2. The Borexino Collaboration, "Comprehensive Measurement of *pp*-Chain Solar Neutrinos," *Nature* 562, no. 7728 (October 25, 2018): 505–510, doi:10.1038/s41586-018-0624-y; The Borexino Collaboration, "Neutrinos from the Primary Proton-Proton Fusion Process in the Sun," *Nature* 512, no. 7515 (August 28, 2014): 383–386, doi:10.1038/nature13702.
3. D. Jeschke et al., "Recent Results from Borexino," *Journal of Physics: Conference Series* 798, no. 1 (January 2017): id. 012114, doi:10.1088/1742-6596/798/1/012114; M. Pallavicini et al., "First Real-Time Detection of Solar pp Neutrinos by Borexino," *EPJ Web of Conferences* 121 (July 2016): id. 01001, doi:10.1051/epjconf/201612101001.
4. Marcelo Emilio et al., "Measuring the Solar Radius from Space during the 2003 and 2006 Mercury Transits," *Astrophysical Journal* 750, no. 2 (May 10, 2012): id. 135, doi:10.1088/0004-637X/750/2/135.
5. Mark S. Miesch et al., "Structure and Evolution of Giant Cells in Global Models of Solar Convection," *Astrophysical Journal* 673, no. 1 (January 20, 2008): 557–575, doi:10.1086/523838.
6. Rachel Howe, "Solar Interior Rotation and Its Variation," *Living Reviews in Solar Physics* 6, no. 1 (February 2009): id. 1, doi:10.12942/lrsp-2009-1; Ariane Schad and Markus Roth, "Inference of Solar Rotation from Perturbations of Acoustic Mode Eigenfunctions," *Astrophysical Journal* 890, no. 1 (February 10, 2020): id. 32, doi:10.3847/1538-4357/ab65ec.

7. P. Charbonneau et al., "Helioseismic Constraints on the Structure of the Solar Tachocline," *Astrophysical Journal* 527, no. 1 (December 10, 1999): 445–460, doi:10.1086/308050; M. Dikpati, "The Importance of the Solar Tachocline," *Advances in Space Research* 38, no. 5 (May 2006): 839–844, doi:10.1016/j.asr.2005.07.016.
8. Pavel A. Denissenkov, "A Model of Magnetic Braking of Solar Rotation That Satisfies Observational Constraints," *Astrophysical Journal* 719, no. 1 (August 10, 2010): 28–44, doi:10.1088/0004-637X/719/1/28.
9. P. A. Gilman, "The Tachocline and the Solar Dynamo," *Astronomische Nachrichten* 326, nos. 3–4 (April 2005): 208–217, doi:10.1002/asna.200410378.
10. A. Sule, G. Rüdiger, and R. Arlt, "A Numerical MHD Model for the Solar Tachocline with Meridional Flow," *Astronomy and Astrophysics* 437, no. 3 (July 2005): 1061–1067, doi:10.1051/0004-6361:20042086.
11. Sule, Rüdriger, and Arlt, "A Numerical MHD Model," 1061–1067.
12. Martin Asplund et al., "The Chemical Composition of the Sun," *Annual Review of Astronomy and Astrophysics* 47 (September 2009): 481–522, doi:10.1146/annurev.astro.46.060407.145222.
13. Aldo M. Serenelli et al., "New Solar Composition: The Problem with Solar Models Revisited," *Astrophysical Journal* 705, no. 2 (November 10, 2009): L123–L127, doi:10.1088/0004-637X/705/2/L123.
14. Maria Bergemann and Aldo Serenelli, "Solar Abundance Problem," in *Determination of Atmospheric Parameters of B-, A-, F-, and G-Type Stars*, ed. E. Niemczura, B. Smalley, and W. Pych, GeoPlanet: Earth and Planetary Sciences (Berlin: Springer, Cham, 2014): 245–258, doi:10.1007/978-3-319-06956-2_21.
15. Francesco L. Villante, "Constraints on the Opacity Profile of the Sun from Helioseismic Observables and Solar Neutrino Flux Measurements," *Astrophysical Journal* 724, no. 1 (November 20, 2010): 98–110, doi:10.1088/0004-637X/724/1/98.
16. James E. Bailey et al., "A Higher-Than-Predicted Measurement of Iron Opacity at Solar Interior Temperatures," *Nature* 517, no. 7532 (January 1, 2015): 56–59, doi:10.1038/nature14048.
17. Núria Vinyoles et al., "A New Generation of Standard Solar Models," *Astrophysical Journal* 835, no. 2 (February 1, 2017): id. 202, doi:10.3847/1538-4357/835/2/202.
18. Anil K. Pradhan and Sultana N. Nahar, "Recalculation of Astrophysical Opacities: Overview, Methodology and Atomic Calculations," in *Workshop on Astrophysical Opacities*, ed. Claudio Mendoza, Sylvaine Turck-Chièze, and James Colgan, ASP Conference Series, vol. 515 (San Francisco: Astronomical Society of the Pacific, 2018), 79–88.
19. Borexino Collaboration, "Comprehensive Measurement of *pp*-Chain," 505–510.
20. K. Abe et al., "Solar Neutrino Measurements in Super-Kamiokande-IV," *Physical Review D* 94, no. 5 (September 1, 2016): id. 052010, doi:10.1103/PhysRevD.94.052010.
21. B. Aharmim et al., "Combined Analysis of All Three Phases of Solar Neutrino Data from the Sudbury Neutrino Observatory," *Physical Review C* 88, no. 2 (August 2013): id. 025501, doi:10.1103/PhysRevC.88.025501.
22. M. Agostini et al. (Borexino Collaboration), "Sensitivity to Neutrinos from the Solar CNO Cycle in Borexino," *European Physical Journal C* 80 (November 26, 2020): id. 1091, doi:10.1140/epjc/s10052-020-08534-2.
23. Gioacchino Ranucci, "First Detection of Solar Neutrinos from the CNO Cycle with Borexino," (presentation on behalf of the Borexino Collaboration, Neutrino 2020 Virtual Conference, June 23, 2020), indico.fnal.gov/event/43209/contributions/187871/

attachments/129210/158592/borexino_cno_neutrino2020.pdf.
24. Ansgar Reiners, "Observations of Cool-Star Magnetic Fields," *Living Reviews in Solar Physics* 9, no. 1 (December 2012): id. 1, doi:10.12942/lrsp-2012-1.
25. Greg Kopp, "An Assessment of the Solar Irradiance Record for Climate Studies," *Journal of Space Weather and Space Climate* 4 (2014): id. A14, doi:10.1051/swsc/2014012.
26. Timo Reinhold et al., "The Sun Is Less Active Than Other Solar-Like Stars," *Science* 368, no. 6490 (May 1, 2020): 518–521, doi:10.1126/science.aay3821.
27. M. Dasi-Espuig et al., "Modelling Total Solar Irradiance since 1878 from Simulated Magnetograms," *Astronomy and Astrophysics* 570 (October 2014): id. A23, doi:10.1051/0004-6361/201424290; M. Dasi-Espuig et al., "Reconstruction of Spectral Solar Irradiance since 1700 from Simulated Magnetograms," *Astronomy and Astrophysics* 590 (June 2016): id. A63, doi:10.1051/0004-6361/201527993.
28. Ilya G. Usoskin, "A History of Solar Activity over Millennia," *Living Reviews in Solar Physics* 14 (2017): id. 3, doi:10.1007/s41116-017-0006-9.
29. C.-J. Wu et al., "Solar Total and Spectral Irradiance Reconstruction over the Last 9,000 Years," *Astronomy and Astrophysics* 620 (December 2018): id. A120, doi:10.1051/0004-6361/201832956; Usoskin, "History of Solar Activity."
30. Colin P. Johnstone, Michael Bartel, and Manuel Güdel, "The Active Lives of Stars: A Complete Description of Rotation and XUV Evolution of F, G, K, and M Dwarfs," *Astronomy and Astrophysics* 649 (May 2021): id. A96, doi:10.1051/0004-6361/202038407; Sylvaine Turck-Chièze, Laurent Piau, and Sébastien Couvidat, "The Solar Energetic Balance Revisited by Young Solar Analogs, Helioseismology, and Neutrinos," *Astrophysical Journal Letters* 731, no. 2 (April 20, 2011): id L29, doi:10.1088/2041-8205/731/2/L29; Ilídio Lopes and Joseph Silk, "Planetary Influence on the Young Sun's Evolution: The Solar Neutrino Probe," *Monthly Notices of the Royal Astronomical Society* 435, no. 3 (November 1, 2013): 2109–2115, doi:10.1093/mnras/stt1427; K. Oláh et al., "Young Solar Type Active Stars: The TYC 2627-638-1 System," *Astronomy and Astrophysics* 515 (June 2010): id. A81, doi:10.1051/0004-6361/200912892.
31. Wendy Stenzel, "Kepler by the Numbers—Mission Statistics," infographic, NASA, October 30, 2018, nasa.gov/kepler/missionstatistics.
32. Hiroyuki Maehara et al., "Superflares on Solar-Type Stars," *Nature* 485, no. 7399 (May 24, 2012): 478–481, doi:10.1038/nature11063.
33. Maehara et al., "Superflares on Solar-Type Stars," figure 2 on page 479.
34. Elias Loomis, "On the Great Auroral Exhibition of Aug. 28th to Sept. 4th, 1859, and on Auroras Generally; 8th article," *American Journal of Science* 96, s2-32 (November 1861): 318–335, doi:10.2475/ajs.s2-32.96.318.
35. B. T. Tsurutani et al., "The Extreme Magnetic Storm of 1–2 September 1859," *Journal of Geophysical Research: Space Physics* 108, no. A7 (2003): 1268–1275, doi:10.1029/2002JA009504.
36. Stephen Battersby, "Core Concept: What Are the Chances of a Hazardous Solar Superflare?," *Proceedings of the National Academy of Sciences, USA* 116, no. 47 (November 19, 2019): 23368–23370, doi:10.1073/pnas.1917356116.
37. Takuya Shibayama et al., "Superflares on Solar-Type Stars Observed with *Kepler*. I. Statistical Properties of Superflares," *Astrophysical Journal Supplement Series* 209, no. 1 (November 2013): id. 5, doi:10.1088/0067-0049/209/1/5.
38. Hiroyuki Maehara et al., "Statistical Properties of Superflares on Solar-Type Stars Based on 1-Minute Cadence Data," *Earth, Planets and Space* 67 (April 2015): id. 59, doi:10.1186/

s40623-015-0217-z.

39. Shibayama et al., "Superflares on Solar-Type Stars Observed."
40. Yuta Notsu et al., "Superflares on Solar-Type Stars Observed with *Kepler* II. Photometric Variability of Superflare-Generating Stars: A Signature of Stellar Rotation and Starspots," *Astrophysical Journal* 771, no. 2 (July 10, 2013): id. 127, doi:10.1088/0004-637X/771/2/127.
41. Yuta Notsu et al., "Do *Kepler* Superflare Stars Really Include Slowly Rotating Sun-Like Stars?—Results Using APO 3.5 m Telescope Spectroscopic Observations and *Gaia*-DR2 Data," *Astrophysical Journal* 876, no. 1 (May 1, 2019): id. 58, doi:10.3847/1538-4357/ab14e6.
42. A. McQuillan, T. Mazeh, and S. Aigrain, "Rotation Periods of 34,030 *Kepler* Main-Sequence Stars: The Full Autocorrelation Sample," *Astrophysical Journal Supplement Series* 211, no. 2 (April 2014): id. 24, doi:10.1088/0067-0049/211/2/24.
43. Herschel B. Snodgrass and Roger K. Ulrich, "Rotation of Doppler Features in the Solar Photosphere," *Astrophysical Journal* 351 (March 1, 1990): 309–316, doi:10.1086/168467.
44. Reinhold et al., "The Sun Is Less Active," 519.
45. Reinhold et al., "The Sun Is Less Active," 518–521.
46. Jinghua Zhang et al., "Solar-Type Stars Observed by LAMOST and Kepler," *Astrophysical Journal Letters* 894, no. 1 (May 1, 2020): id. L11, doi:10.3847/2041-8213/ab8795.
47. Travis S. Metcalfe, "A Stellar Perspective on the Magnetic Future of the Sun," *Proceedings of the International Astronomical Union* 13, no. S340 (February 2018): 213–216, doi:10.1017/S1743921318000947.
48. J.-E. Solheim, "The Sunspot Cycle Length—Modulated by Planets?," *Pattern Recognition in Physics* 1, no. 1 (December 4, 2013): 159–164, doi:10.5194/prp-1-159-2013.
49. Jennifer L. van Saders et al., "Weakened Magnetic Braking as the Origin of Anomalously Rapid Rotation in Old Field Stars," *Nature* 529, no. 7585 (January 14, 2016): 181–184, doi:10.1038/nature16168; Travis S. Metcalfe, "The Sun's Magnetic Midlife Crisis," *Physics Today* 71, no. 6 (June 2018): 70–71, doi:10.1063/PT.3.3956.
50. Travis S. Metcalfe, Ricky Egeland, and Jennifer van Saders, "Stellar Evidence That the Solar Dynamo May Be in Transition," *Astrophysical Journal Letters* 826, no. 1 (July 20, 2016): id. L2, doi:10.3847/2041-8205/826/1/L2; Travis S. Metcalfe and Jennifer van Saders, "Magnetic Evolution and the Disappearance of Sun-Like Activity Cycles," *Solar Physics* 292, no. 9 (September 2017): id. 126, doi:10.1007/s11207-017-1157-5.
51. I describe and document this feature of the Sun's orbit in my book *Improbable Planet: How Earth Became Humanity's Home* (Grand Rapids, MI: Baker Books, 2016), 40–41.
52. I describe and document these and other narrow time windows crucial for global human civilization in my book *Weathering Climate Change: A Fresh Approach* (Covina, CA: RTB Press, 2020), chapters 16–17.

Chapter 10: Our Planetary System

1. Michel Mayor and Didier Queloz, "A Jupiter-Mass Companion to a Solar-Type Star," *Nature* 378, no. 6555 (November 23, 1995): 355–359, doi:10.1038/378355a0; R. Paul Butler and Geoffrey W. Marcy, "A Planet Orbiting 47 Ursae Majoris*," *Astrophysical Journal* 464, no. 2 (June 20, 1996): L153–L156, doi:10.1086/310102; Geoffrey W. Marcy and R. Paul Butler, "A Planetary Companion to 70 Virginis*," *Astrophysical Journal Letters* 464, no. 2 (June 20, 1996): L147–L151, doi:10.1086/310096.
2. Astronomers employ six different methods for detecting exoplanets: radial velocities, transits, gravitational microlensing, reflected light variations, direct imaging, and stellar flare echoes. Details are available in the following papers: Jonathan Lunine, Bruce Macintosh,

and Stanton Peale, "The Detection and Characterization of Exoplanets," *Physics Today* 62, no. 5 (May 2009): 46–51, doi:10.1063/1.3141941; Chris Mann et al., "A Framework for Planet Detection with Faint Light-Curve Echoes," *Astronomical Journal* 156, no. 5 (May 2018): id. 200, doi:10.3847/1538-3881/aadc5e; S. Chapinet et al., "A Compact System of Small Planets around a Former Red-Giant Star," *Nature* 480, no. 7378 (December 22, 2011): 496–499, doi:10.1038/nature10631.

3. "Catalog," Extrasolar Planets Encyclopaedia, Exoplanet TEAM, accessed September 4, 2021, exoplanet.eu/catalog/.
4. "Catalog," accessed September 4, 2021.
5. Elisa V. Quintana et al., "An Earth-Sized Planet in the Habitable Zone of a Cool Star," *Science* 344, no. 6181 (April 18, 2014): 277–280, doi:10.1126/science.1249403.
6. Kristen Menou, "Water-Trapped Worlds," *Astrophysical Journal* 774, no. 1 (September 1, 2013): id. 51, doi:10.1088/0004-637X/774/1/51.
7. Allison Youngblood et al., "The MUSCLES Treasury Survey. IV. Scaling Relations for Ultraviolet, Ca II K, and Energetic Particle Fluxes from M Dwarfs," *Astrophysical Journal* 843, no. 1 (July 1, 2017): id. 31, doi:10.3847/1538-4357/aa76dd.
8. Cecilia Garraffo et al., "The Threatening Magnetic and Plasma Environment of the TRAPPIST-1 Planets," *Astrophysical Journal Letters* 843, no. 2 (July 19, 2017): id. L33, doi:10.3846/2041-8213/aa79ed.
9. Glyn Collinson et al., "The Electric Wind of Venus: A Global and Persistent 'Polar Wind'-Like Ambipolar Electric Field Sufficient for the Direct Escape of Heavy Ionospheric Ions: Venus Has Potential," *Geophysical Research Letters* 43 (June 2016): 5926–5934, doi:10.1002/2016GL068327.
10. Collinson et al., "The Electric Wind," 5926–5934.
11. Hugh Ross, "Complex Life's Narrow Requirements for Atmospheric Gases," *Today's New Reason to Believe* (blog), Reasons to Believe, July 1, 2019, reasons.org/explore/blogs/todays-new-reason-to-believe/complex-life-s-narrow-requirements-for-atmospheric-gases; Hugh Ross, "Tiny Habitable Zones for Complex Life," *Today's New Reason to Believe* (blog), Reasons to Believe, March 4, 2019, reasons.org/explore/blogs/todays-new-reason-to-believe/tiny-habitable-zones-for-complex-life; James Green et al., "When the Moon Had a Magnetosphere," *Science Advances* 6, no. 42 (October 14, 2020): id. eabc0865, doi:10.1126/sciadv.abc0865.
12. Without adequate incident ultraviolet radiation on a planet, the synthesis of many life-essential biochemicals cannot occur. However, too much incident ultraviolet radiation will damage or destroy life. The range of orbital distances from the host star for an acceptable amount of incident ultraviolet radiation is much smaller than it is for liquid water to possibly exist on a planet's surface. Furthermore, only for host stars that are virtually identical to the Sun is it possible for the ultraviolet and liquid water habitable zones to overlap at the same time. Jianpo Guo et al., "Habitable Zones and UV Habitable Zones around Host Stars," *Astrophysics and Space Science* 325, no. 1 (January 2010): id. 25, doi:10.1007/s10509-009-0173-9; Andrea P. Buccino, Guillermo A. Lemarchand, and Pablo J. D. Mauas, "Ultraviolet Radiation Constraints around the Circumstellar Habitable Zones," *Icarus* 183, no. 2 (August 2006): 491–503, doi:10.1016/j.icarus.2006.03.007; Charles H. Lineweaver, Yeshe Fenner, and Brad K. Gibson, "The Galactic Habitable Zone and the Age Distribution of Complex Life in the Milky Way," *Science* 303, no. 5654 (January 2, 2004): 59–62, doi:10.1126/science.1092322.
13. "Catalog," accessed September 5, 2021.

14. Robin M. Canup, "Lunar-Forming Collisions with Pre-Impact Rotation," *Icarus* 196, no. 2 (August 2008): 518–538, doi:10.1016/j.icarus.2008.03.011; Randal C. Paniello, James M. D. Day, and Frédéric Moynier, "Zinc Isotopic Evidence for the Origin of the Moon," *Nature* 490, no. 7420 (October 18, 2012): 376–379, doi:10.1038/nature11507; Seth A. Jacobson et al., "Highly Siderophile Elements in Earth's Mantle as a Clock for the Moon-Forming Event," *Nature* 508, no. 7494 (April 3, 2014): 84–87, doi:10.1038/nature13172; Hugh Ross, *Improbable Planet: How Earth Became Humanity's Home* (Grand Rapids, MI: Baker Books, 2016), 48–57.
15. "Catalog," accessed September 6, 2021. Of the 17 planets, Kepler 42d and Kepler 1520b were not included in the average density calculation. The measured mass for Kepler 42d was an upper limit only, which if used to calculate the planet's density, yields a density greater than the densest element in the periodic table. Kepler 1520b's density measures less than 0.001 grams/cubic centimeter. Hence, it is a super-puff planet, not a rocky planet.
16. "Catalog," accessed September 6, 2021.
17. Michelle Kunimoto and Jaymie M. Matthews, "Searching the Entirety of Kepler Data. II. Occurrence Rate Estimates for FGK Stars," *Astronomical Journal* 159, no. 6 (June 1, 2020): id. 248, doi:10.3847/1538-3881/ab88b0.
18. "Discovery: Exoplanet Catalog," Exoplanet Exploration Program and the Jet Propulsion Laboratory for NASA's Astrophysics Division, accessed September 6, 2021, exoplanets.nasa.gov/discovery/exoplanet-catalog/.
19. Joseph R. Schmitt et al., "Planet Hunters. VI. An Independent Characterization of KOI-351 and Several Long Period Planet Candidates from the *Kepler* Archival Data," *Astronomical Journal* 148, no. 2 (August 1, 2014): id. 28, doi:10.1088/0004-6256/148/2/28.
20. Stephen R. Kane, "The Impact of Stellar Distances on Habitable Zone Planets," *Astrophysical Journal Letters* 861, no. 2 (July 10, 2018): id. L21, doi:10.3847/2041-8213/aad094.
21. "Discovery: Exoplanet Catalog," accessed September 6, 2021.
22. I also explain why in my book *Improbable Planet*, 43–93.
23. "Discovery: Exoplanet Catalog," accessed September 6, 2021.
24. Simon L. Grimm et al., "The Nature of the TRAPPIST-1 Exoplanets," *Astronomy and Astrophysics* 613 (May 2018): id. A68, p. 1, doi:10.1051/0004-6361/201732233.
25. J. M. Alcalá et al., "2MASS J15491331-3539118: A New Low-Mass Wide Companion of the GQ Lup System," *Astronomy and Astrophysics* 635 (March 2020): id. L1, doi:10.1051/0004-6361/201937309; Ya-Lin Wu et al., "An ALMA and MagAO Study of the Substellar Companion GQ Lup B*," *Astrophysical Journal* 836, no. 2 (February 20, 2017): id. 223, doi:10.3847/1538-4357/aa5b96.
26. "Catalog," accessed September 6, 2021.
27. Jonathan Horner, James B. Gilmore, and Dave Waltham, "The Influence of Jupiter, Mars and Venus on Earth's Orbital Evolution," *Proceedings of the 15th Australian Space Research Conference* (Canberra, Australian Capital Territory, September 29–October 1, 2015), ed. Wayne Short and Graziella Caprarelli (Australia: National Space Society of Australia, 2016), 81, arxiv.org/pdf/1708.03448.pdf.
28. Mayor and Queloz, "A Jupiter-Mass Companion," 355–359; Butler and Marcy, "A Planet Orbiting 47 Ursae Majoris," L153–L156; Marcy and Butler, "A Planetary Companion to 70 Virginis," L147–L151.
29. "Catalog," accessed September 6, 2021.
30. Wei Zhu and Yanqin Wu, "The Super Earth–Cold Jupiter Relations," *Astronomical Journal* 156, no. 3 (September 1, 2018): id. 92, doi:10.3847/1538-3881/aad22a.

31. Dong Lai and Bonan Pu, "Hiding Planets behind a Big Friend: Mutual Inclinations of Multi-Planet Systems with External Companions," *Astronomical Journal* 153, no. 1 (January 1, 2017): id. 42, doi:10.3847/1538-3881/153/1/42.
32. "Catalog," accessed September 6, 2021.
33. "Catalog," accessed September 6, 2021.
34. Aviv Ofir et al., "An Independent Planet Search in the *Kepler* Dataset," *Astronomy and Astrophysics* 561 (January 2014): id. A103, doi:10.1051/0004-6361/201220935.
35. Jessica E. Libby-Roberts et al., "The Featureless Transmission Spectra of Two Super-Puff Planets," *Astronomical Journal* 159, no. 2 (February 1, 2020): id. 57, doi:10.3847/1538-3881/ab5d36; Sarah Millholland, "Tidally Induced Radius Inflation of Sub-Neptunes," *Astrophysical Journal* 886, no. 1 (November 20, 2019): id. 72, doi:10.3847/1538-4357/ab4c3f; Lile Wang and Fei Dai, "Dusty Outflows in Planetary Atmospheres: Understanding 'Super-Puffs' and Transmission Spectra of Sub-Neptunes," *Astrophysical Journal Letters* 873, no. 1 (March 1, 2019): id. L1, doi:10.3847/2041-8213/ab0653.
36. Zhu and Wu, "Super Earth–Cold Jupiter Relations," p. 4.
37. Zhu and Wu, p. 2.
38. Geoffrey W. Marcy et al., "Masses, Radii, and Orbits of Small *Kepler* Planets: The Transition from Gaseous to Rocky Planets," *Astrophysical Journal Supplement Series* 210, no. 2 (February 2014): id. 20, doi:10.1088/0067-0049/210/2/20; Yanqin Wu and Yoram Lithwick, "Density and Eccentricity of *Kepler* Planets," *Astrophysical Journal* 772, no. 1 (July 20, 2013): id. 74, doi:10.1088/0004-637X/772/1/74.
39. "Catalog," accessed September 6, 2021.
40. Rachel B. Fernandes et al., "Hints for a Turnover at the Snow Line in the Giant Planet Occurrence Rate," *Astrophysical Journal* 874, no. 1 (March 20, 2019): id. 81, doi:10.3847/1538-4357/ab0300; Robert A. Wittenmyer, "The Anglo-Australian Planet Search XXIV: The Frequency of Jupiter Analogs," *Astrophysical Journal* 819, no. 1 (March 1, 2016): id. 28, doi:10.3847/0004-637X/819/1/28.
41. Karen Meech and Sean N. Raymond, "Origin of Earth's Water: Sources and Constraints," submitted December 9, 2019, chapter to appear in *Planetary Astrobiology*, ed. Victoria Meadows et al., arXiv:1912.04361.
42. Zhu and Wu, "Super Earth–Cold Jupiter Relations," p. 6.
43. "Catalog," accessed September 6, 2021.
44. "Catalog," accessed September 6, 2021. No planet masses greater than 30 times Jupiter's mass were included in the calculations since nearly all astronomers acknowledge such massive planets are in fact brown dwarf stars.
45. I have written extensively about planetary habitable zones in these articles and books: Hugh Ross, "Tiny Habitable Zones for Complex Life," *Today's New Reason to Believe* (blog), Reasons to Believe, March 4, 2019, reasons.org/explore/blogs/todays-new-reason-to-believe/tiny-habitable-zones-for-complex-life; Hugh Ross, "Complex Life's Narrow Requirements for Atmospheric Gases," *Today's New Reason to Believe* (blog), Reasons to Believe, July 1, 2019, reasons.org/explore/blogs/todays-new-reason-to-believe/complex-life-s-narrow-requirements-for-atmospheric-gases; Hugh Ross, *Weathering Climate Change: A Fresh Approach* (Covina, CA: RTB Press, 2020), 174–177; Ross, *Improbable Planet*, 81–93.
46. Dave Waltham, "Testing Anthropic Selection: A Climate Change Example," *Astrobiology* 11, no. 2 (March 2011): 105–114, doi:10.1089/ast.2010.0475; Russell Deitrick et al., "Exo-Milankovitch Cycles. II. Climates of G-Dwarf Planets in Dynamically Hot Systems," *Astronomical Journal* 155, no. 6 (June 1, 2018): id. 266, doi:10.3847/1538-3881/aac214;

Ross, *Weathering Climate Change*, 109–116.

47. Dave Waltham, "The Large-Moon Hypothesis: Can It Be Tested?," *International Journal of Astrobiology* 5, no. 4 (October 2006): 327–331, doi:10.1017/S1473550406003120; Dave Waltham, "Half a Billion Years of Good Weather: Gaia or Good Luck?," *Astronomy and Geophysics* 48, no. 3 (June 2007): 3.22–3.24, doi:10.1111/j.1468-4004.2007.48322.x.
48. "Catalog," accessed September 6, 2021.
49. Barbara E. McArthur et al., "New Observational Constraints on the υ Andromedae System with Data from the *Hubble Space Telescope* and Hobby-Eberly Telescope," *Astrophysical Journal* 715, no. 2 (June 1, 2010): 1203–1220, doi:10.1088/0004-637X/715/2/1203; S. Curiel et al., "A Fourth Planet Orbiting υ Andromedae," *Astronomy and Astrophysics* 525 (January 2011): id. A78, doi:10.1051/0004-6361/201015693.
50. McArthur et al., "New Observational Constraints," 1203–1220; Danielle Piskorz et al., "Detection of Water Vapor in the Thermal Spectrum of the Non-Transiting Hot Jupiter Upsilon Andromedae b," *Astronomical Journal* 154, no. 2 (August 1, 2017): id. 78, doi:10.3847/1538-3881/aa7dd8.
51. McArthur et al., "New Observational Constraints," 1203–1220; Piskorz et al., "Detection of Water Vapor."
52. Russell Deitrick et al., "The Three-Dimensional Architecture of the υ Andromedae Planetary System," *Astrophysical Journal* 798, no. 1 (January 1, 2015): id. 46, doi:10.1088/0004-637X/798/1/46.
53. "Catalog," accessed September 6, 2021.
54. "Catalog," accessed September 6, 2021.
55. "Catalog," accessed September 7, 2021.

Chapter 11: Planetary Migration and Orbital Configuration

1. "Catalog," Extrasolar Planets Encyclopaedia, Exoplanet TEAM, accessed September 6, 2021, exoplanet.eu/catalog/.
2. Hidekazu Tanaka, Taku Takeuchi, and William R. Ward, "Three-Dimensional Interaction between a Planet and an Isothermal Gaseous Disk. I. Corotation and Lindblad Torques and Planet Migration," *Astrophysical Journal* 565, no. 2 (February 1, 2002): 1257–1274, doi:10.1086/324713; Gennaro D'Angelo and Stephen H. Lubow, "Three-Dimensional Disk-Planet Torques in Locally Isothermal Disk," *Astrophysical Journal* 724, no. 1 (November 20, 2010): 730–747, doi:10.1088/0004-637X/724/1/730; C. Yu et al., "Type I Planet Migration in Nearly Laminar Disks: Long-Term Behavior," *Astrophysical Journal* 712, no. 1 (March 20, 2010): 198–208, doi:10.1088/0004-637X/712/1/198.
3. Sahl Rowther and Farzana Meru, "Planet Migration in Self-Gravitating Discs: Survival of Planets," *Monthly Notices of the Royal Astronomical Society* 496, no. 2 (August 2020): 1598–1609, doi:10.1093/mnras/staa1590; Shigeru Ida et al., "A New and Simple Prescription for Planet Orbital Migration and Eccentricity Damping by Planet-Disc Interactions Based on Dynamical Friction," *Monthly Notices of the Royal Astronomical Society* 494, no. 4 (June 2020): 5666–5674, doi:10.1093/mnras/staa1073; Alissa Bans, Arieh Königl, and Ana Uribe, "Type I Planet Migration in a Magnetized Disk. II. Effect of Vertical Angular Momentum Transport," *Astrophysical Journal* 802, no. 1 (March 20, 2015): id. 55, doi:10.1088/0004-637X/802/1/55.
4. Jürgen Blum and Gerhard Wurm, "The Growth Mechanisms of Macroscopic Bodies in Protoplanetary Disks," *Annual Review of Astronomy and Astrophysics* 46 (September 2008): 21–56, doi:10.1146/annurev.astro.46.060407.145152; Chamkor Singh and Marco G. Mazza, "Early-Stage Aggregation in Three-Dimensional Charged Granular Gas," *Physical Review E*

97, no. 2 (February 2018): id. 022904, doi:10.1103/PhysRevE.97.022904.

5. M. C. Wyatt, "Resonant Trapping of Planetesimals by Planet Migration: Debris Disk Clumps and Vega's Similarity to the Solar System," *Astrophysical Journal* 598, no. 2 (December 1, 2003): 1321–1340, doi:10.1086/379064; A. Del Popolo, S. Yeşilyurt, and E. N. Ercan, "Evolution of Planetesimal Discs and Planetary Migration," *Monthly Notices of the Royal Astronomical Society* 339, no. 2 (February 2003): 556–568, doi:10.1046/j.1365-8711.2003.06194.x; Clément Baruteau, Farzana Meru, and Sijme-Jan Paardekooper, "Rapid Inward Migration of Planets Formed by Gravitational Instability," *Monthly Notices of the Royal Astronomical Society* 416, no. 3 (September 2011): 1971–1982, doi:10.1111/j.1365-2966.2011.19172.x.
6. Andrew J. Winter et al., "Stellar Clustering Shapes the Architecture of Planetary Systems," *Nature* 586, no. 7830 (October 22, 2020): 528–532, doi:10.1038/s41586-020-2800-0.
7. Isamu Matsuyama, Doug Johnstone, and Norman Murray, "Halting Planet Migration by Photoevaporation from the Central Source," *Astrophysical Journal* 585, no. 2 (March 10, 2003): L143–L146, doi:10.1086/374406.
8. Aurélien Crida, Frédéric Masset, and Alessandro Morbidelli, "Long Range Outward Migration of Giant Planets, with Application to Fomalhaut b," *Astrophysical Journal* 705, no. 2 (November 10, 2009): L148–L152, doi:10.1088/0004-637X/705/2/L148.
9. Kevin J. Walsh and Alessandro Morbidelli, "The Effect of an Early Planetesimal-Driven Migration of the Giant Planets on Terrestrial Planet Formation," *Astronomy and Astrophysics* 526 (February 2011): id. A126, doi:10.1051/0004-6361/201015277.
10. David Nesvorný, "Young Solar System's Fifth Giant Planet?," *Astrophysical Journal Letters* 742, no. 2 (December 1, 2011): id. L22, doi:10.1088/2041-8205/742/2/L22; David Nesvorný and Alessandro Morbidelli, "Statistical Study of the Early Solar System's Instability with Four, Five, and Six Giant Planets," *Astronomical Journal* 144, no. 4 (October 1, 2012): id. 117, doi:10.1088/0004-6256/144/4/117; Konstantin Batygin, Michael E. Brown, and Hayden Betts, "Instability-Driven Dynamical Evolution Model of a Primordially Five-Planet Outer Solar System," *Astrophysical Journal Letters* 744, no. 1 (January 1, 2012): id. L3, doi:10.1088/2041-8205/744/1/L3; Konstantin Batygin and Michael E. Brown, "Evidence for a Distant Giant Planet in the Solar System," *Astronomical Journal* 151, no. 1 (February 2016): id. 22, doi:10.3847/0004-6256/151/2/22; Benjamin C. Bromley and Scott J. Kenyon, "Making Planet Nine: A Scattered Giant in the Outer Solar System," *Astrophysical Journal* 826, no. 1 (July 20, 2016): id. 64, doi:10.3847/0004-637X/826/1/64; Konstantin Batygin et al., "The Planet Nine Hypothesis," *Physics Reports* 805 (May 3, 2019): 1–53, doi:10.1016/j.physrep.2019.01.009; Matthew S. Clement and Nathan A. Kaib, "Orbital Precession in the Distant Solar System: Further Constraining the Planet Nine Hypothesis with Numerical Simulations," *Astronomical Journal* 159, no. 6 (June 2020): id. 285, doi:10.3847/1538-3881/ab9227; Hugh Ross, "What Does a Ninth Planet Mean for the Creation Model?," *Today's New Reason to Believe* (blog), Reasons to Believe, September 5, 2016, reasons.org/explore/blogs/todays-new-reason-to-believe/what-does-a-ninth-planet-mean-for-the-creation-model.
11. Matthew S. Clement et al., "Mars' Growth Stunted by an Early Giant Planet Instability," *Icarus* 311 (September 1, 2018): 340–356, doi:10.1016/j.icarus.2018.04.008; Matthew S. Clement, Sean N. Raymond, and Nathan A. Kaib, "Excitation and Depletion of the Asteroid Belt in the Early Instability Scenario," *Astronomical Journal* 157, no. 1 (January 1, 2019): id. 38, doi:10.3847/1538-3881/aaf21e; Rogerio Deienno et al., "Excitation of a Primordial Cold Asteroid Belt as an Outcome of Planetary Instability," *Astrophysical Journal* 864, no. 1 (September 1, 2018): id. 50, doi:10.3847/1538-4357/aad55d; R. Brasser et al., "Constructing the Secular Architecture of the Solar System II: The Terrestrial Planets," *Astronomy and*

Astrophysics 507, no. 2 (November 2009): 1053–1065, doi:10.1051/0004-6361/200912878; Walsh and Morbidelli, "The Effect of an Early Planetesimal-Driven Migration"; Nesvorný and Morbidelli, "Statistical Study of the Early Solar System's Instability"; Rogerio Deienno et al., "Constraining the Giant Planets' Initial Configuration from Their Evolution: Implications for the Timing of the Planetary Instability," *Astronomical Journal* 153, no. 4 (April 1, 2017): id. 153, doi:10.3847/1538-3881/aa5eaa.

12. Clement, Raymond, and Kaib, "Excitation and Depletion of the Asteroid Belt," id. 38.
13. Rogerio Deienno et al., "Is the Grand Tack Model Compatible with the Orbital Distribution of Main Belt Asteroids?," *Icarus* 272 (July 1, 2016): 114–124, doi:10.1016/j.icarus.2016.02.043.
14. R. Brasser et al., "Analysis of Terrestrial Planet Formation by the Grand Tack Model: System Architecture and Tack Location," *Astrophysical Journal* 821, no. 2 (April 20, 2016): id. 75, doi:10.3847/0004-637X/821/2/75.
15. Raúl O. Chametla et al., "Capture and Migration of Jupiter and Saturn in Mean Motion Resonance in a Gaseous Protoplanetary Disc," *Monthly Notices of the Royal Astronomical Society* 492, no. 4 (March 2020): 6007–6018, doi:10.1093/mnras/staa260.
16. Patryk Sofia Lykawka and Takashi Ito, "Constraining the Formation of the Four Terrestrial Planets in the Solar System," *Astrophysical Journal* 883, no. 2 (October 1, 2019): id. 130, doi:10.3847/1538-4357/ab3b0a.
17. A. Toliou, A. Morbidelli, and K. Tsiganis, "Magnitude and Timing of the Giant Planet Instability: A Reassessment from the Perspective of the Asteroid Belt," *Astronomy and Astrophysics* 592 (August 2016): id. A72, doi:10.1051/0004-6361/201628658; R. Brasser, K. J. Walsh, and D. Nesvorný, "Constraining the Primordial Orbits of the Terrestrial Planets," *Monthly Notices of the Royal Astronomical Society* 433, no. 4 (August 21, 2013): 3417–3427, doi:10.1093/mnras/stt986.
18. R. G. Strom, S. Marchi, and R. Malhotra, "Ceres and the Terrestrial Planets Impact Cratering Record," *Icarus* 302 (March 1, 2018): 104–108, doi:10.1016/j.icarus.2017.11.013; S. Marchi et al., "High-Velocity Collisions from the Lunar Cataclysm Recorded in Asteroidal Meteorites," *Nature Geoscience* 6, no. 4 (April 2013): 303–307, doi:10.1038/ngeo1769; William F. Bottke et al., "An Archaean Heavy Bombardment from a Destabilized Extension of the Asteroid Belt," *Nature* 486, no. 7396 (May 3, 2012): 78–82, doi:10.1038/nature10967; David A. Minton, James E. Richardson, and Caleb I. Fassett, "Re-Examining the Main Asteroid Belt as the Primary Source of Ancient Lunar Craters," *Icarus* 247 (February 2015): 172–190, doi:10.1016/j.icarus.2014.10.018.
19. Andrew Shannon, Alan P. Jackson, and Mark C. Wyatt, "Oort Cloud Asteroids: Collisional Evolution, the Nice Model, and the Grand Tack," *Monthly Notices of the Royal Astronomical Society* 485, no. 4 (June 2019): 5511–5518, doi:10.1093/mnras/stz776.
20. Rafael de Sousa Ribeiro et al., "Dynamical Evidence for an Early Giant Planet Instability," *Icarus* 339 (March 15, 2020): id. 113605, doi:10.1016/j.icarus.2019.113605.
21. Konstantin Batygin and Greg Laughlin, "Jupiter's Decisive Role in the Inner Solar System's Early Evolution," *Proceedings of the National Academy of Sciences, USA* 112, no. 14 (April 7, 2015): 4214–4217, doi:10.1073/pnas.1423252112.
22. Batygin and Laughlin, "Jupiter's Decisive Role," 4214.
23. Edwin S. Kite and Eric B. Ford, "Habitability of Exoplanet Waterworlds," *Astrophysical Journal* 864, no. 1 (September 1, 2018): id. 75, doi:10.3847/1538-4357/aad6e0; Fergus Simpson, "Bayesian Evidence for the Prevalence of Waterworlds," *Monthly Notices of the Royal Astronomical Society* 468, no. 3 (July 2017): 2803–2815, doi:10.1093/mnras/stx516; Nadejda Marounina and Leslie A. Rogers, "Hot and Steamy, Cold and Icy, or Temperate

and Habitable: Modeling the Early Evolution of Water World Exoplanets," *American Astronomical Society: Division for Extreme Solar Systems* 51 (August 2019): id. 321.02, ui.adsabs.harvard.edu/abs/2019ESS.....432102M/abstract; Simon L. Grimm et al., "The Nature of the TRAPPIST-1 Exoplanets," *Astronomy and Astrophysics* 613 (May 2018): id. A68, p. 1, doi:10.1051/0004-6361/201732233.

24. Mikhail Marov, "The Formation and Evolution of the Solar System," *Oxford Research Encyclopedia of Planetary Science* (May 24, 2018): id. 2, doi:10.1093/acrefore/9780190647926.013.2; H. Lammer et al., "Constraining the Early Evolution of Venus and Earth through Atmospheric Ar, Ne Isotope and Bulk K/U Ratios," *Icarus* 339 (March 15, 2020): id. 113551, doi:10.1016/j.icarus.2019.113551; A. Morbidelli et al., "Building Terrestrial Planets," *Annual Review of Earth and Planetary Sciences* 40 (May 2012): 251–275, doi:10.1146/annurev-earth-042711-105319; Francis M. McCubbin and Jessica J. Barnes, "Origin and Abundances of H_2O in the Terrestrial Planets, Moon, and Asteroids," *Earth and Planetary Science Letters* 526 (November 15, 2019): id. 115771, doi:10.1016/j.epsl.2019.115771.
25. Gerrit Budde, Christoph Burkhardt, and Thorsten Kleine, "Molybdenum Isotopic Evidence for the Late Accretion of Outer Solar System Material to Earth," *Nature Astronomy* 3, no. 8 (August 2019): 736–741, doi:10.1038/s41550-019-0779-y.
26. Sean N. Raymond and Andre Izidoro, "Origin of Water in the Inner Solar System: Planetesimals Scattered Inward during Jupiter and Saturn's Rapid Gas Accretion," *Icarus* 297 (November 15, 2017): 134–148, doi:10.1016/j.icarus.2017.06.030; Thomas S. Kruijer et al., "Age of Jupiter Inferred from the Distinct Genetics and Formation Times of Meteorites," *Proceedings of the National Academy of Sciences USA* 114, no. 26 (June 27, 2017): 6712–6716, doi:10.1073/pnas.1704461114; Kevin J. Walsh et al., "A Low Mass for Mars from Jupiter's Early Gas-Driven Migration," *Nature* 475, no. 7355 (July 14, 2011): 206–209, doi:10.1038/nature10201; Gerrit Budde et al., "Molybdenum Isotopic Evidence for the Origin of Chondrules and a Distinct Genetic Heritage of Carbonaceous and Non-Carbonaceous Meteorites," *Earth and Planetary Science Letters* 454 (November 15, 2016): 293–303, doi:10.1016/j.epsl.2016.09.020.
27. C. M. O'D. Alexander et al., "The Provenances of Asteroids, and Their Contributions to the Volatile Inventories of the Terrestrial Planets," *Science* 337, no. 6095 (August 10, 2012): 721–723, doi:10.1126/science.1223474; Adam R. Sarafian et al., "Early Accretion of Water in the Inner Solar System from a Carbonaceous Chondrite-Like Source," *Science* 346, no. 6209 (October 31, 2014): 623–626, doi:10.1126/science.1256717; Lydia J. Hallis et al., "Evidence for Primordial Water in Earth's Deep Mantle," *Science* 350, no. 6262 (November 13, 2015): 795–797, doi:10.1126/science.aac4834; Jun Wu et al., "Origin of Earth's Water: Chondritic Inheritance Plus Nebular Ingassing and Storage of Hydrogen in the Core," *Journal of Geophysical Research: Planets* 123, no. 10 (October 2018): 2691–2712, doi:10.1029/2018JE005698.
28. Hongping Deng et al., "Primordial Earth Mantle Heterogeneity Caused by the Moon-Forming Giant Impact?," *Astrophysical Journal* 887, no. 2 (December 20, 2019): id. 211, doi:10.3847/1538-4357/ab50b9; A. V. Byalko and M. I. Kuzmin, "Fragments of the Moon Formation: Geophysical Consequences of the Giant Impact," *Journal of Experimental and Theoretical Physics* 129, no. 4 (December 2019): 511–520, doi:10.1134/S1063776119100182; John B. Biersteker and Hilke E. Schlichting, "Losing Oceans: The Effects of Composition on the Thermal Component of Impact-Driven Atmospheric Loss," *Monthly Notices of the Royal Astronomical Society* 501, no. 1 (February 2021): 587–595, doi:10.1093/mnras/staa3614.

29. Batygin and Laughlin, "Jupiter's Decisive Role," 4214–4217.
30. "Catalog," accessed March 18, 2021.
31. "Catalog," accessed March 18, 2021.
32. E. I. Chiang, D. Fischer, and E. Thommes, "Excitation of Orbital Eccentricities of Extrasolar Planets by Repeated Resonance Crossings," *Astrophysical Journal* 564, no. 2 (January 10, 2002): L105–L109, iopscience.iop.org/article/10.1086/338961/pdf.
33. Chiang, Fischer, and Thommes, "Excitation of Orbital Eccentricities," L105–L109.
34. Daniel Malmberg, Melvyn B. Davies, and Douglas C. Heggie, "The Effects of Fly-Bys on Planetary Systems," *Monthly Notices of the Royal Astronomical Society* 411, no. 2 (February 2011): 859–877, doi:10.1111/j.1365-2966.2010.17730.x; Daohai Li, Alexander J. Mustill, and Melvyn B. Davies, "Flyby Encounters between Two Planetary Systems II: Exploring the Interactions of Diverse Planetary System Architectures," *Monthly Notices of the Royal Astronomical Society* 496, no. 2 (August 2020): 1149–1165, doi:10.1093/mnras/staa1622.
35. Chametla et al., "Capture and Migration of Jupiter and Saturn," 6007.
36. K. S. Noll et al., "HST Spectroscopic Observations of Jupiter after the Impact of Comet Shoemaker-Levy 9," *Science* 267, no. 5202 (March 3, 1995): 1307–1313, doi:10.1126/science.7871428; Andrew P. Ingersoll and Hiroo Kanamori, "Waves from the Collisions of Comet Shoemaker-Levy 9 with Jupiter," *Nature* 374, no. 6524 (April 20, 1995): 706–708, doi:10.1038/374706a0.
37. T. A. Michtchenko and S. Ferraz-Mello, "Resonant Structure of the Outer Solar System in the Neighborhood of the Planets," *Astronomical Journal* 122, no. 1 (July 1, 2001): 474–481, doi:10.1086/321129.
38. Russell Deitrick et al., "Exo-Milankovitch Cycles. I. Orbits and Rotation States," *Astronomical Journal* 155, no. 2 (February 1, 2018): id. 60, doi:10.3847/1538-3881/aaa301; Russell Deitrick et al., "Exo-Milankovitch Cycles. II. Climates of G-Dwarf Planets in Dynamically Hot Systems," *Astronomical Journal* 155, no. 6 (June 1, 2018): id. 266, doi:10.3847/1538-3881/aac214; Hugh Ross, *Weathering Climate Change: A Fresh Approach* (Covina, CA: RTB Press, 2020), 81–94.
39. J. Laskar and M. Gastineau, "Existence of Collisional Trajectories of Mercury, Mars and Venus with the Earth," *Nature* 459, no. 7248 (June 11, 2009): 817–819, doi:10.1038/nature08096; Jacques Laskar, "Chaotic Diffusion in the Solar System," *Icarus* 196, no. 1 (July 2008): 1–15, doi:10.1016/j.icarus.2008.02.017.
40. Kimmo Innanen, Seppo Mikkola, and Paul Wiegert, "The Earth-Moon System and the Dynamical Stability of the Inner Solar System," *Astronomical Journal* 116, no. 4 (October 1998): 2055–2057, doi:10.1086/300552.
41. Jonathan Horner, James B. Gilmore, and Dave Waltham, "The Role of Jupiter in Driving Earth's Orbital Evolution: An Update," in *Proceedings of the 14th Australian Space Research Conference* (University of South Australia, Adelaide, South Australia, September 29–October 1, 2014), ed. Wayne Short and Iver Cairns (Australia: National Space Society of Australia, 2016), 25–38, arxiv.org/pdf/1511.06043.pdf.
42. Ross, *Weathering Climate Change*, 81–93, 143–147, 167–177, 229–238.
43. Jonathan Horner, James B. Gilmore, and Dave Waltham, "The Influence of Jupiter, Mars and Venus on Earth's Orbital Evolution," in *Proceedings of the 15th Australian Space Research Conference* (Canberra, Australian Capital Territory, September 29–October 1, 2015), ed. Wayne Short and Graziella Caprarelli (Australia: National Space Society of Australia, 2016), 81–100, arxiv.org/pdf/1708.03448.pdf.

Chapter 12: Small Solar System Bodies

1. Rebecca G. Martin et al., "Asteroid Belt Survival through Stellar Evolution: Dependence on the Stellar Mass," *Monthly Notices of the Royal Astronomical Society: Letters* 494, no. 1 (May 2020): L17–L21, doi:10.1093/mnrasl/slaa030; Xavier P. Koenig and Lori E. Allen, "Disk Evolution in W5: Intermediate-Mass Stars at 2–5 Myr," *Astrophysical Journal* 726, no. 1 (January 1, 2011): id. 18, doi:10.1088/0004-637X/726/1/18; A. Meredith Hughes, Gaspard Duchêne, and Brenda C. Matthews, "Debris Disks: Structure, Composition, and Variability," *Annual Review of Astronomy and Astrophysics* 56 (September 2018): 541–591, doi:10.1146/annurev-astro-081817-052035.
2. Farisa Y. Morales et al., "Common Warm Dust Temperatures around Main-Sequence Stars," *Astrophysical Journal Letters* 730, no. 2 (April 1, 2011): id. L29, doi:10.1088/2041-8205/730/2/L29; D. E. Trilling et al., "Debris Disks around Sun-Like Stars," *Astrophysical Journal* 674, no. 2 (February 20, 2008): 1086–1105, doi:10.1086/525514.
3. J. S. Greaves and M. C. Wyatt, "Debris Discs and Comet Populations around Sun-Like Stars: The Solar System in Context," *Monthly Notices of the Royal Astronomical Society* 404, no. 4 (June 2010): 1944–1951, doi:10.1111/j.1365-2966.2010.16415.x; Trilling et al., "Debris Disks," 1086–1105.
4. Greaves and Wyatt, "Debris Discs and Comet Populations," 1944–1951.
5. Rebecca G. Martin and Mario Livio, "On the Formation and Evolution of Asteroid Belts and Their Potential Significance for Life," *Monthly Notices of the Royal Astronomical Society: Letters* 428, no. 1 (January 2013): L11–L15, doi:10.1093/mnrasl/sls003.
6. "Catalog," Extrasolar Planets Encyclopaedia, Exoplanet TEAM, accessed August 6, 2020, exoplanet.eu/catalog/.
7. Martin and Livio, "On the Formation and Evolution," L11–L15.
8. Martin and Livio, "On the Formation and Evolution."
9. E. V. Pitjeva and N. P. Pitjev, "Masses of the Main Asteroid Belt and the Kuiper Belt from the Motions of Planets and Spacecraft," *Astronomy Letters* 44, nos. 8–9 (August 2018): 554–566, doi:10.1134/S1063773718090050; G. A. Krasinsky et al., "Hidden Mass in the Asteroid Belt," *Icarus* 158, no. 1 (July 2002): 98–105, doi:10.1006/icar.2002.6837.
10. J. L. Elliot et al., "The Deep Ecliptic Survey: A Search for Kuiper Belt Objects and Centaurs. II. Dynamical Classification, the Kuiper Belt Plane, and the Core Population," *Astronomical Journal* 129, no. 2 (February 2005): 1117–1162, doi:10.1086/427395.
11. Matthew S. Tiscareno and Renu Malhorta, "The Dynamics of Known Centaurs," *Astronomical Journal* 126, no. 6 (December 2003): 3122–3131, doi:10.1086/379554.
12. Scott S. Sheppard et al., "A Wide-Field CCD Survey for Centaurs and Kuiper Belt Objects," *Astronomical Journal* 120, no. 5 (November 2000): 2687–2694, doi:10.1086/316805.
13. Chadwick A. Trujillo, David C. Jewitt, and Jane X. Luu, "Population of the Scattered Kuiper Belt," *Astrophysical Journal Letters* 529, no. 2 (February 1, 2000): L103–L106, doi:10.1086/312467; Pitjeva and Pitjev, "Main Asteroid Belt and the Kuiper Belt," 554–66.
14. Luke Dones et al., "Origin and Evolution of the Cometary Reservoirs," *Space Science Reviews* 197 (November 2015): 191–269, doi:10.1007/s11214-015-0223-2.
15. Harold F. Levison et al., "Origin of the Structure of the Kuiper Belt during a Dynamical Instability in the Orbits of Uranus and Neptune," *Icarus* 196, no. 1 (July 2008): 258–273, doi:10.1016/j.icarus.2007.11.035.
16. Joseph M. Hahn, "The Secular Evolution of the Primordial Kuiper Belt," *Astrophysical Journal* 595, no. 1 (September 20, 2003): 531–549, doi:10.1086/377195; Scott J. Kenyon and Jane X. Luu, "Accretion in the Early Kuiper Belt. II. Fragmentation," *Astronomical Journal*

118, no. 2 (August 1999): 1101–1119, doi:10.1086/300969.

17. A. Di Ruscio et al., "Analysis of *Cassini* Radio Tracking Data for the Construction of INPOP19a: A New Estimate of the Kuiper Belt Mass," *Astronomy and Astrophysics* 640 (August 2020): id. A7, doi:10.1051/0004-6361/202037920.
18. Levison et al., "Secular Evolution of Kuiper Belt," 531–49.
19. David Nesvorný, "Jumping Neptune Can Explain the Kuiper Belt Kernel," *Astronomical Journal* 150, no. 3 (September 2015): id. 68, doi:10.1088/0004-6256/150/3/68; A. Morbidelli, H. S. Gaspar, and D. Nesvorný, "Origin of the Peculiar Eccentricity Distribution of the Inner Cold Kuiper Belt," *Icarus* 232 (April 2014): 81–87, doi:10.1016/j.icarus.2013.12.023; Wesley C. Fraser et al., "The Absolute Magnitude Distribution of Kuiper Belt Objects," *Astrophysical Journal* 782, no. 2 (February 20, 2014): id. 100, doi:10.1088/0004-637X/782/2/100; Elliot et al., "Deep Ecliptic Survey," 1117–1162; Levison et al., "Secular Evolution of Kuiper Belt," 531–549.
20. J. A. Correa-Otto and M. F. Calandra, "Stability in the Most External Region of the Oort Cloud: Evolution of the Ejected Comets," *Monthly Notices of the Royal Astronomical Society* 490, no. 2 (December 2019): 2495–2506, doi:10.1093/mnras/stz2671.
21. Paul R. Weissmann, "The Mass of the Oort Cloud," *Astronomy and Astrophysics* 118, no. 1 (February 1983): 90–94, articles.adsabs.harvard.edu/pdf/1983A%26A...118...90W.
22. Giorgi Kokaia and Melvyn B. Davies, "Stellar Encounters with Giant Molecular Clouds," *Monthly Notices of the Royal Astronomical Society* 489, no. 4 (November 2019): 5165–5180, doi:10.1093/mnras/stz813.
23. Paul R. Weissman and Harold F. Levison, "Origin and Evolution of the Unusual Object 1996 PW: Asteroids from the Oort Cloud?," *Astrophysical Journal Letters* 488, no. 2 (October 20, 1997): L133–L136, doi:10.1086/310940.
24. D. Hutsemékers et al., "Isotopic Abundances of Carbon and Nitrogen in Jupiter-Family and Oort Cloud Comets," *Astronomy and Astrophysics: Letters* 440, no. 2 (September 2005): L21–L24, doi:10.1051/0004-6361:200500160; Takafumi Ootsubo et al., "Grain Properties of Oort Cloud Comets: Modeling the Mineralogical Composition of Cometary Dust from Mid-Infrared Emission Features," *Planetary and Space Science* 55, no. 9 (June 2007): 1044–1049, doi:10.1016/j.pss.2006.11.012; Michael J. Mumma et al., "Parent Volatiles in Comet 9P/Tempel 1: Before and After Impact," *Science Express* 310, no. 5746 (October 14, 2005): 270–274, doi:10.1126/science.1119337.
25. Laurette Piani et al., "Earth's Water May Have Been Inherited from Material Similar to Enstatite Meteorites," *Science* 369, no. 6507 (August 28, 2020): 1110–1113, doi:10.1126/science.aba1948.
26. Cheng Chen et al., "Late Delivery of Nitrogen to the Earth," *Astronomical Journal* 157, no. 2 (February 1, 2019): id. 80, doi:10.3847/1538-3881/aaf96a.
27. Philip A. Bland and Natalya A. Artemieva, "The Rate of Small Impacts on Earth," *Meteoritics and Planetary Science* 41, no. 4 (April 2006): 607–631, doi:10.1111/j.1945-5100.2006.tb00485.x.
28. Heather Pringle, "New Respect for Metal's Role in Ancient Arctic Cultures," *Science* 277, no. 5327 (August 8, 1997): 766–767, doi:10.1126/science.277.5327.766.
29. Donald W. Davis, "Sub-Million-Year Age Resolution of Precambrian Igneous Events by Thermal Extraction-Thermal Ionization Mass Spectrometer Pb Dating of Zircon: Application to Crystallization of the Sudbury Impact Melt Sheet," *Geology* 36, no. 5 (May 2008): 383–386, doi:10.1130/G234502A.1; Joseph A. Petrus, Doreen E. Ames, and Balz S. Kamber, "On the Track of the Elusive Sudbury Impact: Geochemical Evidence for a

Chrondrite or Comet Bolide," *Terra Nova* 27, no. 1 (February 2015): 9–20, doi:10.1111/ter.12125.

30. Tom Jewiss, "The Mining History of the Sudbury Area," *Rocks and Minerals in Canada* (Spring 1983), posted by Earth Science Museum, University of Waterloo, accessed September 3, 2021, uwaterloo.ca/earth-sciences-museum/resources/mining-canada/mining-history-sudbury-area.
31. Jewiss, "Mining History of the Sudbury Area."
32. Jason Kirk et al., "The Origin of Gold in South Africa," *American Scientist* 91, no. 6 (November 2003): 534–541, doi:10.1511/2003.38.907. A pdf is available at https://www.researchgate.net/publication/240968643_The_Origin_of_Gold_in_South_Africa.
33. Kirk et al., "Gold in South Africa," 534–541.
34. Wolf Uwe Reimold et al., "Economic Mineral Deposits in Impact Structures: A Review," in *Impact Tectonics*, ed. Christian Koeberl and Herbert Henkel (Berlin: Springer, January 2005), 479–552, doi:10.1007/3-540-27548-7_20.
35. I provide detailed descriptions of these events in Hugh Ross, *Weathering Climate Change: A Fresh Approach* (Covina, CA: RTB Press, 2020), 129–133, 143–147, 153–161, 229–238.
36. James Goff et al., "The Eltanin Asteroid Impact: Possible South Pacific Palaeomegatsunami Footprint and Potential Implications for the Pliocene-Pleistocene Transition," *Journal of Quaternary Science* 27, no. 7 (October 2012): 660–670, doi:10.1002/jqs.2571; Ross, *Weathering Climate Change*, 130–133.
37. Winfried H. Schwarz et al.,"Coeval Ages of Australasian, Central American and Western Canadian Tektites Reveal Multiple Impacts 790 ka Ago," *Geochimica et Cosmochimica Acta* 178 (April 1, 2016): 307–319, doi:10.1016/j.gca.2015.12.037; Richard A. Muller, "Avalanches at the Core-Mantle Boundary," *Geophysical Research Letters* 29, no. 19 (October 12, 2002): 41-1–41-4, doi:10.1029/2002GL015938; Aaron J. Cavosie et al., "New Clues from Earth's Most Elusive Impact Crater: Evidence of Reidite in Australasian Tektites from Thailand," *Geology* 46, no. 3 (March 1, 2018): 203–206, doi:10.1130/G39711.1; Kerry Sieh et al., "Australasian Impact Crater Buried under the Bolaven Volcanic Field, Southern Laos," *Proceedings of the National Academy of Sciences, USA* 117, no. 3 (January 21, 2020): 1346–1353, doi:10.1073/pnas.1904368116; Ross, *Weathering Climate Change*, 229–238.
38. Kurt H. Kjær et al., "A Large Impact Crater beneath Hiawatha Glacier in Northwest Greenland," *Science Advances* 4, no. 11 (November 14, 2018): id. eaar8173, doi:10.1126/sciadv.aar8173; James H. Wittke et al., "Evidence for the Deposition of 10 Million Tonnes of Impact Spherules across Four Continents 12,800 Y Ago," *Proceedings of the National Academy of Sciences, USA* 110, no. 23 (June 4, 2013): E2088–E2097, doi:10.1073/pnas.1301760110; Ross, *Weathering Climate Change*, 153–161.
39. Hugh Ross, *Improbable Planet: How Earth Became Humanity's Home* (Grand Rapids, MI: Baker Books, 2016), 119–197.

Chapter 13: The Lunar Interior

1. "219 Planet Moons," Go Astronomy, March 2021, go-astronomy.com/planets/planet-moons.htm, access date September 3, 2021.
2. Mark A. Wieczorek et al., "The Constitution and Structure of the Lunar Interior," *Reviews in Mineralogy and Geochemistry* 60, no. 1 (January 2006): 221–364, doi:10.2138/rmg.2006.60.3.
3. I provide a detailed description of the Moon-forming event in *Improbable Planet: How Earth Became Humanity's Home* (Grand Rapids, MI: Baker Books, 2016), 48–58.
4. J. O. Dickey et al., "Lunar Laser Ranging: A Continuing Legacy of the Apollo Program,"

Science 265, no. 5171 (July 22, 1994): 482–490, doi:10.1126/science.265.5171.482.

5. Kimmo Innanen, Seppo Mikkola, and Paul Wiegert, "The Earth-Moon System and the Dynamical Stability of the Inner Solar System," *Astronomical Journal* 116, no. 4 (October 1998): 2055–2057, doi:10.1086/300552.
6. Simon J. Lock, Sarah T. Stewart, and Matija Ćuk, "The Energy Budget and Figure of Earth during Recovery from the Moon-Forming Giant Impact," *Earth and Planetary Science Letters* 530 (January 15, 2020): id. 115885, doi:10.1016/j.epsl.2019.115885; Natsuki Hosono et al., "Terrestrial Magma Ocean Origin of the Moon," *Nature Geoscience* 12, no. 6 (June 2019): 418–423, doi:10.1038/s41561-019-0354-2.
7. Lock, Stewart, and Ćuk, "Energy Budget and Figure of Earth"; Hosono et al., "Terrestrial Magma Ocean Origin," 418–423.
8. Lock, Stewart, and Ćuk; Hosono et al., 418–423.
9. Dave Waltham, "Anthropic Selection for the Moon's Mass," *Astrobiology* 4, no. 4 (Winter 2004): 460–461, doi:10.1089/ast.2004.4.460.
10. J. Laskar and P. Robutel, "The Chaotic Obliquity of the Planets," *Nature* 361, no. 6413 (February 18, 1993): 608–612, doi:10.1038/361608a0.
11. Gongjie Li and Konstantin Batygin, "On the Spin-Axis Dynamics of a Moonless Earth," *Astrophysical Journal* 790, no. 1 (July 20, 2014): id. 69, doi:10.1088/0004-637X/790/1/69; Laskar and Robutel, "Chaotic Obliquity of the Planets," 608–612; Neil F. Comins, *What If the Moon Didn't Exist?: Voyages to Earths That Might Have Been* (New York: HarperPerennial, 1995).
12. André Berger, "Obliquity and Precession for the Last 5,000,000 Years," *Astronomy and Astrophysics* 51, no. 1 (July 1976): 127–135, researchgate.net/publication/234372369_Obliquity_and_precession_for_the_last_5_000_000_years.
13. Waltham, "Anthropic Selection," 463.
14. D. Waltham, "Our Large Moon Does Not Stabilize Earth's Axis," *EPSC Abstracts* 8, (European Planetary Science Congress, University College London, London, UK, September 8–13, 2013), id. EPSC2013-37, davidwaltham.com/wp-content/uploads/2013/03/EPSC2013-37.pdf; Waltham, "Anthropic Selection," 460–461.
15. Dave Waltham, "Half a Billion Years of Good Weather: Gaia or Good Luck?," *Astronomy and Geophysics* 48, no. 3 (June 2007): 3.22–3.24, doi:10.1111/j.1468-4004.2007.48322.x; Dave Waltham, "The Large-Moon Hypothesis: Can It Be Tested," *International Journal of Astrobiology* 5, no. 4 (October 2006): 327–331, doi:10.1017/S1473550406003120.
16. Meng-Hua Zhu et al., "Reconstructing the Late-Accretion History of the Moon," *Nature* 571, no. 7764 (July 11, 2019): 226–229, doi:10.1038/s41586-019-1359-0.
17. Zhu et al., "The Late-Accretion History," 226–229; James M. D. Day, "Low Retention of Impact Material by the Moon," *Nature* 571, no. 7764 (July 11, 2019): 177–178, doi:10.1038/d41586-019-02066-w.
18. Laura R. Prugh and Christopher D. Golden, "Does Moonlight Increase Predation Risk? Meta-Analysis Reveals Divergent Responses of Nocturnal Mammals to Lunar Cycles," *Journal of Animal Ecology* 83, no. 2 (March 2014): 504–514, doi:10.1111/1365-2656.12148; M. S. Palmer et al., "A 'Dynamic' Landscape of Fear: Prey Responses to Spatiotemporal Variations in Predation Risk across the Lunar Cycle," *Ecology Letters* 20, no. 11 (November 2017): 1364–1373; Hugh Ross, "Lunar Designs Optimize Life for Both Predators and Prey," *Today's New Reason to Believe* (blog), Reasons to Believe, October 23, 2018, reasons.org/explore/blogs/todays-new-reason-to-believe/lunar-designs-optimize-life-for-both-predators-and-prey.
19. Xiao Tang et al., "Estimation of Lunar FeO Abundance Based on Imaging by LRO Diviner,"

Research in Astronomy and Astrophysics 16, no. 2 (February 2016): id. 24, doi:10.1088/1674-4527/16/2/024; M. Naito et al., "Iron Distribution of the Moon Observed by the Kaguya Gamma-Ray Spectrometer: Geological Implications for the South Pole-Aitken Basin, the Orientale Basin, and the Tycho Crater," *Icarus* 310 (August 2018): 21–31, doi:10.1016/j.icarus.2017.12.005; O. L. Kuskov, E. V. Kronrod, and V. A. Kronrod, "Geochemical Constraints on the Cold and Hot Models of the Moon's Interior: 1-Bulk Composition," *Solar System Research* 52, no. 6 (November 2018): 467–479, doi:10.1134/S0038094618060047; Jiachao Liu and Jie Li, "Solidification of Lunar Core from Melting Experiments on the Fe-Ni-S System," *Earth and Planetary Science Letters* 530 (January 2020): id. 115834, doi:10.1016/j.epsl.2019.115834.

20. V. Viswanathan et al., "Observational Constraint on the Radius and Oblateness of the Lunar Core-Mantle Boundary," *Geophysical Research Letters* 46, no. 13 (July 2019): 7295–7303, doi:10.1029/2019GL082677.
21. Viswanathan et al., "Observational Constraint," 7295–7303.
22. Viswanathan et al., "Observational Constraint," 7295.
23. Hélène Piet, James Badro, and Philippe Gillet, "Geochemical Constraints on the Size of the Moon-Forming Giant Impact," *Geophysical Research Letters* 44, no. 23 (December 16, 2017): 11,770–11,777, doi:10.1002/2017GL075225.
24. Hongping Deng et al., "Primordial Earth Mantle Heterogeneity Caused by the Moon-Forming Giant Impact?," *Astrophysical Journal* 887, no. 2 (December 20, 2019): id. 211, doi:10.3847/1538-4357/ab50b9.
25. Erick J. Cano, Zachary D. Sharp, and Charles K. Shearer, "Distinct Oxygen Isotope Compositions of the Earth and Moon," *Nature Geoscience* 13, no. 4 (April 2020): 270–274, doi:10.1038/s41561-020-0550-0.
26. Mark A. Wieczorek et al., "The Crust of the Moon as Seen by GRAIL," *Science* 339, no. 6120 (February 8, 2013): 671–675, doi:10.1126/science.1231530.
27. Wieczorek et al., "Crust of the Moon," 671–675; Philippe Lognonné, Jeannine Gagnepain-Beyneix, and Hugues Chenet, "A New Seismic Model of the Moon: Implications for Structure, Thermal Evolution, and Formation of the Moon," *Earth and Planetary Science Letters* 211, nos. 1–2 (June 15, 2003): 27–44, doi:10.1016/S0012-821X(03)00172-9; A. Khan and K. Mosegaard, "An Inquiry into the Lunar Interior: A Nonlinear Inversion of the Apollo Lunar Seismic Data," *Journal of Geophysical Research: Planets* 107, no. E6 (June 2002): id. 5036, doi:10.1029/2001JE001658.
28. Albert Einstein, "Die Grundlage der allgemeinen Relativitätstheorie," *Annalen der Physik* 49 (1916): 769–822. The English translation is in Albert Einstein, Herman Minkowski, H. A. Lorentz, and Hermann Weyl, *The Principle of Relativity: A Collection of Original Memoirs on the Special and General Theory of Relativity*, notes by A. Sommerfeld and trans. by W. Perrett and G. B. Jeffrey (London: Methuen and Co., 1923), 109–164.
29. Einstein, "Die Grundlage der allgemeinen Relativitätstheorie."
30. Frank Watson Dyson, Arthur Stanley Eddington, and C. Davidson, "IX. A Determination of the Deflection of Light by the Sun's Gravitational Field, from Observations Made at the Total Eclipse of May 29, 1919," *Philosophical Transactions of the Royal Society of London, Series A* 220 (January 1, 1920): 291–333, doi:10.1098/rsta.1920.0009.
31. Saied Mighani et al., "The End of the Lunar Dynamo," *Science Advances* 6, no. 1 (January 1, 2020): id. eaax0883, doi:10.1126/sciadv.aax0883.
32. V. N. Zharkov, "On the History of the Lunar Orbit," *Solar System Research* 34, no. 1 (January 2000): p. 1, ui.adsabs.harvard.edu/abs/2000SoSyR..34....1Z/abstract.

33. James Green et al., "When the Moon Had a Magnetosphere," *Science Advances* 6, no. 42 (October 14, 2020): id. eabc0865, doi:10.1126/sciadv.abc0865; science.org/doi/10.1126/sciadv.abc0865.
34. John A. Tarduno et al., "Absence of a Long-Lived Lunar Paleomagnetosphere," *Science Advances* 7, no. 32 (August 4, 2021): id. eab7647, doi:10.1126/sciadv.abi7647.
35. Tim Elliott, "A Chip Off the Old Block," in Tim Elliott and Sarah T. Stewart, "Shadows Cast on the Moon's Origin," *Nature* 504, no. 7478 (December 5, 2013): 90, doi:10.1038/504090a.

Chapter 14: Earth's Core Features

1. S. B. Smithson et al., "Seismic Results at Kola and KTB Deep Scientific Boreholes: Velocities, Reflections, Fluids, and Crustal Composition," *Tectonophysics* 329, nos. 1–4 (December 31, 2000): 301–317, doi:10.1016/S0040-1951(00)00200-6.
2. I describe this fine-tuning of earthquake activity (plate tectonics) in two previous books: *Improbable Planet: How Earth Became Humanity's Home* (Grand Rapids, MI: Baker Books, 2016), 134–139, 171–175, 181–189, 194–197, 200–204; *Weathering Climate Change: A Fresh Approach* (Covina, CA: RTB Press, 2020), 99–102, 133–140, 168–171.
3. Mary M. Reagan et al., "The Effect of Nickel on the Strength of Iron Nickel Alloys: Implications for the Earth's Inner Core," *Physics of the Earth and Planetary Interiors* 283 (October 2018): 43–47, doi:10.1016/j.pepi.2018.08.003; Z. G. Bazhanova, V. V. Roizen, and A. R. Oganov, "High-Pressure Behavior of the Fe-S System and Composition of the Earth's Inner Core," *Physics-Uspekhi* 60, no. 10 (October 2017): 1025–1032, doi:10.3367/UFNe.2017.03.038079; D. Alfè, M. J. Gillan, and G. D. Price, "Temperature and Composition of the Earth's Core," *Contemporary Physics* 48, no. 2 (2007): 63–80, doi:10.1080/00107510701529653.
4. Samuel Thompson et al., "Compression Experiments to 126 GPa and 2500 K and Thermal Equation of State of Fe_3S: Implications for Sulfur in the Earth's Core," *Earth and Planetary Science Letters* 534 (March 15, 2020): id. 116080, doi:10.1016/j.epsl.2020.116080; Shigehiko Tateno et al., "Fe_2S: The Most Fe-Rich Iron Sulfide at the Earth's Inner Core Pressures," *Geophysical Research Letters* 46, no. 21 (November 16, 2019): 11,944–11,949, doi:10.1029/2019GL085248; E. Edmund et al., "Velocity-Density Systematics of Fe-5wt%Si: Constraints on Si Content in the Earth's Core," *Journal of Geophysical Research: Solid Earth* 124, no. 4 (April 2019): 3436–3447, doi:10.1029/2018JB016904; Tilak Das et al., "First-Principles Prediction of Si-Doped Fe Carbide as One of the Possible Constituents of Earth's Inner Core," *Geophysical Research Letters* 44, no. 17 (September 16, 2017): 8776–8784, doi:10.1002/2017GL073545; Hitoshi Gomi, Yingwei Fei, and Takashi Yoshino, "The Effects of Ferromagnetism and Interstitial Hydrogen on the Equations of States of hcp and dhcp FeHx: Implications for the Earth's Inner Core," *American Mineralogist* 103, no. 8 (August 1, 2018): 1271–1281, doi:10.2138/am-2018-6295 Alfè, Gillan, and Price, "Temperature and Composition," 63–80; Bazhanova, Roizen, and Oganov, "High-Pressure Behavior," 1025–1032.
5. Haruka Ozawa et al., "High-Pressure Melting Experiments on Fe-Si Alloys and Implications for Silicon as a Light Element in the Core," *Earth and Planetary Science Letters* 456 (December 15, 2016): 47–54, doi:10.1016/j.epsl.2016.08.042; Thompson et al., "Compression Experiments," id. 116080; Tateno et al., "Most Fe-Rich," 11,944–11,949; Edmund et al., "Velocity-Density Systematics," 3436–3447.
6. Shunpei Yokoo et al., "Melting Experiments on Liquidus Phase Relations in the Fe-S-O Ternary System under Core Pressures," *Geophysical Research Letters* 46, no. 10 (May 28, 2019): 5137–5145, doi:10.1029/2019GL082277.

7. Hrvoje Tkalčić and Thanh-Son Phạm, "Shear Properties of Earth's Inner Core Constrained by a Detection of *J* Waves in Global Correlation Wavefield," *Science* 362, no. 6412 (October 19, 2018): 329–332, doi:10.1126/science.aau7649; Jessica C. E. Irving, "Earth's Soft Heart," *Science* 362, no. 6412 (October 19, 2018): 294, doi:10.1126/science.aav2296.
8. R. Deguen, T. Alboussière, and S. Labrosse, "Double-Diffusive Translation of Earth's Inner Core," *Geophysical Journal International* 214, no. 1 (July 2018): 88–107, doi:10.1093/gji/ggy120; Alfè, Gillan, and Price, "Temperature and Composition," 63–80.
9. Youjun Zhang et al., "Reconciliation of Experiments and Theory on Transport Properties of Iron and the Geodynamo," *Physical Review Letters* 125, no. 7 (August 14, 2020): id. 078501, doi:10.1103/PhysRevLett.125.078501.
10. Adam M. Dziewonski and Don L. Anderson, "Preliminary Reference Earth Model," *Physics of the Earth and Planetary Interiors* 25, no. 4 (June 1981): 297–356, doi:10.1016/0031-9201(81)90046-7.
11. A. J. Biggin et al., "Paleomagnetic Field Intensity Variations Suggest Mesoproterozoic Inner-Core Nucleation," *Nature* 526, no. 7572 (October 8, 2015): 245–248, doi:10.1038/nature15523.
12. Richard K. Bono et al., "Young Inner Core Inferred from Ediacaran Ultra-Low Geomagnetic Field Intensity," *Nature Geoscience* 12, no. 2 (February 2019): 143, doi:10.1038/s41561-018-0288-0.
13. P. Driscoll and D. Bercovici, "On the Thermal and Magnetic Histories of Earth and Venus: Influences of Melting, Radioactivity, and Conductivity," *Physics of the Earth and Planetary Interiors* 236 (November 2014): 36–51, doi:10.1016/j.pepi.2014.08.004; Christopher J. Davies, "Cooling History of Earth's Core with High Thermal Conductivity," *Physics of the Earth and Planetary Interiors* 247 (October 2015): 65–79, doi:10.1016/j.pepi.2015.03.007; Stéphane Labrosse, "Thermal Evolution of the Core with a High Thermal Conductivity," *Physics of the Earth and Planetary Interiors* 247 (October 2015): 36–55, doi:10.1016/j.pepi.2015.02.002.
14. Anatoly B. Belonoshko, Rajeev Ahuja, and Börje Johansson, "Stability of the Body-Centered-Cubic Phase of Iron in the Earth's Inner Core," *Nature* 424, no. 6952 (August 28, 2003): 1032–1034, doi:10.1038/nature01954; Anatoly B. Belonoshko et al., "Stabilization of Body-Centered Cubic Iron under Inner-Core Conditions," *Nature Geoscience* 10 (April 2017): 312–316, doi:10.1038/ngeo2892.
15. Davide Gambino et al., "Longitudinal Spin Fluctuations in bcc and Liquid Fe at High Temperature and Pressure Calculated with a Supercell Approach," *Physical Review B* 102, no. 1 (July 1, 2020): id. 014402, doi:10.1103/PhysRevB.102.014402; Belonoshko et al., "Stabilization of Body-Centered Cubic Iron," 312–316.
16. Ryosuke Sinmyo, Kei Hirose, and Yasuo Ohishi, "Melting Curve of Iron to 290 GPa Determined in a Resistance-Heated Diamond-Anvil Cell," *Earth and Planetary Science Letters* 510 (March 15, 2019): 45–52, doi:10.1016/j.epsl.2019.01.006; Nguyen Ba Duc et al., "Investigation of the Melting Point, Debye Frequency and Temperature of Iron at High Pressure," *European Physical Journal B* 93, no. 6 (June 2020): id. 115, doi:10.1140/epjb/e2020-10083-8; S. Anzellini et al., "Melting of Iron at Earth's Inner Core Boundary Based on Fast X-Ray Diffraction," *Science* 340, no. 6131 (April 26, 2013): 464–466, doi:10.1126/science.1233514; Dongzhou Zhang et al., "Temperature of Earth's Core Constrained from Melting of Fe and $Fe_{0.9}Ni_{0.1}$ at High Pressures," *Earth and Planetary Science Letters* 447 (August 1, 2016): 72–83, doi:10.1016/j.epsl.2016.04.026; Wen-Jin Zhang et al., "Melting Curves and Entropy of Melting of Iron under Earth's Core Conditions," *Physics of the Earth and*

Planetary Interiors 244 (July 2015): 69–77, doi:10.1016/j.pepi.2014.10.011; O. L. Anderson, D. G. Isaak, and V. E. Nelson, "The High-Pressure Melting Temperature of Hexagonal Close-Packed Iron Determined from Thermal Physics," *Journal of Physics and Chemistry Solids* 64, no. 11 (November 2003): 2125–2131, doi:10.1016/S0022-3697(03)00112-4; Tao Sun et al., "Melting Properties from *ab initio* Free Energy Calculations: Iron at the Earth's Inner Core Boundary," *Physical Review B* 98, no. 22 (December 1, 2018): id. 224301, doi:10.1103/PhysRevB.98.224301.

17. R. Torchio et al., "Melting Curve and Phase Relations of Fe-Ni Alloys: Implications for the Earth's Core Composition," *Geophysical Research Letters* 47, no. 14 (July 28, 2020): id. E2020GL088169, doi:10.1029/2020GL088169; Tetsuya Komabayashi et al., "Phase Relations in the System Fe-Ni-Si to 200 GPa and 3900 K and Implications for Earth's Core," *Earth and Planetary Science Letters* 512 (April 15, 2019): 83–88, doi:10.1016/j.epsl.2019.01.056; Sinmyo, Hirose, and Ohishi, "Melting Curve of Iron," 45–52; Zhang et al., "Temperature of Earth's Core," 72–83.
18. Anatoly B. Belonoshko et al., "Low Viscosity of the Earth's Inner Core," *Nature Communications* 10 (June 6, 2019): id. 2483, doi:10.1038/s41467-019-10346-2.
19. Scott Burdick, Lauren Waszek, and Vedran Lekić, "Seismic Tomography of the Uppermost Inner Core," *Earth and Planetary Science Letters* 528 (December 15, 2019): id. 115789, doi:10.1016/j.epsl.2019.115789; Tanja Pejić et al., "Transdimensional Bayesian Attenuation Tomography of the Upper Inner Core," *Journal of Geophysical Research: Solid Earth* 124, no. 2 (February 2019): 1929–1943, doi:10.1029/2018JB016400; Tanja Pejić et al., "Attenuation Tomography of the Upper Inner Core," *Journal of Geophysical Research: Solid Earth* 122, no. 4 (April 2017): 3008–3032, doi:10.1002/2016JB013692; Hrvoje Tkalčić, "Complex Inner Core of the Earth: The Last Frontier of Global Seismology," *Reviews of Geophysics* 53, no. 1 (March 2015): 59–94, doi:10.1002/2014rg000469.
20. Dongdong Tian and Lianxing Wen, "Seismological Evidence for a Localized Mushy Zone at the Earth's Inner Core Boundary," *Nature Communications* 8, no. 1 (August 2017): id. 165, doi:10.1038/s41467-017-00229-9.
21. S. C. Singh, M. A. J. Taylor, and J. P. Montagner, "On the Presence of Liquid in Earth's Inner Core," *Science* 287, no. 5462 (March 31, 2000): 2471–2474, doi:10.1126/science.287.5462.2471; Arwen Deuss, "Normal Mode Constraints on Shear and Compressional Wave Velocity of the Earth's Inner Core," *Earth and Planetary Science Letters* 268, nos. 3–4 (April 30, 2008): 364–375, doi:10.1016/j.epsl.2008.01.029; M. Lasbleis, M. Kervazo, and G. Choblet, "The Fate of Liquids Trapped during the Earth's Inner Core Growth," *Geophysical Research Letters* 47, no. 2 (January 28, 2020): id. E2019GL085654, doi:10.1029/2019GL085654.
22. Ludovic Huguet et al., "Structure of a Mushy Layer under Hypergravity with Implications for Earth's Inner Core," *Geophysical Journal International* 204, no. 3 (March 2016): 1729–1755, doi:10.1093/gji/ggv554; Ikuro Sumita et al., "A Model for Sedimentary Compaction of a Viscous Medium and Its Application to Inner-Core Growth," *Geophysical Journal International* 124, no. 2 (February1996): 502–524, doi:10.1111/j.1365-246X.1996.tb07034.x.
23. Anna M. Mäkinen, Arwen Deuss, and Simon A. T. Redfern, "Anisotropy of Earth's Inner Core Intrinsic Attenuation from Seismic Normal Mode Models," *Earth and Planetary Science Letters* 404 (October 15, 2014): 354–364, doi:10.1016/j.epsl.2014.08.009.
24. Xianwei Sha and Ronald E. Cohen, "Lattice Dynamics and Thermodynamics of bcc Iron under Pressure: First-Principles Linear Response Study," *Physical Review B* 73, no. 10 (March 1, 2006): id. 104303, doi:10.1103/PhysRevB.73.104303; Belonoshko et al., "Stability of the Body-Centered-Cubic Phase," 1032–1034.

25. Belonoshko et al., "Low Viscosity."
26. A. Cao and B. Romanowicz, "Constraints on Shear Wave Attenuation in the Earth's Inner Core from an Observation of PKJKP," *Geophysical Research Letters* 36, no. 9 (May 2009): id. L09301, doi:10.1029/2009GL038342.
27. Janneke de Jong, Lennart de Groot, and Arwen Deuss, "Observing the Signature of the Magnetic Field's Behaviour in the Radial Variation of Inner Core Anisotropy," *22nd EGU General Assembly*, held online, May 4–8, 2020: id. 20504.
28. Kenneth P. Kodama et al., "Palaeointensity of the 1.3 Billion-Yr-Old Gardar Basalts, Southern Greenland Revisited: No Evidence for Onset of Inner Core Growth," *Geophysical Journal International* 217, no. 3 (June 2019): 1974–1987, doi:10.1093/gji/ggz126; Aleksey V. Smirnov et al., "Palaeointensity, Core Thermal Conductivity and the Unknown Age of the Inner Core," *Geophysical Journal International* 205, no. 2 (May 1, 2016): 1190–1195, doi:10.1093/gji/ggw080.
29. J. A. Jacobs, "The Earth's Inner Core," *Nature* 172, no. 4372 (August 15, 1953): 297–298, doi:10.1038/172297a0.
30. Zuihong Zou, Keith D. Koper, and Vernon F. Cormier, "The Structure at the Base of the Outer Core Inferred from Seismic Waves Diffracted around the Inner Core," *Journal of Geophysical Research: Solid Earth* 113, no. B5 (May 2008): id. B05314, doi:10.1029/2007JB005316; Jenny Wong, Christopher J. Davies, and Chris A. Jones, "A Boussinesq Slurry Model of the F-Layer at the Base of Earth's Outer Core," *Geophysical Journal International* 214, no. 3 (September 2018): 2236–2249, doi:10.1093/gji/ggy245.
31. Toshiki Ohtaki et al., "Seismological Evidence for Laterally Heterogeneous Lowermost Outer Core of the Earth," *Journal of Geophysical Research: Solid Earth* 123, no. 12 (December 2018): 10,903–10,917, doi:10.1029/2018JB015857.
32. Wong, Davies, and Jones, "Boussinesq Slurry Model," 2236–2249.
33. Shin-ichi Takehiro and Youhei Sasaki, "Penetration of Steady Fluid Motions into an Outer Stable Layer Excited by MHD Thermal Convection in Rotating Spherical Shells," *Physics of the Earth and Planetary Interiors* 276 (March 2018): 258–264, doi:10.1016/j.pepi.2017.03.001; V. Lesur, K. Whaler, and I. Wardinski, "Are Geomagnetic Data Consistent with Stably Stratified Flow at the Core-Mantle Boundary?," *Geophysical Journal International* 201, no. 2 (May 2015): 929–946, doi:10.1093/gji/ggv031.
34. Sinmyo, Hirose, and Ohishi, "Melting Curve of Iron," 45–52; Duc et al., "Investigation of the Melting Point"; Komabayashi et al., "Phase Relations in the System," 83–88.
35. Sinmyo, Hirose, and Ohishi, "Melting Curve of Iron," 45–52; Duc et al., "Investigation of the Melting Point"; Komabayashi et al., "Phase Relations in the System," 83–88.
36. Brian J. Anderson et al., "The Magnetic Field of Mercury," *Space Science Reviews* 152, nos. 1–4 (May 2010): 307–339, doi:10.1007/s11214-009-9544-3.
37. Robert J. Lillis et al., "Time History of the Martian Dynamo from Crater Magnetic Field Analysis," *Journal of Geophysical Research: Planets* 118, no. 7 (July 2013): 1488–1511, doi:10.1002/jgre.20105.
38. Håkan Svedhem et al., "Venus as a More Earth-Like Planet," *Nature* 450, no. 7170 (November 29, 2007): 629–632, doi:10.1038/nature06432.
39. Saied Mighani et al., "The End of the Lunar Dynamo," *Science Advances* 6, no. 1 (January 1, 2020): id. eaax0883, doi:10.1126/sciadv.aax0883; Ian Garrick-Bethell et al., "Early Earth Magnetism," *Science* 323, no. 5912 (January 16, 2009): 356–359, doi:10.1126/science.1166804; Erin K. Shea et al., "A Long-Lived Lunar Core Dynamo," *Science* 335, no. 6067 (January 27, 2012): 453–456, doi:10.1126/science.1215359; Benjamin P. Weiss and Sonia

M. Tikoo, "The Lunar Dynamo," *Science* 346, no. 6214 (December 5, 2014): id. 1246753, doi:10.1126/science.1246753; Ian Garrick-Bethell et al., "Further Evidence for Early Lunar Magnetism from Troctolite 76535," *Journal of Geophysical Research: Planets* 122, no. 1 (January 2017): 76–93, doi:10.1002/2016JE005154.

40. M. G. Kivelson, K. K. Khurana, and M. Volwerk, "The Permanent and Inductive Magnetic Moments of Ganymede," *Icarus* 157, no. 2 (June 2002): 507–522, doi:10.1006/icar.2002.6834.
41. Alexandra Witze, "Greenland Rocks Suggest Earth's Magnetic Field Is Older Than We Thought," *Nature* 576, no. 7787 (December 19, 2019): id. 347, doi:10.1038/d41586-019-03807-7; Bernard Marty et al., "Nitrogen Partial Pressure in the Archean Atmosphere from Analysis of Hydrothermal Quartz," *American Geophysical Union*, Fall Meeting 2012 (December 2012): abstract id. V54b-04.
42. John A. Tarduno et al., "A Hadean to Paleoarchean Geodynamo Recorded by Single Zircon Crystals," *Science* 349, no. 6247 (July 31, 2015): 521–524, doi:10.1126/science.aaa9114; Matthew S. Dare et al., "Detrital Magnetite and Chromite in Jack Hills Quartzite Cobbles: Further Evidence for the Preservation of Primary Magnetizations and New Insights into Sediment Provenance," *Earth and Planetary Science Letters* 451 (October 1, 2016): 298–314, doi:10.1016/j.epsl.2016.05.009; B. P. Weiss et al., "Paleomagnetism of Hadean and Archean Detrital Zircons from the Jack Hills, Western Australia," *American Geophysical Union*, Fall Meeting 2016 (December 2016): abstract id. V11D-05; R. D. Cottrell et al., "The Hadean to Paleoarchean Geodynamo: Microconglomerate Tests from Siliciclastic Metasedimentary Rocks from the Southern Cross Terrane of Western Australia," *American Geophysical Union*, Fall Meeting 2016 (December 2016): abstract id. DI13A-2344.
43. Bernard Marty et al., "Nitrogen Isotopic Composition and Density of the Archean Atmosphere," *Science* 342, no. 6154 (October 4, 2013): 101–104, doi:10.1126/science.1240971; Marty et al., "Nitrogen Partial Pressure," abstract id. V54b-04.
44. John A. Tarduno, Eric G. Blackman, and Eric E. Mamajek, "Detecting the Oldest Geodynamo and Attendant Shielding from the Solar Wind: Implications for Habitability," *Physics of the Earth and Planetary Interiors* 233 (August 2014): 68–87, doi:10.1016/j.pepi.2014.05.007; Marty et al., "Nitrogen Partial Pressure," abstract id. V54b-04.
45. Crystal Y. Shi et al., "Formation of an Interconnected Network of Iron Melt at Earth's Lower Mantle Conditions," *Nature Geoscience* 6, no. 11 (November 2013): 971–975, doi:10.1038/ngeo1956.
46. Tushar Mittal et al., "Precipitation of Multiple Light Elements to Power Earth's Early Dynamo," *Earth and Planetary Science Letters* 532 (February 15, 2020): id. 116030, doi:10.1016/j.epsl.2019.116030.
47. Behnam Seyed-Mahmoud, Gary Henderson, and Keith Aldridge, "A Numerical Model for Elliptical Instability of the Earth's Fluid Outer Core," *Physics of the Earth and Planetary Interiors* 117, nos. 1–4 (January 2000): 51–61, doi:10.1016/S0031-9201(99)00086-2; D. Cébron et al., "Magnetohydrodynamic Simulations of the Elliptical Instability in Triaxial Ellipsoids, *Geophysics and Astrophysics Fluid Dynamics* 106, nos. 4–5 (August 2012): 524–546, doi:10.1080/03091929.2011.641961.
48. Wolfram Research, Inc., Mathematica's ElementData Function (2020), Champaign, IL, accessed 9/03/2021, periodictable.com/Properties/A/UniverseAbundance.an.log.html.
49. Wolfram Research, Inc., Mathematica's ElementData Function (2020).
50. M. Agostini et al. (Borexino Collaboration), "Comprehensive Geoneutrino Analysis with Borexino," *Physical Review D* 101, no. 1 (January 2020): id. 012009, doi:10.1103/PhysRevD.101.012009.

51. Lars Stixrude, Roberto Scipioni, and Michael P. Desjarlais, "A Silicate Dynamo in the Early Earth," *Nature Communications* 11 (February 2020): id. 935, doi:10.1038/s41467-020-14773-4.
52. David Gubbins, "The Distinction between Geomagnetic Excursions and Reversals," *Geophysical Journal International* 137, no. 1 (April 1999): F1–F3, doi:10.1046/j.1365-246x.1999.00810.x.
53. A. J. Biggin et al., "Palaeomagnetic Field Intensity Variations Suggest Mesoproterozoic Inner-Core Nucleation," *Nature* 526, no. 7572 (October 8, 2015): 245–248, doi:10.1038/nature15523.
54. Xiaoya Zhan, Keke Zhang, and Rixiang Zhu, "A Full-Sphere Convection-Driven Dynamo: Implications for Ancient Geomagnetic Field," *Physics of the Earth and Planetary Interiors* 187, nos. 3–4 (August 2011): 328–335, doi:10.1016/j.pepi.2011.02.007.
55. P. Driscoll and D. Bercovici, "On the Thermal and Magnetic Histories of Earth and Venus: Influences of Melting, Radioactivity, and Conductivity," *Physics of the Earth and Planetary Interiors* 236 (November 2014): 36–51, doi:10.1016/j.pepi.2014.08.004; Stéphane Labrosse, "Thermal Evolution of the Core with a High Thermal Conductivity," *Physics of the Earth and Planetary Interiors* 247 (October 2015): 36–55, doi:10.1016/j.pepi.2015.02.002; Christopher J. Davies, "Cooling History of Earth's Core with High Thermal Conductivity," *Physics of the Earth and Planetary Interiors* 247 (October 2015): 65–79, doi:10.1016/j.pepi.2015.03.007.
56. Richard K. Bono et al., "Young Inner Core Inferred from Ediacaran Ultra-Low Geomagnetic Field Intensity," *Nature Geoscience* 12, no. 2 (February 2019): 143–147, doi:10.1038/s41561-018-0288-0.
57. Peter Driscoll, "Geodynamo Recharged," *Nature Geoscience* 12, no. 2 (February 2019): 83–84, doi:10.1038/s41561-019-0301-2.
58. Florian Lhuillier et al., "Impact of Inner-Core Size on the Dipole Field Behaviour of Numerical Dynamo Simulations," *Geophysical Journal International* 218, no. 1 (July 2019): 179–189, doi:10.1093/gji/ggz146.
59. Michael W. McElhinny and Jo Lock, "Global Paleomagnetic Database Supplement Number One: Update to 1992," *Surveys in Geophysics* 14, no. 3 (May 1993): 303–329, doi:10.1007/BF00690947.
60. Bradford M. Clement, "Dependence of the Duration of Geomagnetic Polarity Reversals on Site Latitude," *Nature* 428, no. 6983 (April 8, 2004): 637–640, doi:10.1038/nature02459.
61. N. R. Nowaczyk et al., "Dynamics of the Laschamp Geomagnetic Excursion from Black Sea Sediments," *Earth and Planetary Science Letters* 351–352 (October 15, 2012): 54–69, doi:10.1016/j.epsl.2012.06.050.
62. Manasvi Lingam, "Revisiting the Biological Ramifications of Variations in Earth's Magnetic Field," *Astrophysical Journal Letters* 874, no. 2 (April 1, 2019): id. L28, doi:10.3847/2041-8213/ab12eb.
63. Eric Gaidos et al., "Thermodynamic Limits on Magnetodynamos in Rocky Exoplanets," *Astrophysical Journal* 718, no. 2 (August 1, 2010): 596–609, doi:10.1088/0004-637X/718/2/596.
64. Glenn LeDrew, "The Real Starry Sky," *Journal of the Royal Astronomical Society of Canada* 95, no. 1 (February 2001): 32, rasc.ca/sites/default/files/publications/JRASC-2001-02.pdf.

Chapter 15: Earth's Mantle

1. D. Kim et al., "Sequencing Seismograms: A Panoptic View of Scattering in the Core-Mantle Boundary Region," *Science* 368, no. 6496 (June 12, 2020): 1223–1228, doi:10.1126/science.aba8972.

2. Maxim D. Ballmer et al., "Compositional Mantle Layering Revealed by Slab Stagnation at ~1000-km Depth," *Science Advances* 1, no. 11 (December 10, 2015): id. E1500815, doi:10.1126/sciadv.1500815; Maxim D. Ballmer et al., "Persistence of Strong Silica-Enriched Domains in the Earth's Lower Mantle," *Nature Geoscience* 10, no. 3 (March 2017): 236–240, doi:10.1038/ngeo2898; Lauren Waszek, Nicholas C. Schmerr, and Maxim D. Ballmer, "Global Observations of Reflectors in the Mid-Mantle with Implications for Mantle Structure and Dynamics," *Nature Communications* 9 (January 2018): id. 385, doi:10.1038/s41467-017-02709-4.
3. Lujendra Ojha et al., "Depletion of Heat Producing Elements in the Martian Mantle," *Geophysical Research Letters* 46, no. 22 (November 28, 2019): 12756–12763, doi:10.1029/2019GL085234.
4. Francis Lucazeau, "Analysis and Mapping of an Updated Terrestrial Heat Flow Data Set," *Geochemistry, Geophysics, Geosystems* 20, no. 8 (August 2019): 4000–4024, doi:10.1029/2019GC008389.
5. Lucazeau, "Analysis and Mapping," 4000–4024.
6. Andrew C. Kren, Peter Pilewskie, and Odele Coddington, "Where Does Earth's Atmosphere Get Its Energy?," *Journal of Space Weather and Space Climate* 7 (January 2017): id. A10, doi:10.1051/swsc/2017007.
7. W. F. McDonough, O. Šrámek, and S. A. Wipperfurth, "Radiogenic Power and Geoneutrino Luminosity of the Earth and Other Terrestrial Bodies through Time," *Geochemistry, Geophysics, Geosystems* 21, no. 7 (July 2020): id. e2019GC008865, doi:10.1029/2019GC008865; M. Agostini et al. (Borexino Collaboration), "Comprehensive Geoneutrino Analysis with Borexino," *Physical Review D* 101, no. 1 (January 1, 2020): id. 012009, doi:10.1103/PhysRevD.101.012009; The KamLAND Collaboration, "Partial Radiogenic Heat Model for Earth Revealed by Geoneutrino Measurements," *Nature Geoscience* 4, no. 9 (September 2011): 647–651, doi:10.1038/ngeo1205; Lucazeau, "Analysis and Mapping," 4000–4024.
8. Mario Fischer-Gödde et al., "Ruthenium Isotope Vestige of Earth's Pre-Late-Veneer Mantle Preserved in Archaean Rocks," *Nature* 579, no. 7798 (March 12, 2020): 240–244, doi:10.1038/s41586-020-2069-3; María Isabel Varas-Reus et al., "Selenium Isotopes as Tracers of a Late Volatile Contribution to Earth from the Outer Solar System," *Nature Geoscience* 12, no. 9 (September 2019): 779–782, doi:10.1038/s41561-019-0414-7; Francis Albarède, "Volatile Accretion History of the Terrestrial Planets and Dynamic Implications," *Nature* 461, no. 7268 (October 29, 2009): 1227–1233, doi:10.1038/nature08477.
9. Oleg Abramov, David A. Kring, and Stephen J. Mojzsis, "The Impact Environment of the Hadean Earth," *Geochemistry* 73, no. 3 (October 2013): 227–248, doi:10.1016/j.chemer.2013.08.004; Jian Wang et al., "Hidden Eoarchean Crust in the Southwestern Central Asian Orogenic Belt," *Lithos* 360–361 (May 2020): id. 105437, doi:10.1016/j.lithos.2020.105437; R. G. Strom, S. Marchi, and R. Malhotra, "Ceres and the Terrestrial Planets Impact Cratering Record," *Icarus* 302 (March 1, 2018): 104–108, doi:10.1016/j.icarus.2017.11.013.
10. I provide the data and calculations in my book, *Improbable Planet: How Earth Became Humanity's Home* (Grand Rapids, MI: Baker Books, 2016), 167–168.
11. Hugh Ross, *Why the Universe Is the Way It Is* (Grand Rapids, MI: Baker Books, 2008), 45–47.
12. Ross, *Improbable Planet*, 43–77, 113–115.
13. William Thomson, "4. On the Secular Cooling of the Earth," *Proceedings of the Royal Society of Edinburgh* 4 (1862): 610–611, doi:10.1017/S0370164600035124. A PDF is available at courses.seas.harvard.edu/climate/eli/Courses/EPS281r/Sources/Earth-age-and-thermal-history/

more/Kelvin-1863-excerpts.pdf.
14. Emily Sarafian et al., "Experimental Constraints on the Damp Peridotite Solidus and Oceanic Mantle Potential Temperature," *Science* 355, no. 6328 (March 3, 2017): 942–945, doi:10.1126/science.aaj2165.
15. Ricardo Arevalo Jr., William F. McDonough, and Mario Luong, "The K/U Ratio of the Silicate Earth: Insights into Mantle Composition, Structure, and Thermal Evolution," *Earth and Planetary Science Letters* 278, nos. 3–4 (February 25, 2009): 361–369, doi:10.1016/j.epsl.2008.12.023.
16. Tushar Mittal et al., "Precipitation of Multiple Light Elements to Power Earth's Early Dynamo," *Earth and Planetary Science Letters* 532 (February 15, 2020): id. 116030, doi:10.1016/j.epsl.2019.116030.
17. Ryosuke Sinmyo, Kei Hirose, and Yasuo Ohishi, "Melting Curve of Iron to 290 GPa Determined in a Resistance-Heated Diamond-Anvil Cell," *Earth and Planetary Science Letters* 510 (March 15, 2019): 45–52, doi:10.1016/j.epsl.2019.01.006; Tetsuya Komabayashi et al., "Phase Relations in the System Fe-Ni-Si to 200 GPa and 3900 K and Implications for Earth's Core," *Earth and Planetary Science Letters* 512 (April 15, 2019): 83–88, doi:10.1016/j.epsl.2019.01.056; Esteban Gazel et al., "Plume-Subduction Interaction in Southern Central America: Mantle Upwelling and Slab Melting," *Lithos* 121, nos. 1–4 (January 2011): 117–134, doi:10.1016/j.lithos.2010.10.008.
18. Takashi Nakagawa and Paul J. Tackley, "Influence of Combined Primordial Layering and Recycled MORB on the Coupled Thermal Evolution of Earth's Mantle and Core," *Geochemistry, Geophysics, Geosystems* 15, no. 3 (March 2014): 619–633, doi:10.1002/2013GC005128; Takashi Nakagawa and Paul J. Tackley, "Influence of Plate Tectonic Mode on the Coupled Thermochemical Evolution of Earth's Mantle and Core," *Geochemistry, Geophysics, Geosystems* 16, no. 10 (October 2015): 3400–3413, doi:10.1002/2015GC005996.
19. P. J. Tackley et al., "Planetary Lithosphere-Outer Core-Inner Core-Mantle Coupled Evolution over the Entire Age of the Solar System," *American Geophysical Union*, Fall Meeting 2016 (December 2016): abstract #GP12A-07.
20. Juan Rodriguez-Gonzalez et al., "Water in Geodynamical Models of Mantle Convection and Plate Tectonics," EGU General Assembly 2018, (proceedings from the conference held April 8–13, 2018 in Vienna, Austria): 8656.

Chapter 16: Earth's Crustal Interior

1. Nikolas I. Christensen and Walter D. Mooney, "Seismic Velocity Structure and Composition of the Continental Crust: A Global View," *Journal of Geophysical Research: Solid Earth* 100, no. B6 (June 10, 1995): 9761–9788, doi:10.1029/95JB00259.
2. Leszek Czechowski and Marek Grad, "The Stress Field and Its Role in the Evolution of Asthenosphere and Lithosphere," EGU General Assembly 2017, (proceedings from the conference, held April 23–28, 2017 in Vienna, Austria): 4670.
3. Katrin Mierdel et al., "Water Solubility in Aluminous Orthopyroxene and the Origin of Earth's Asthenosphere," *Science* 315, no. 5810 (January 19, 2007): 364–368, doi:10.1126/science.1135422.
4. I describe these features and why Earth may be unique in possessing them in *Improbable Planet: How Earth Became Humanity's Home* (Grand Rapids, MI: Baker Books, 2016), 111–118, 121–123, 134–139, 158, 200–204.
5. These numbers are derived from the aluminum-to-iron abundance ratios by mass in the universe, Earth's crust, and Earth's mantle, not the percentage of aluminum in Earth's

crust and mantle relative to the percentage in the universe. Hydrogen, helium, methane, and ammonia—gases which rocky bodies are unable to retain gravitationally—dominate the universe's abundance of ordinary matter (based on elements in the periodic table). Thus, aluminum-to-iron abundance ratio yields a true comparison of Earth's aluminum richness relative to the average in other rocky bodies. Citation for the mantle aluminum and iron abundances: Rhea K. Workman and Stanley R. Hart, "Major and Trace Element Composition of the Depleted MORB Mantle (DMM)," *Earth and Planetary Science Letters* 231, nos. 1–2 (February 28, 2005): 53–72, doi:10.1016/j.epsl.2004.12.005. Citation for the crust aluminum and iron abundances: W. M. Haynes, ed., "Abundance of Elements in the Earth's Crust and in the Sea," *CRC Handbook of Chemistry and Physics*, 97th ed. (Boca Raton, FL: CRC Press, 2016), 14–17.

6. Christensen and Mooney, "Seismic Velocity Structure," 9761–9788.
7. Peter Bird, "An Updated Digital Model of Plate Boundaries," *Geochemistry, Geophysics, Geosystems* 4, no. 3 (March 2003): article #9, 1027, doi:10.1029/2001GC000252.
8. George F. Cooper et al., "Variable Water Input Controls Evolution of the Lesser Antilles Volcanic Arc," *Nature* 582, no. 7813 (June 25, 2020): 525–529, doi:10.1038/s41586-020-2407-5.
9. Wolfgang Bach and Gretchen L. Früh-Green, "Alteration of the Oceanic Lithosphere and Implications for Seafloor Processes," *Elements* 6, no. 3 (June 1, 2010): 173–178, doi:10.2113/gselements.6.3.173.
10. Cooper et al., "Variable Water Input," 525–529.
11. I devoted an entire chapter on the Sun's luminosity history in *Improbable Planet*, 143–164.
12. Ross, *Improbable Planet*, 94–219.
13. Terry T. Isson and Noah J. Planavsky, "Reverse Weathering as a Long-Term Stabilizer of Marine pH and Planetary Climate," *Nature* 560, no. 7719 (August 23, 2018): 471–475, doi:10.1038/s41586-018-0408-4; S. Rahman, R. C. Aller, and J. K. Cochran, "The Missing Silica Sink: Revisiting the Marine Sedimentary Si Cycle Using Cosmogenic ^{32}Si," *Global Biogeochemical Cycles* 31, no. 10 (October 2017): 1559–1578, doi:10.1002/2017GB005746; Hugh Ross, "Highly Fine-Tuned Reverse Weathering Stabilized Earth's Early Climate," *Today's New Reason to Believe* (blog), Reasons to Believe, September 10, 2018, reasons.org/explore/blogs/todays-new-reason-to-believe/highly-fine-tuned-reverse-weathering-stabilized-earth-s-early-climate.
14. Daniella M. Rempe and William E. Dietrich, "Direct Observations of Rock Moisture, a Hidden Component of the Hydrologic Cycle," *Proceedings of the National Academy of Sciences, USA* 115 (March 13, 2018): 2664–2669, doi:10.1073/pnas.1800141115; Hugh Ross, "Weathered Bedrock: Key to Advanced Life on Earth," *Today's New Reason to Believe* (blog), Reasons to Believe, May 7, 2018, reasons.org/explore/blogs/todays-new-reason-to-believe/weathered-bedrock-key-to-advanced-life-on-earth.
15. T. T. Isson et al., "Evolution of the Global Carbon Cycle and Climate Regulation on Earth," *Global Biogeochemical Cycles* 34, no. 2 (February 2020): id. e2018GB006061, doi:10.1029/2018GB006061; K. Wallmann et al., "Silicate Weathering in Anoxic Marine Sediments," *Geochimica et Cosmochimica Acta* 72, no. 12 (June 15, 2008): 2895–2918, doi:10.1016/j.gca.2008.03.026; Laurence A. Coogan and Kathryn M. Gillis, "Low-Temperature Alteration of the Seafloor: Impacts on Ocean Chemistry," *Annual Review of Earth and Planetary Sciences* 46 (May 2018): 21–45, doi:10.1146/annurev-earth-082517-010027.
16. Isson et al., "Global Carbon Cycle."
17. Isson et al., "Global Carbon Cycle."

18. Hubert Staudigel et al., "Cretaceous Ocean Crust at DSDP Sites 417 and 418: Carbon Uptake from Weathering versus Loss by Magmatic Outgassing," *Geochimica et Cosmochimica Acta* 53, no. 11 (November 1989): 3091–3094, doi:10.1016/0016-7037(89)90189-0; Patrick V. Brady and Sigurdur R. Gíslason, "Seafloor Weathering Controls on Atmospheric CO_2 and Global Climate," *Geochimica et Cosmochimica Acta* 61, no. 5 (March 1997): 965–973, doi:10.1016/S0016-7037(96)00385-7; Guo-Liang Zhang and Christopher Smith-Duque, "Seafloor Basalt Alteration and Chemical Change in the Ultra Thinly Sedimented South Pacific," *Geochemistry, Geophysics, Geosystems* 15, no. 7 (July 2014): 3066–3080, doi:10.1002/2013GC005141.
19. Terry Plank and Craig E. Manning, "Subducting Carbon," *Nature* 574, no. 7778 (October 17, 2019): 343–352, doi:10.1038/s41586-019-1643-z; Isson et al., "Global Carbon Cycle"; Yizhuo Sun et al., "Stability and Migration of Slab-Derived Carbonate-Rich Melts above the Transition Zone," *Earth and Planetary Science Letters* 531 (February 1, 2020): id. 116000, doi:10.1016/j.epsl.2019.116000.
20. David J. Des Marais, "Isotopic Evolution of the Biogeochemical Carbon Cycle during the Precambrian," *Reviews in Mineralogy and Geochemistry: Stable Isotope Geochemistry* 43, no. 1, ed. John W. Valley and David Cole (2001): 555–578, doi:10.2138/gsrmg.43.1.555.
21. Megan S. Duncan and Rajdeep Dasgupta, "Rise of Earth's Atmospheric Oxygen Controlled by Efficient Subduction of Organic Carbon," *Nature Geoscience* 10, no. 5 (May 2017): 387–392, doi:10.1038/ngeo2939.
22. F. P. Bundy et al., "The Pressure-Temperature Phase and Transformation Diagram for Carbon; Updated through 1994," *Carbon* 34, no. 2 (1996): 141–153, doi:10.1016/0008-6223(96)00170-4.
23. Heinrich D. Holland, "Volcanic Gases, Black Smokers, and the Great Oxidation Event," *Geochimica et Cosmochimica Acta* 66, no. 21 (November 1, 2002): 3811–3826, doi:10.1016/S0016-7037(02)00950-x; Timothy W. Lyons, Christopher T. Reinhard, and Noah J. Planavsky, "The Rise of Oxygen in Earth's Early Ocean and Atmosphere," *Nature* 506, no. 7488 (February 20, 2014): 307–315, doi:10.1038/nature13068; Genming Luo et al., "Rapid Oxygenation of Earth's Atmosphere 2.33 Billion Years Ago," *Science Advances* 2, no. 5 (May 13, 2016): id. e1600134, doi:10.1126/sciadv.1600134; Heinrich D. Holland, "Why the Atmosphere Became Oxygenated: A Proposal," *Geochimica et Cosmochimica Acta* 73, no. 18 (September 15, 2009): 5241–5255, doi:10.1016/j.gca.2009.05.070.
24. C. Brenhin Keller et al., "Neoproterozoic Glacial Origin of the Great Unconformity," *Proceedings of the National Academy of Sciences, USA* 116, no. 4 (January 22, 2019): 1136–1145, doi:10.1073/pnas.1804350116; Jon M. Husson and Shanan E. Peters, "Atmospheric Oxygenation Driven by Unsteady Growth of the Continental Sedimentary Reservoir," *Earth and Planetary Science Letters* 460 (February 15, 2017): 68–75, doi:10.1016/j.epsl.2016.12.012; Setareh Shahkarami et al., "The Ediacaran-Cambrian Boundary: Evaluating Stratigraphic Completeness and the Great Unconformity," *Precambrian Research* 345 (August 2020): id. 105721, doi:10.1016/j.precamres.2020.105721.
25. Keller et al., "Neoproterozoic Glacial Origin," 1136–1145.
26. Douglas Erwin and James Valentine, *The Cambrian Explosion: The Construction of Animal Biodiversity* (New York: W. H. Freeman, 2013); Hugh Ross, *Improbable Planet*, 172–178.
27. Stephan V. Sobolev and Michael Brown, "Surface Erosion Events Controlled the Evolution of Plate Tectonics on Earth," *Nature* 570, no. 7759 (June 6, 2019): 52–57, doi:10.1038/s41586-019-1258-4.

Chapter 17: Interior Design Implications

1. David Sloan et al., ed., *Fine-Tuning in the Physical Universe* (New York: Cambridge University Press, 2020); John D. Barrow and Frank J. Tipler, *The Anthropic Cosmological Principle* (New York: Oxford University Press, 1986); Paul Davies, *The Cosmic Blueprint: New Discoveries in Nature's Creative Ability to Order the Universe* (New York: Simon and Schuster, 1988); Paul Davies, *The Cosmic Jackpot: Why Our Universe Is Just Right for Life* (Boston: Houghton Mifflin Harcourt, 2007); Hugh Ross, *The Creator and the Cosmos*, 4th ed. (Covina, CA: RTB Press, 2018).
2. Hugh Ross, *Improbable Planet: How Earth Became Humanity's Home* (Grand Rapids, MI: Baker Books, 2016); Hugh Ross, *Weathering Climate Change* (Covina, CA: RTB Press, 2020).
3. Job 26:14 (NIV).
4. Ecclesiastes 3:11 (Amplified Bible).
5. Romans 2:14–15; 3:10–12, 23 (NIV).
6. John 14:6 (NIV).

Appendix: Solar Elemental Abundance—Rocky Planet Configuration Link

1. Jorge Meléndez et al., "The Peculiar Solar Composition and Its Possible Relation to Planet Formation," *Astrophysical Journal Letters* 704, no. 1 (October 10, 2009): L66–L70, doi:10.1088/0004-637X/704/1/L66.
2. Megan Bedell et al., "The Chemical Homogeneity of Sun-Like Stars in the Solar Neighborhood," *Astrophysical Journal* 865, no. 1 (September 20, 2018): id. 68, doi:10.3847/1538-4357/aad908.
3. Marília Carlos et al., "The Li-Age Correlation: The Sun Is Unusually Li Deficient for Its Age," *Monthly Notices of the Royal Astronomical Society* 485, no. 3 (May 2019): 4052–4059, doi:10.1093/mnras/stz681.
4. Walter Nichiporuk and Carleton B. Moore, "Lithium, Sodium, and Potassium Abundances in Carbonaceous Chrondrites," *Geochimica et Cosmochimica Acta* 38, no. 11 (November 1974): 1691–1694, doi:10.1016/0016-7037(74)90186-0; D. Krankowsky and O. Müller, "Isotopic Composition and Abundance of Lithium in Meteoritic Matter," *Geochimica et Cosmochimica Acta* 31, no. 10 (October 1967): 1833–1842, doi:10.1016/0016-7037(67)90125-1; James M. D. Day et al., "Evidence for High-Temperature Fractionation of Lithium Isotopes during Differentiation of the Moon," *Meteoritics and Planetary Science* 51, no. 6 (June 2016): 1046–1062, doi:10.1111/maps.12643.
5. James N. Connelly et al., "The Absolute Chronology and Thermal Processing of Solids in the Solar Protoplanetary Disk," *Science* 338, no. 6107 (November 2, 2012): 651–655, doi:10.1126/science.1226919; E. G. Adelberger et al., "Solar Fusion Cross Sections. II. The *pp* Chain and CNO Cycles," *Review of Modern Physics* 83, no. 1 (January–March 2011): 195–246, doi:10.1103/RevModPhys.83.195.
6. I. Baraffe et al., "Lithium Depletion in Solar-Like Stars: Effect of Overshooting Based on Realistic Multi-Dimensional Simulations," *Astrophysical Journal Letters* 845, no. 1 (August 10, 2017): id. L6, doi:10.3847/2041-8213/aa82ff; J. Christensen-Dalsgaard et al., "A More Realistic Representation of Overshoot at the Base of the Solar Convective Envelope as Seen by Helioseismology," *Monthly Notices of the Royal Astronomical Society* 414, no. 2 (June 2011): 1158–1174, doi:10.1111/j.1365-2966.2011.18460.x; S. Basu, "Helioseismic Evidence for Mixing in the Sun," in *Chemical Abundances and Mixing in Stars in the Milky Way and Its Satellites*, (proceedings of the ESO-Arcetrie Workshop held in Castiglione della Pescaia, Italy, September 13–17, 2004), ed. S. Randich and L. Pasquini (Berlin: Springer Nature,

2006), 284–287.

7. M. Rempel, "Overshoot at the Base of the Solar Convection Zone: A Semianalytical Approach," *Astrophysical Journal* 607, no. 2 (June 1, 2004): 1046–1064, doi:10.1086/383605.
8. Carlos et al., "Li-Age Correlation," 4052–4059.
9. Garik Israelian et al., "Lithium in Stars with Exoplanets," *Astronomy and Astrophysics* 414, no. 2 (February 2004): 601–611, doi:10.1051/0004-6361:20034398.
10. Y. Q. Chen and G. Zhao, "A Comparative Study on Lithium Abundances in Solar-Type Stars with and without Planets," *Astronomical Journal* 131, no. 3 (March 1, 2006): 1816–1821, doi:10.1086/499946.
11. Garik Israelian et al., "Enhanced Lithium Depletion in Sun-Like Stars with Orbiting Planets," *Nature* 462, no. 7270 (November 12, 2009): 189–191, doi:10.1038/nature08483.
12. Carlos et al., "Li-Age Correlation," 4052–4059.
13. "Catalog," Extrasolar Planets Encyclopaedia, Exoplanet TEAM, accessed September 3, 2021, exoplanet.eu/catalog/.
14. "Catalog," accessed September 3, 2021.
15. Simon L. Grimm et al., "The Nature of the TRAPPIST-1 Exoplanets," *Astronomy and Astrophysics* 613 (May 2018): id. A68, doi:10.1051/0004-6361/201732233.
16. Grimm et al., "TRAPPIST-1 Exoplanets" 1.
17. Jorge Meléndez et al., "Peculiar Solar Composition," L69.
18. Maria M. Katsova et al., "Superflare G and K Stars and the Lithium Abundance," *The 19th Cambridge Workshop on Cool Stars, Stellar Systems, and the Sun (CS19)*, ed. G. A. Feiden (presented at Uppsala, Sweden, June 6–10, 2016), id. 124, doi:10.5281/zenodo.59176; Y. Takeda et al., "Behavior of Li Abundances in Solar-Analog Stars* II. Evidence of the Connection with Rotation and Stellar Activity," *Astronomy and Astrophysics* 515 (June 2010): id. A93, doi:10.1051/0004-6361/200913897.

Index

About the Author

Hugh Ross is founder and president of Reasons to Believe (RTB), an organization dedicated to demonstrating the compatibility of science and the Christian faith.

With a degree in physics from the University of British Columbia and a PhD in astronomy from the University of Toronto, Hugh continued his research on quasars and galaxies as a postdoctoral fellow at the California Institute of Technology before transitioning to full-time ministry. In addition to founding and leading RTB, he remains on the pastoral staff at Christ Church Sierra Madre. His writings include journal and magazine articles and numerous books—*The Creator and the Cosmos*, *Why the Universe Is the Way It Is*, and *Improbable Planet*, among others. He has spoken on hundreds of university campuses as well as at conferences and churches around the world.

Hugh lives in Southern California with his wife, Kathy.

About Reasons to Believe

We at Reasons to Believe seek to dispel the idea that religious beliefs and scientific studies should be kept separate. Our scholar team, consisting of three PhD scientists and a philosopher-theologian, offers distinctive and fascinating insights on topics ranging from biblical creation to cutting-edge biotechnology.

Our intent is to create a space where ideas and ideologies can be explored fearlessly and where a spirit of curiosity is welcomed. We aim to present research and start a conversation—because people deserve respect and a safe forum for discussing their views.

For more information, visit reasons.org.

For inquiries, contact us via:
818 S. Oak Park Rd.
Covina, CA 91724
(855) REASONS | (855) 732-7667
ministrycare@reasons.org